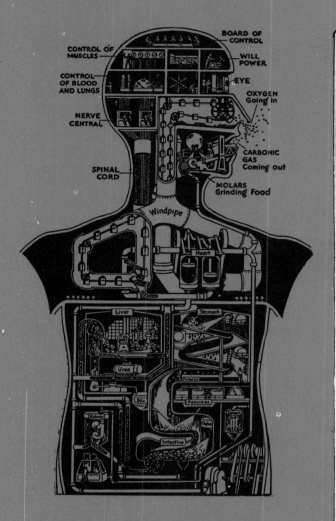

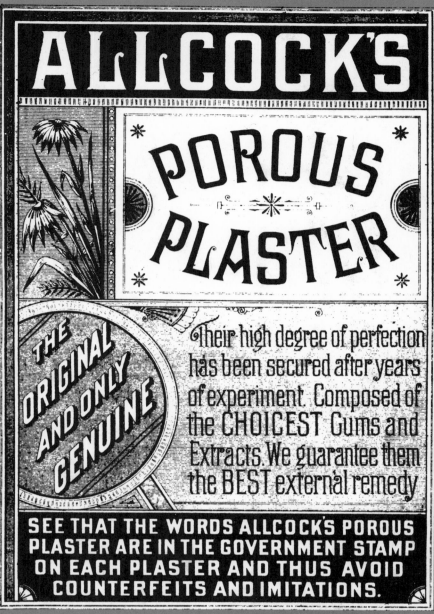

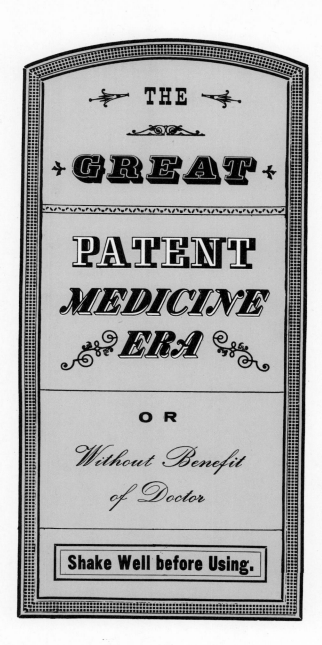

THE GREAT

PATENT

MEDICINE ERA

OR

Without Benefit of Doctor

Shake Well before Using.

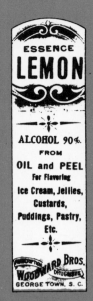

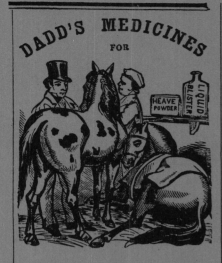

THE GREAT

PATENT MEDICINE ERA

OR

Without Benefit of Doctor

BY *Adelaide Hechtlinger*

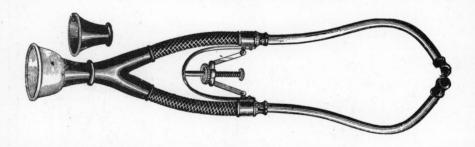

Madison Square Press

Grosset & Dunlap, Inc.

A NATIONAL GENERAL COMPANY

PUBLISHERS

NEW YORK

Nervousness in the Home.

We are all familiar with the ruin worked in the home by disturbed nerves, the breaking down of the closer ties between husband and wife, and the influence for ill under which children grow up to mature years. It is under such conditions that the seeds of disease are sown which bear bitter fruit in the present and future generations. The nervousness of the father or the mother becomes uncontrollable. No amount of will power will keep it down, unless the nerves are brought into subjection by effective means.

Disturbed nerves break down domestic happiness.

The advent of nervousness into the home is a storm signal which must be heeded or the domestic fabric will soon be tottering to its fall. So lamentably true is this that when the first indications of nervousness appear they must be heeded promptly, that help may be found before the harsh words are spoken which, induced by a nervous condition, have a force in them sufficient to mar the hopes and lives of all.

Get Dr. Greene's advice when nervousness first appears.

THE FARM-YARD, THE ONLY PLACE TO FIND PURE COW'S MILK.

COPYRIGHT © 1970 BY GROSSET & DUNLAP, INC. ALL RIGHTS RESERVED. PUBLISHED SIMULTANEOUSLY IN CANADA. LIBRARY OF CONGRESS CATALOG CARD NUMBER: 70-122554. PRINTED IN THE UNITED STATES OF AMERICA.

BOOK DESIGN BY JOS. TRAUTWEIN

Contents

BUGGY CASES,

72 FULTON STREET, NEW YORK.

In writing them, please mention this list.

FAT FOLKS, TAKE Dr. ROSE'S OBESITY POWDERS

THEY REDUCE THE WEIGHT IN A COMPARATIVELY SHORT TIME.

Retail price, $1.00; our price, 3 boxes for $1.65; per box 58o

TOO MUCH FAT IS A DISEASE and a source of great annoyance to those afflicted. It impairs the strength and produces fatty degeneration of the heart, which sometimes leads to a premature death. All people who have obesity are troubled with sluggish circulation and labored action of the heart. The patient feels lazy and burdensome. There is a sluggish condition of the whole system, while they are not exactly sickly, there is a feeling that all is not right.

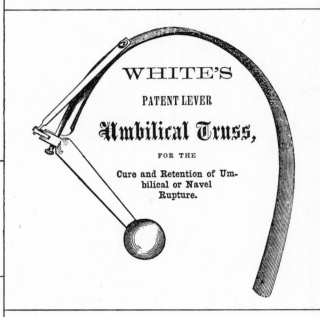

WHITE'S PATENT LEVER Umbilical Truss,

FOR THE

Cure and Retention of Umbilical or Navel Rupture.

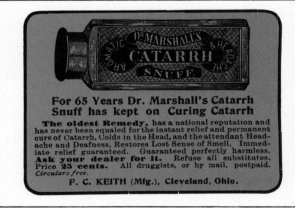

For 65 Years Dr. Marshall's Catarrh Snuff has kept on Curing Catarrh

The oldest Remedy, has a national reputation and has never been equaled for the instant relief and permanent cure of Catarrh, Colds in the Head, and the attendant Headache and Deafness, Restores Lost Sense of Smell. Immediate relief guaranteed. Guaranteed perfectly harmless. **Ask your dealer for it.** Refuse all substitutes. **Price 25 cents.** All druggists, or by mail, postpaid. *Circulars free.*

F. C. KEITH (Mfg.), Cleveland, Ohio.

Liquor Agency rules in New Hampshire.—1. All liquor to be A No. 1, and sold cheap for cash. 2. Children under ten years of age will not be allowed to get drunk on the premises unless accompanied by their parents. 3. No liquor will be sold to any person who cannot walk a board-fence, and distinctly pronounce the name of "Erastus Richardson" without slipping; "Rassus Risson" won't do. 4. Intoxicating liquors will be sold for medicinal purposes, except on nights and Sundays, when they will be sold in cases of sickness only.—Give RUSH's Pain Cure a fair trial.

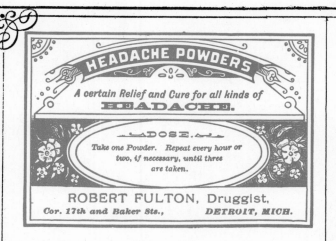

HEADACHE POWDERS

A certain Relief and Cure for all kinds of
HEADACHE.

— DOSE. —

Take one Powder. Repeat every hour or
two, if necessary, until three
are taken.

ROBERT FULTON, Druggist,
Cor. 17th and Baker Sts., DETROIT, MICH.

My dear Mrs. Pinkham: I cannot
praise LYDIA E. PINKHAM'S VEGETABLE
COMPOUND too highly for its the only medicine I ever tried which cured me. I *suffered*
much during my *first menstrual period*, I
felt weak and dizzy, my thoughts became
sluggish, I had headaches, backaches and
fainting spells ; pains in the back and
lower limbs. After taking Vegetable
Compound a short time I was in perfect health, felt buoyant and full of life.
MISS M. CARTLEDGE,
553 Whitehall St., Atlanta, Ga.
Director Hillside Womans Golf Club.

THE HYGEIA HOTEL,
Old Point Comfort, Va.

Deservedly World-Famed, this immense and unique caravansary is situated a few
yards from Fort Monroe, and lies along a beautiful sandy beach, washed by the waters of Chesapeake
Bay and Hampton Roads. The wonderfully equable climate makes it an

ALL-THE-YEAR-ROUND RESORT,

Unsurpassed in healthfulness and general attraction. It is the rendezvous for prominent people from
all sections, and an atmosphere of comfort, luxury and refinement pervades the place.

Turkish, Russian, Electric and Hot Sea Baths.
The latter celebrated for their efficiency in rheumatic troubles.

Glass-Enclosed Verandas. Music by the U. S. Artillery School Band.

Average temperature for winter, 48 degrees. Pure ocean air; free from Malaria, and heavily
charged with ozone, the great blood purifier. Nervousness and insomnia speedily, and, in most
cases, permanently relieved. All things considered,

The Most Comfortable and Delightful Resort at which to Spend the Winter Months in the United States.

Send for Descriptive Pamphlet. **F. N. PIKE, Manager.**

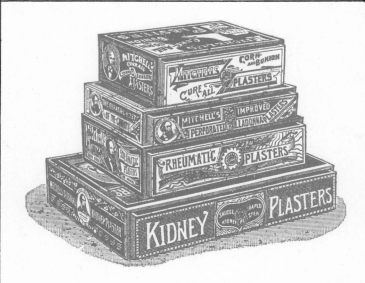

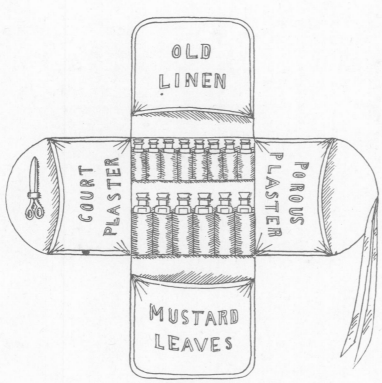

Traveller's Medicine Case.

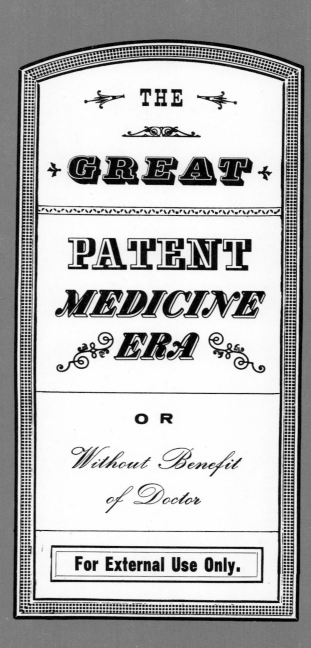

THE

GREAT

PATENT

MEDICINE ERA

OR

Without Benefit of Doctor

For External Use Only.

Introduction

THE HAND THAT DOES IT.

IT IS NOT the purpose of this book to replace the doctor. The volume is a period piece and should be regarded as such. Yet the writer recalls some of these remedies being mentioned by her elders as sure-fire cures and strangely enough, very often they helped. Whether the illness would have been alleviated through the normal course of events or whether the home remedies actually helped, remains a moot question.

In the days before 1900, much medical treatment was domestic and primitive. It was not easy to secure the services of the one physician in the area. Usually if the physician were available, the money with which to pay was not, so physicians were called only in the strictest of emergencies. Every family had its home medical books and supply of medicines, usually herbs, and other nostrums listed in the books. There were also superstitions. If they did not help there usually was someone in the community who was handy in caring for the sick and had a particular system of cures which was made up of homemade science, empiricism, and superstition.

Since Indian influence was strong, many settlers relied upon the herb and root doctors who used remedies obtained from forest and garden. Many pioneers practiced their cures in the Indian fashion as an avocation either to be neighborly or helpful. Others became "doctors" and advertised their success in curing various ailments.

Herb recipes in the Middle West were not confined to herbals and formal works. They were passed along from person to person, copied down in odd places, recorded in household remedy books, and published in almanacs and newspapers. Many of them were adopted by botanic medical schools. Some were administered for specific ills while others were taken just on general principles.

Since herbs were used in remedies so widely, root and herb collecting and cultivating be-came a routine activity for many pioneers. For a dollar one was able to get several dozen cures for assorted ailments as well as the latest and best information on how to get rid of freckles, curl hair, produce ink, kill rats, make soft soap, keep potatoes from rotting and many other things pertaining to both man and beast.

The frontiersman, self-reliant, proud and generally poor, seldom called the doctor, since it was considered a waste of time and money. Furthermore, most physicians' crude medicine was not usually helpful.

The pioneer turned to patent medicines if his home remedies did not help him, before he would resort to calling the doctor. All papers carried advertisements extolling the virtues of various patent medicines. Country peddlers carried the medicines, as well as drugs and herbs that customers were unable to grow.

In the days before 1900 the woman of the house made the medicines, usually so strong that the teaspoon was considered the maximum-sized measure. A tablespoonful would probably have killed the patient. Often the medicine was doled out in drops. Powders were a big thing, but it took careful preparation to administer them properly. All sorts of plasters and poultices were applied and when they were removed the patient usually felt better—just at the thought that the torture of the cure was over. Medicines were horrible-tasting, stinging, gagging, and strong. Often the patient was cured after one dose, as the idea of a second dose was too appalling to consider.

While it is not suggested that the remedies from this book be used—quite the contrary— it should be borne in mind that folk medicine has made many important contributions to scientific medicine. The basic principles used today in some of our newest and most effective drugs have often come from these old-time remedies.

Books
to Aid
the Afflicted

The American pioneers not only suffered the diseases that they had suffered "back home," but also new diseases, previously unknown. Usually it was felt that the new climate and environment were responsible for these ailments, and to alleviate their sufferings they adopted many Indian remedies. They also used remedies for old diseases to help them combat the new. Whenever a cure worked (or seemed to work) it was written down.

Eventually enterprising authors and publishers put them into book form for general use. In addition to the standard works on medicine found in the home, there were other, related kinds of books that dealt with specific topics such as marriage and health. Cookbooks had sections on home medication. And books for the farmer, mechanic or businessman also contained sections on the proper care of man and beast.

Despite the growing number of volumes, there remained many ailments the cure for which was to be found in no book. This problem was neatly solved. Many of the books contained certificates which entitled the purchaser to a free consultation by mail with the "doctor" author of the book.

The following title pages illustrate how many different types of books took care of the individual's health problems.

SEARCH *ON*

LIGHTS HEALTH

Light on Dark Corners.

A COMPLETE SEXUAL SCIENCE

—AND—

A GUIDE TO PURITY AND PHYSICAL MANHOOD.

Advice to Maiden, Wife, and Mother.

LOVE, COURTSHIP AND MARRIAGE.

BY

PROF. B. G. JEFFERIS, M. D., PH. D.,
CHICAGO, ILL.,
AND
J. L. NICHOLS, A. M.

EIGHTEENTH EDITION.

PUBLISHED BY

J. L. NICHOLS & CO.

NAPERVILLE, ILL. ———— TORONTO, ONT.

SOLD ONLY BY SUBSCRIPTION.

1897.

Spencerville Allen: to Chic March 7th 1873

Receipt to cure the chills and fevers given by Ark. Blocker take 1 oz yellow Root Pulverized 2 oz Peruvian Bark 1 oz carbonate of Iron 20 grains Quinine in one quart of Whiskey, 15 grains Quinine and 20 grains of carbonate of Iron divide into 4 Powders to be taken ever 3 hours apart as the fever leaves The Bitters to be taken ½ hour before each meal

---

THE PEOPLE'S HOME MEDICAL BOOK

BOOK I
OF THE
PEOPLE'S
HOME
LIBRARY

BY

T. J. RITTER M.D.

GRADUATE OF BOTH THE ALLOPATHIC
AND HOMEOPATHIC SCHOOLS.
FORMERLY ASST. TO THE CHAIR OF THE
THEORY AND PRACTICE OF MEDICINE,
MICHIGAN STATE UNIVERSITY,
ANN ARBOR, MICH.

PUBLISHED BY

THE R. C. BARNUM CO.

CLEVELAND, OHIO.

1914

THE HOUSEHOLD GUIDE;

OR

Practical Helps for Every Home.

HOME NURSING AND HOME REMEDIES;

INSECT EXTERMINATION;

PROF. HENKEL'S ILLUSTRATIONS OF THE

EFFECTS OF ALCOHOL AND CIGARETTES;

A CYCLOPEDIA OF

New Receipts and Celebrated Prescriptions;

Hints and Helps on Health,
Care of Children, etc.

BY

PROF. B. G. JEFFERIS, M. D., Ph. D.,
CHICAGO, ILLS.

— ALSO —

A COMPLETE COOK BOOK

BY

MRS. J. L. NICHOLS AND ANNA HOLVERSON.

SIXTH EDITION.

Published by
J. L. NICHOLS, NAPERVILLE, ILLS.,
To whom all communications must be addressed.
1893.

Certificate of Membership

This Certifies that the Bearer being a subscriber to the "**Household Physician**" is enrolled as a member of **Physicians Medical Society** for one year from the date of this Certificate and is entitled to receive free, prompt and competent advice from the chief of staff in answer to any query of a medical nature.

This further certifies that the Bearer will receive free consultation including prescriptions and medical advice.

In seeking advice and treatment by mail be careful to state definitely symptoms of ailment, also full name and post office address. Enclosing two cent stamp for reply. Address all communications to Chief of Staff, Staff Headquarters, 95 Milk St. Boston, Mass.

Date _____ Agent _____ **Physicians Medical Society.**

This certificate must be dated, and signed by the Agent.

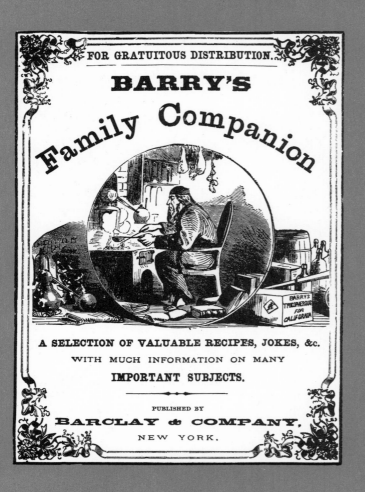
Certificate

This CERTIFIES that .... has purchased "THE PEOPLE'S HOME LIBRARY," and that he is entitled for five years to absolutely free consultation with DR. W. C. FAIR, V. S., concerning the diseases, symptoms, treatment, breeding or feeding of any live stock owned by himself or any member of his family.

Subscriber's Address ....

(SEAL) DR. W. C. FAIR, V. S.

By ...., Agent.

Date ...., 19...

NOTE—Do not forget to cut out and enclose this certificate, which will be promptly returned to you with a reply. Also enclose a two-cent stamp. Address, DR. W. C. FAIR, V. S., 625 Long Ave., Cleveland, Ohio. State symptoms fully, telling just how the animal acts. A fee of ONE DOLLAR will be charged for each consultation with those who are not subscribers.

THE

DOCTOR AT HOME.

Illustrated.

TREATING THE DISEASES

OF

MAN AND THE HORSE.

A practical hand-book for the non-professional. Written in plain, simple language so as to be easily understood by the common people. It treats all of the common diseases of the human family, and gives a large number of excellent receipts and favorite prescriptions for various diseases, with engravings to illustrate many points of interest. Also, an Essay on Hygiene, a Table of Doses, with proportional doses for children; and, in Part Second, the Diseases of the Horse are plainly treated, with the plainest and best treatment that can be given under most circumstances; and a Table of Doses for the Horse, a Table showing the Age of the Horse, a large number of excellent receipts for the Horse, and a large amount of other valuable information.

BY

DR. B. J. KENDALL & CO.,

ENOSBURGH FALLS, VT., U. S. A.,

AUTHORS OF

"A TREATISE ON THE HORSE AND HIS DISEASES."

PRINTED AT STEAM PRINTING HOUSE OF DR. B. J. KENDALL CO.
ENOSBURGH FALLS, VT.

1888.

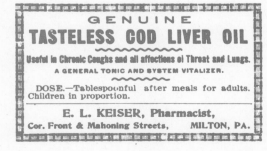

Parts
of the Body

In those books that dealt primarily with home medicine there usually was included a set of diagrams showing the various parts of the body so that the subscriber would know what the author was writing about. When the subscriber wished to read about an ailment in any particular part of the body, he could turn to the pertinent diagram and thus more easily follow the author's discussion.

Many of these diagrams are very good and were the forerunners of the overlay transparencies that are found in various science books today which are published for the student and professional.

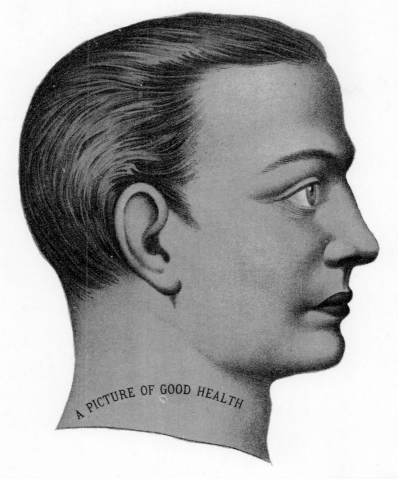

A PICTURE OF GOOD HEALTH

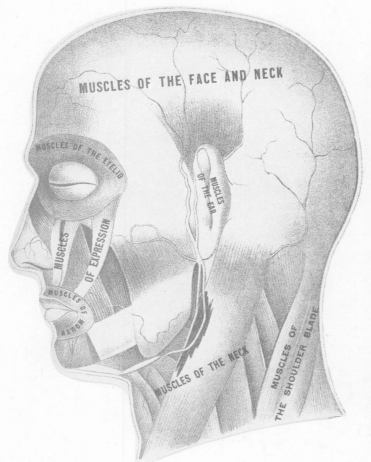

MUSCLES OF THE FACE AND NECK

MUSCLES OF THE EYELID

MUSCLES OF THE EAR

MUSCLES OF EXPRESSION

MUSCLES OF MOUTH

MUSCLES OF THE NECK

MUSCLES OF THE SHOULDER BLADE

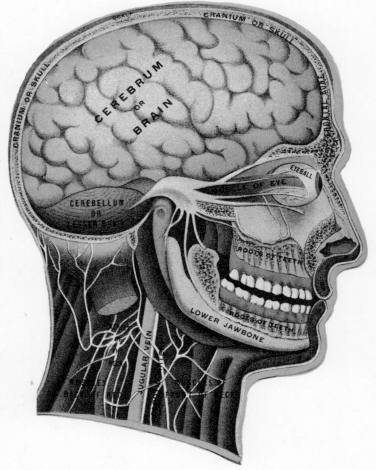

SCALP

CRANIUM OR SKULL

CRANIUM OR SKULL

CEREBRUM OR BRAIN

FRONTAL LOBE

EYEBALL

MUSCLE OF EYE

CEREBELLUM OR LESSER BRAIN

ROOTS OF TEETH

ROOTS OF TEETH

LOWER JAWBONE

JUGULAR VEIN

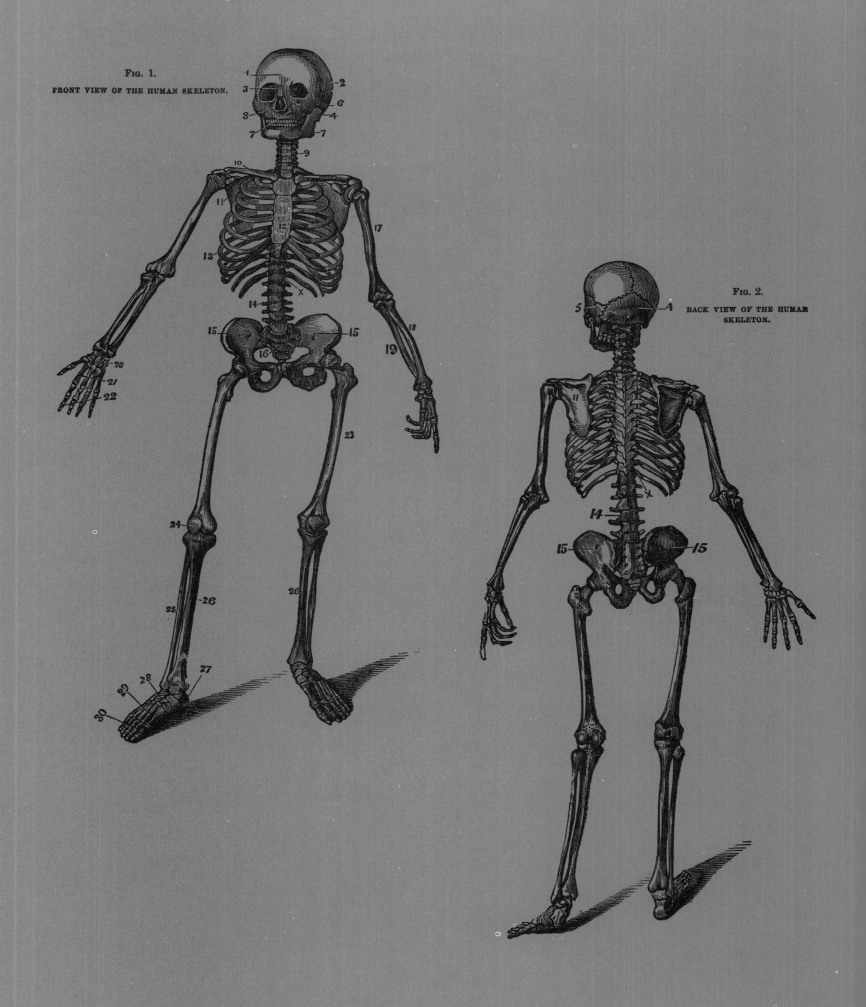

FIG. 1.

FRONT VIEW OF THE HUMAN SKELETON.

FIG. 2.

BACK VIEW OF THE HUMAN
SKELETON.

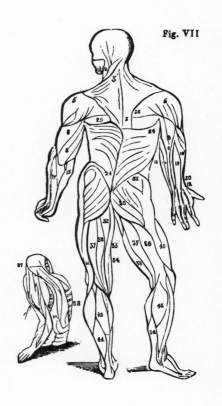

Fig. VII

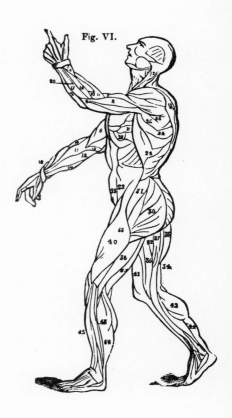

Fig. VI.

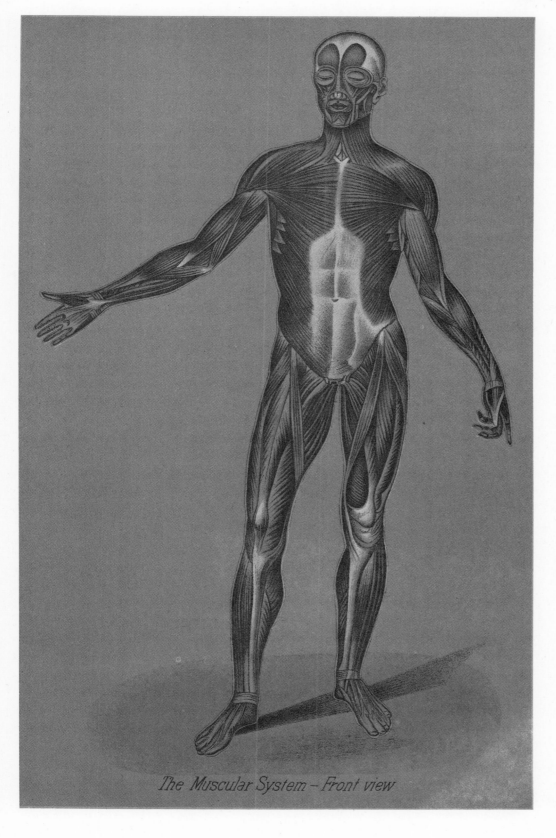

The Muscular System – Front view

Symptoms

*How was the wife or mother of a patient to
know the nature of the ailment?
In those books that dealt primarily
with medicine for the layman, there always was a section that listed the
various symptoms and what diseases they suggested.
The "home doctor" isolated the symptoms, decided what the patient was suffering from,
and then looked up the medication prescribed by
the author of the book.
The patient was then treated accordingly.
If the patient was fortunate,
the diagnosis was correct and perhaps the medication proper.
By sheer luck, a patient often managed to survive both a serious illness
and the medication provided.
Sometimes, though, the patient would have recovered regardless.
It was necessary that readers should understand
the temperament and constitution of the body so that
they might intelligently diagnose the case.*

Fig. 79.

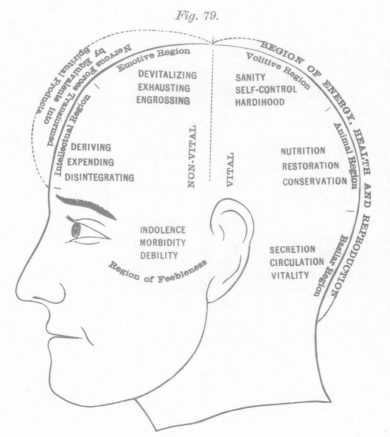

Man has *thinking, warming, nourishing,* and *moving* powers. For the performance of each of these great functions, he has organs of the best possible construction.

FOR THINKING, he has a *brain.* If this be *large in proportion to his other organs,* it gives a character, a cast, a peculiarity to his whole organization. Everything about him is subordinate to his brain. We recognize him, at once, as a thinking and feeling being. He has an intellectual *look.* There is a delicacy, a refinement, a sensitiveness, a studious habit, an air of thoughtfulness about him, which determine his traits, his tone, his temper, his whole character. Hence it is proper to say he has a *cephalic* or thinking *temperament.*

THE LUNGS AND HEART, devoted to renewing and circulating the blood, are placed in the *chest* or *thorax.* If *these be large in man in proportion to other organs,* he is characterized by great activity of circulation, by a large supply of red blood, and by the general indications of a full, warm, and bounding life. This activity gives him his tone and temper, and shows that his is the *thoracic* or *calorific temperament.*

IN THE GREAT CAVITY OF THE AB-DOMEN is done the work of receiving, digesting, and disposing of the materials which nourish the body. If the organs which do this work *be large in proportion to others,* the body is fed to repletion, and the whole organization speaks of the table. The habit, the look, the temper, are all sluggish. This is the *abdominal* or *alimentary temperament.*

THE BONES AND MUSCLES are instruments by which the *movements* of the body are performed. If these *be the largest,* in proportion, of any in the body, then the locomotive powers are in higher perfection than any others. There is largeness of person, energy of movement, and greatness of endurance. The whole case of the person partakes of the strength and coarseness of bone and muscle. This is the *muscular* or *locomotive temperament.*

This gives us four temperaments—

I. THE CEPHALIC TEMPERAMENT, denoted by large brain, activity of mind, and general delicacy of organization.

II. THE THORACIC TEMPERAMENT, indicated by a large chest, force of circulation, redness of skin, great activity, warmth of temper, and fulness of life.

III. THE ABDOMINAL TEMPERAMENT, denoted by a large development of the stomach, liver, bowels, and lymphatics; by a fulness of belly, fondness of high living, and a disposition to float sluggishly upon the current of the world, rather than to struggle against it.

IV. THE MUSCULAR TEMPERAMENT, indicated by largeness of frame and limbs, coarseness of structure, and a great power of locomotion and endurance.

MEDICATION AND TEMPERAMENTS

The object of speaking of temperaments in this work is to make the reader acquainted with the principles upon which remedies are to be adapted to their development. The philosophical-minded physician will, in prescribing, always keep the temperament in view.

PERSONS OF A CEPHALIC TEMPERAMENT cannot bear powerful medicines,—particularly drastic purges. Their fine, delicate and sensitive organizations would be torn to pieces by doses which would hardly be sufficient in a fully-developed muscular temperament. This should always be borne in mind in prescribing for persons of a large brain and delicate organization.

In this temperament, too, fevers, instead of running a high fiery course, take the low typhoid type, the patient becoming pale, and showing a constant tendency to sink. Such patients would be killed by purging, leeching, cupping, sweating, and starving.

PERSONS OF A THORACIC TEMPERAMENT, having a rapid circulation, and a fulness of blood, are most liable to inflammatory diseases. When fever attacks them, they have what is called a "high fever." If rheumatism comes, it is *acute* rheumatism. Disease takes hold of them smartly. As they do everything with emphasis and energy when well, so when ill, they make a business of it. . . .

Stimulants and tonics generally make such persons worse. They want sedatives, and diaphoretics, and sweats, and purgatives, and leeches, and cups, and low diet, and cold bathing, and whatever else will slacken the ferocious swiftness of their circulation.

THOSE OF THE ABDOMINAL TEMPERAMENT are not particularly subject either to very high fevers, or to those typhoid forms which produce sinking. As in the two temperaments noticed above, their complaints chiefly attack the organs most largely developed. Their diseases affect the stomach, the liver, the spleen, and the bowels. These are the largest organs in their bodies, and are most used; and being overworked, they fall into disease.

As these persons are slothful in all their habits, so their diseases run a sluggish course. They are not so liable to sudden death as persons of either of the preceding temperaments.

These persons will bear larger doses of medicine than either of the preceding. Neither do their constitutions respond as readily to medicine. A physician will be disappointed if he expects to see them recovering as fast under its use.

Fig. 177.

LYMPHATIC TEMPERAMENT.

Fig. 178.

ENCEPHALIC TEMPERAMENT.

SANGUINE TEMPERAMENT.

BILIOUS TEMPERAMENT.

THOSE OF A MUSCULAR TEMPERAMENT, having little fondness for anything but a hardy, active life, are much exposed to the elements. Though strong and long-enduring, the hardship of their lives often breaks them down, and when felled by disease, they are oftentimes shockingly racked and torn by it.

These persons bear large doses of medicine, and when sick, need to be treated with an energy proportioned to the strength of their constitution. Rheumatism, which affects the joints, the ligaments, and the tendons, is an affection from which they suffer severely.

THE CONSTITUTION

In prescribing for disease, it is of very great importance to take notice of the constitution. This is a different matter from the temperaments. Persons of the same temperament are often quite unlike in the strength of their constitution. And those having good natural constitutions, frequently abuse them by improper habits and indulgences, and at length come to have broken and very feeble constitutions.

Some persons' muscles and other tissues are put together as if they were never intended to come apart. Like some of the woods of the forest,—the lignum vitae for example,—they are fine-grained and tough. A real smart boy will wear out an iron rocking-horse sooner than one of these persons can exhaust their constitution by hard work. Others, to outward appearance equally well made, have very little endurance, break down easily under hard work, and lose their flesh from trifling causes.

The state of the constitution, therefore, should always be learned before much medicine is given; for what a person of a strong constitution will need, may greatly injure a feeble person, even of the same temperament.

HABITS—These must likewise be attended to. Persons using stimulants require larger doses of medicine to affect them than other persons.

CLIMATE—Medicines act differently on the same persons in summer and winter. Narcotics act more powerfully in hot weather and climates than in cold, and must be given in smaller doses.

THE SEX—The peculiarities of each sex should never be forgotten in prescribing for the sick. Males are not so sensitive as females. They will bear more medicine, and their nervous system is not so readily excited by it. . . . A mother should know something of the symptoms of disease and to aid this, here is a table of symptoms that will be valuable in every home.

COLOR OF SKIN

YELLOW—Generally means jaundice.

SALLOW YELLOW—When patient is haggard and emaciated means some malignant disease like cancer.

WAXY PALE SKIN—With swelling under eyes indicates Bright's disease.

PALENESS—Is caused by shock or loss of blood.

WHITENESS—Means anemia. Small quantity of blood and of poor quality.

GREENISH WHITE—Shows chlorosis which is commonly called green sickness.

PURPLISH—Cyanosis or mixture of pure and impure blood. Blood not properly purified.

HECTIC OR RED CHEEKS—Means tuberculous constitution.

SINGLE RED CHEEK—When seen with fan-like motion of wings of nose when breathing indicates pneumonia.

TONGUE

STRAWBERRY TONGUE—Scarlet fever. First looks like an unripe and later like a ripe strawberry.

YELLOWISH BROWN—Liver trouble.

WHITISH WITH THICK COATING—Usually some stomach trouble.

COATED ON BACK PART—Dyspepsia and constipation.

CRACKED AND RED—Last stages of peritonitis.

BLUISH OR INKY TONGUE AND LIPS—Addison's disease.

RASH

SCARLET COLOR—Scarlet fever.

BLOTCHY AND MUDDY—Measles.

SCATTERED RAISED SPOTS WITH WHITISH PIMPLES—Chicken pox.

SPITTING

GLAIRY MUCUS—Catarrh.

DARK BLOOD, SPITTING OR VOMITING—Hemorrhage or bleeding from stomach.

Figure 18.

RECEIPTS FOR ALL KINDS OF LINIMENT.

 BARRELL'S
INDIAN LINIMENT.

1 qt. alcohol,
1 oz. tincture ot capsicum,
½ oz. oil of origanum,
½ oz. oil of sassafras,
½ oz. oil of pennyroyal,
½ oz. oil of hemlock.
Mix.

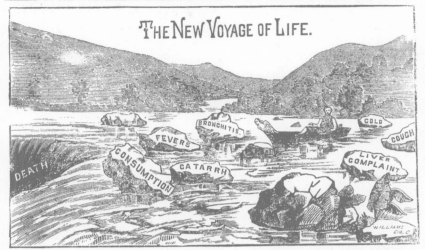

1140   MEDICINES AND THEIR PREPARATIONS.

1. **Headache, congestion of the base of the brain, occipital headache.**—A hot water bottle or small mustard poultice applied to nape of neck in conjunction with hot foot baths, are efficient in these troubles.

2. **Stiff-neck, torticollis or wry neck.**—Bathing with hot alcohol and water, or chloroform or ammonia liniments are useful applications.

3. **Nose bleed (epistaxis).**—Cold applications, as piece of ice or large cold key placed in position 3. Holding a wad of tissue paper between upper lip and teeth under nostril of bleeding side.

4. **Pleurisy.**—Paint with tincture of iodine for acute and chronic pleurisy though hot flaxseed poultices are possibly better for the very painful acute variety. Swathing the lower portion of the chest with firm bandages to prevent too deep breathing gives great relief.

5. **Backache, lumbago.**—Thorough massage of the back muscles in region of No. 5, using some bland and soothing oil like sweet or olive oil is excellent. Avoid irritating applications like mustard poultices but use porous plasters in their place or adhesive plaster straps.

6. **Sciatica.**—Painting course of sciatic nerve with tincture of iodine or the application of three or four fly blisters about three-fourths of an inch square, two or three inches apart, down the back.

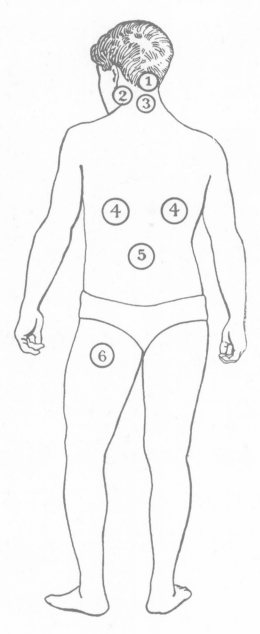

FROTHY, RED BLOOD, SPITTING OR VOMITING—Hemorrhage or bleeding from lungs or lower bronchial tubes.

VOMITING

YELLOW OR GREEN MATERIAL—Usually shows bile.

COFFEE GROUNDS—Malignant growth; probably cancer of stomach.

DARK BLOOD—Bleeding from stomach.

RED, FROTHY, BLOOD—Bleeding from lungs.

PROJECTILE (Vomiting with force)—Usually means meningitis.

BLOATING

OF STOMACH—Indigestion. Dilated stomach.

UNDER EYES—Kidney trouble.

OF FACE—Kidney trouble. Heart trouble. Poor condition generally.

OF ABDOMEN—Cirrhosis or hardening of liver. Tumors of ovaries, etc.

OF LEGS AND FEET—Kidney trouble. Often from pressure on veins.

FEVER

FEVER—Shows rise in temperature. Found in inflammatory diseases such as tonsilitis, gastritis, appendicitis, etc. Also in infectious diseases such as diphtheria, scarlet fever, typhoid fever, etc. . . .

CHILL

CHILL—Indicates lower external temperature. Found in malaria, grip, pneumonia, nervousness, etc.

COUGH

COUGHING—Is often due to irritation from dust or smoking; also to nervousness and indigestion.

DRY, HACKING COUGH—May mean consumption.

COARSE, BARKING COUGH—Whooping cough.

LOOSE COUGH—Due to mucus in air passages.

CRY OF CHILD

CRYING—Usually indicates pain or anger.

BOISTEROUS, TEMPORARY CRY—Anger.

CATCHY, JERKY CRY—Pain.

MOANING, WAILING CRY—Disease.

STOOLS

GREENISH—Improper feeding, usually in children.

WATERY—Generally in cholera infantum.

FREQUENT—Diarrhoea.

INFREQUENT—Constipation.

URINE

BLOODY—Hemorrhage or bleeding from kidneys.

PALE—Generally nervousness. May be diabetes insipidus.

WHITE—Generally from deposits of white gravel.

SWELLINGS

UNDER JAW—Enlarged glands.
SIDE OF JAW IN FRONT OF EAR—Mumps.
FRONT OF NECK—Goitre.

EYES

RED AND INFLAMED—Inflammation of eyes.
ROLLING OF EYES—Generally caused by brain irritation.
CONTRACTED (SMALL) PUPILS—Generally poisoning from opium.
DILATED (ENLARGED) PUPILS—Apoplexy. Poisoning from atropine.

NOSE

MOVEMENT OF NOSTRILS IN BREATHING—Frequently seen in pneumonia.
PICKING NOSE—Often means worms and especially if there is a scratching of rectum.

HEADACHE

FRONT PART, DULL ACHING—Caused by constipation or dyspepsia.
ACHING IN EYES—Generally glasses are needed.
TOP AND BACK OF HEAD—In women, this frequently indicates womb disease.
THROBBING—Congestion.
IN TEMPLES (NEURALGIA)—May be due to bad teeth.

FROTHING AT MOUTH

FROTHING AT MOUTH—Convulsions, paralysis or apoplexy.

HANDS AND FEET

COLD HANDS AND FEET—Poor circulation and low condition. Also seen in last stages of disease before death.

HEAD

OVER EYEBROWS—Catarrh or grip.
NECK (NAPE OF)—Spinal troubles and nervousness.
NECK, CONTINUED STIFFNESS OF NAPE—One of the first symptoms of typhoid fever.

CHEST

IN LUNGS—Pleurisy, pneumonia, consumption.
MUSCLES OF CHEST—Rheumatism or neuritis.
UNDER EDGE OF RIBS—Intercostal neuralgia (Neuritis.)
PAIN IN BREATHING—Generally pleurisy or pneumonia.

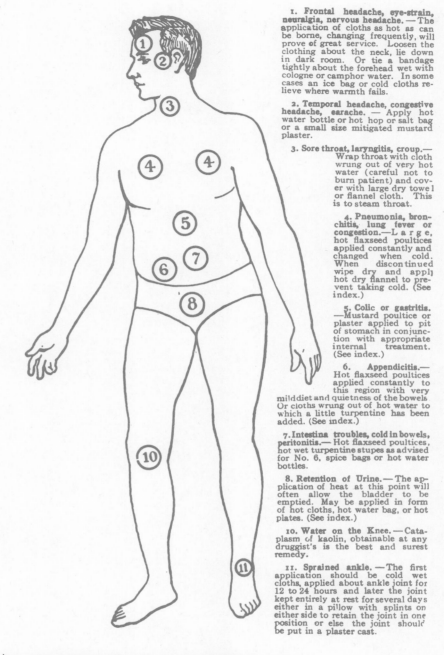

1. **Frontal headache, eye-strain, neuralgia, nervous headache.**—The application of cloths as hot as can be borne, changing frequently, will prove of great service. Loosen the clothing about the neck, lie down in dark room. Or tie a bandage tightly about the forehead wet with cologne or camphor water. In some cases an ice bag or cold cloths relieve where warmth fails.

2. **Temporal headache, congestive headache, earache.** — Apply hot water bottle or hot hop or salt bag or a small size mitigated mustard plaster.

3. **Sore throat, laryngitis, croup.**—Wrap throat with cloth wrung out of very hot water (careful not to burn patient) and cover with large dry towel or flannel cloth. This is to steam throat.

4. **Pneumonia, bronchitis, lung fever or congestion.**—Large, hot flaxseed poultices applied constantly and changed when cold. When discontinued wipe dry and apply hot dry flannel to prevent taking cold. (See index.)

5. **Colic or gastritis.**—Mustard poultice or plaster applied to pit of stomach in conjunction with appropriate internal treatment. (See index.)

6. **Appendicitis.**—Hot flaxseed poultices applied constantly to this region with very mild diet and quietness of the bowels. Or cloths wrung out of hot water to which a little turpentine has been added. (See index.)

7. **Intestine troubles, cold in bowels, peritonitis.**— Hot flaxseed poultices, hot wet turpentine stupes as advised for No. 6, spice bags or hot water bottles.

8. **Retention of Urine.**—The application of heat at this point will often allow the bladder to be emptied. May be applied in form of hot cloths, hot water bag, or hot plates. (See index.)

10. **Water on the Knee.**—Cataplasm of kaolin, obtainable at any druggist's is the best and surest remedy.

11. **Sprained ankle.**—The first application should be cold wet cloths, applied about ankle joint for 12 to 24 hours and later the joint kept entirely at rest for several days either in a pillow with splints on either side to retain the joint in one position or else the joint should be put in a plaster cast.

AROUND HEART—May be heart trouble, muscular rheumatism or heartburn. Heartburn is due to pressure from gas in stomach or bowels.

ABDOMEN

PAINS IN STOMACH—Probably due to indigestion. May be dilation or gas.
IN STOMACH AND RADIATING TO BACK BONE—Ulcer of stomach.
IN STOMACH—May be due to cancer.

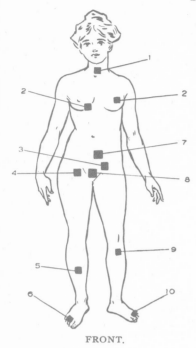

FRONT.

1. Goitre.
2. Diseases of the Breasts.
3. Peritonitis.
4. Diseases of the Ovary.
5. Ulcer of the Leg.
6. Bunions.
7. Abdominal Hernia.
8. Womb Diseases.
9. Varicose Veins.
10. Corns.

BACK.

1. Varicose Veins.
2. Curvature of the Spine.
3. Backache.
4. Varicose Veins.

RIGHTSIDE UNDER RIBS AND LIVER AND HIGHER THAN IN APPENDICITIS—Gall stones.

RUNNING FROM KIDNEY TO BLADDER AND INTO GROIN OR SCROTUM—Usually due to gravel.

BACK

PAIN UNDER RIBS NEAR BACK BONE—Kidney trouble. Kidneys are higher up than most people think.

IN DEEP MUSCLES OF BACK—Lumbago.

VERY LOW IN BACK—Piles or injured bone (Coccyx)

PAIN IN URINATING

PAIN IN PASSING URINE—Local inflammation of urethra or bladder or due to acid or alkaline urine.

COMPARISON OF DISEASES

DIPHTHERIA—First there is a spot or spots on the tonsils or perhaps on the soft palate or uvula, then the membrane quickly forms and perhaps extends to the other parts.

Membrane when forcibly removed leaves a red, raw surface and speedily returns.

Membrane is of a "whitish-yellow-brown" or grayish color.

Bad tongue somewhat the color of the membrane.

Very bad breath.

TONSILITIS—Spot or spots on the tonsils; membrane forms on the tonsils only.

Membrane when it comes off leaves a glistening surface.

Membrane of a whitish–yellow–brown or grayish color.

Bad tongue somewhat the color of the membrane.

Very bad breath.

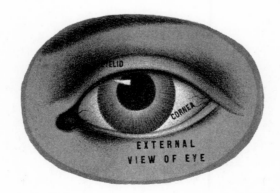

EXTERNAL VIEW OF EYE

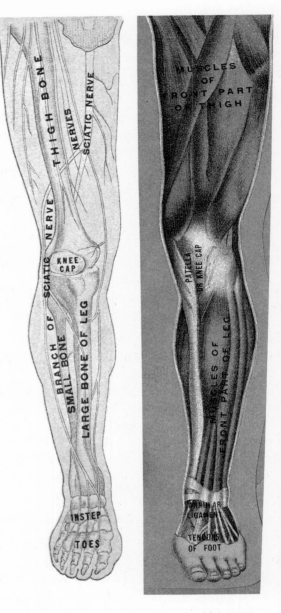

MEASLES—Sneezing, water running from nose, watery eyes and generally a bad cough.

A great deal of fever.

The eruption is generally thick and in blotches or spots.

Eruption appears first in the mouth and on the face.

SMALL-POX—There is first a sense of uneasiness, weariness, and soreness.

Severe pain in the head as if it would fly to pieces. An indescribable pain in the back.

Very bad breath.

Eruption is first seen upon the face and exposed parts of the body in the form of small red points. These enlarge greatly and finally fill with pus.

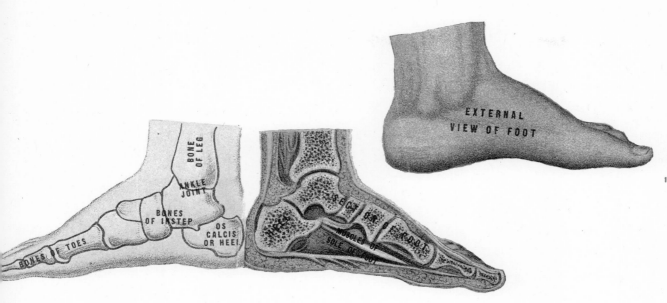

External view of foot. Bones of leg, Ankle Joint, Bones of Instep, Os Calcis or Heel, Bones of Toes. Section of Foot, Muscles of Sole of Foot.

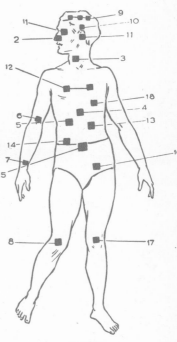

FRONT.

1. Diseases of the Eye.
2. Diseases of the Nose.
3. Diseases of the Throat.
4. Diseases of the Stomach.
5. Diseases of the Liver.
6. Articular Rheumatism.
7. Articular Rheumatism.
8. Rheumatism.
9. Headache.
10. Neuralgia.
11. Diseases of the Ear.
12. Diseases of the Lungs.
13. Diseases of the Bowels.
14. Appendicitis.
15. Diseases of the Bladder.
16. Rupture.
17. Rheumatism.
18. Diseases of the Heart.

Roseola—Eruption is a deep scarlet flush.

Eruption shows in patches and is not uniform over the body.

Eruption first appears on limbs and body.

Tongue may be covered with a thick whitish yellow coating.

There is not generally a sore throat.

Gall stone colic—The pain is generally excruciating.

The pain is generally under the ribs and in the stomach.

There is a history of gall stones.

Generally a bilious complexion.

Appendicitis—The pain may be severe but is generally a severe aching.

The pain is located midway between the navel and the point of the hip bone and does not extend down into the scrotum.

The muscles of the abdomen are tense and hard.

However, since there are more diseases than listed above and many more symptoms, it would be advisable for the person who is treating the sick to look at the list of symptoms which is alphabetically arranged thus:

Abdomen, distended—Chronic Catarrh of the Stomach. Chronic Dyspepsia. Drunkard's Dyspepsia. Chronic Alcoholism.

(through)

Chest, crackling sounds in the, which cough does not change—Pleurisy.

(through)

Feet and legs, swollen ankles—Cancer of the Stomach. Dropsy.

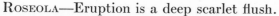

External view of hand.

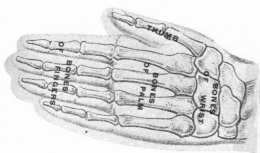

Thumb, Bones of Fingers, Bones of Palm, Bones of Wrist.

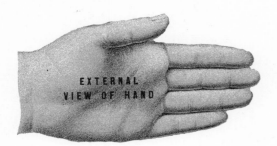

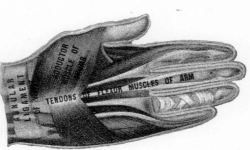

Annular Ligament, Adductor Muscle of Thumb, Tendons of Flexor Muscles of Arm.

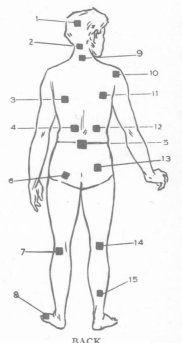

BACK.

1. Headache.
2. Brain Disease.
3. Pleurisy.
4. Kidney Disease.
5. Lumbago.
6. Sciatica.
7. Rheumatism.
8. Gout.
9. Stiff Neck.
10. Rheumatism.
11. Pleurisy.
12. Kidney Disease.
13. Sciatica.
14. Sciatica.
15. Sciatica.

REV. JOHN WESLEY'S

VALUABLE

PRIMITIVE REMEDIES,

OR AN

EASY AND NATURAL METHOD OF CURING
MOST DISEASES.

ALSO

MODERN MEDICINE,

BY

𝔒. 𝔚. 𝔊𝔬𝔯𝔡𝔬𝔫, 𝔐. 𝔇.,

WITH USEFUL AND VALUABLE RECEIPTS.

For Books, address

O. W. GORDON, Editor and Manager.

CHICAGO,

1880.

REV. JOHN WESLEY, A. M.

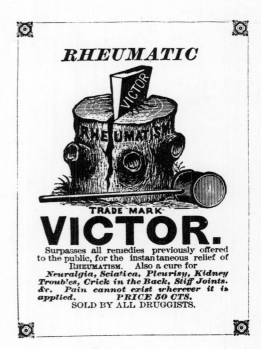

RHEUMATIC

TRADE MARK

VICTOR.

Surpasses all remedies previously offered
to the public, for the instantaneous relief of
RHEUMATISM.   Also a cure for
*Neuralgia, Sciatica, Pleurisy, Kidney
Troubles, Crick in the Back, Stiff Joints.
&c.   Pain cannot exist wherever it is
applied.*   PRICE 50 CTS.
SOLD BY ALL DRUGGISTS.

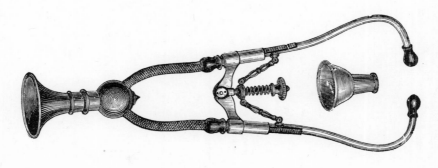

Home Remedy Books

Now that the diagnosis (?) had been made, the next step would be to cure the patient. That was done in one of many ways.

The first method was through the use of remedies found in various books, one of the first of which was a book called *Primitive Physic* published in the United States by Rev. John Wesley in 1747. In his book he says that he wanted to simplify cures so that the common man could be his own doctor.

Other early books included *The Pocumtuc Housewife*, a combined cookbook and medical book, adapted by several ladies in the Connecticut Valley in the early 1800's. Other books published in the early 1800's were *The Indian Doctor's Dispensatory* by Peter Smith, *The Indian Doctor; Dr. John Williams' Last Legacy, A Useful Family Herbal* and *The Family Doctor or Guide to Health*.

Over the years during the 19th century there were many books written and published. Two of the more famous ones were *Dr. Chase's Recipes or Information for Everybody* and *Gunn's Domestic Medicine or Poor Man's Friend in Pain and Sickness*.

Here are excerpts from a number of books published up until 1914. Notice that the Rev. Wesley's original primitive remedies were incorporated into a book by O. W. Gordon, M.D. in 1880. Since the original Wesley book was not touched by Dr. Gordon, all the original quaintness is there.

J. C. Gunn, M.D.

DIARRHŒA MIXTURE

FOR

SUMMER COMPLAINT, DYSENTERY, DIARRHŒA, ETC.

DOSE: ADULTS HALF TEASPOONFUL EVERY THREE HOURS IN WATER.

Chesnee Dairy Co.
CHESNEE, S.C.

Two Hundredth Edition, Revised and Enlarged.

GUNN'S

NEW FAMILY PHYSICIAN:

OR

HOME BOOK OF HEALTH;

FORMING A

COMPLETE HOUSEHOLD GUIDE.

GIVING MANY VALUABLE SUGGESTIONS FOR AVOIDING DISEASE AND PROLONGING LIFE, WITH PLAIN DIRECTIONS
IN CASES OF EMERGENCY, AND POINTING OUT IN FAMILIAR LANGUAGE THE CAUSES,
SYMPTOMS, TREATMENT AND CURE OF DISEASES INCIDENT TO

MEN, WOMEN AND CHILDREN,

WITH THE SIMPLEST AND BEST REMEDIES; PRESENTING A

MANUAL FOR NURSING THE SICK,

AND

DESCRIBING MINUTELY THE PROPERTIES AND USES OF HUNDREDS OF WELL-KNOWN

MEDICINAL PLANTS.

BY JOHN C. GUNN, M. D.,

AUTHOR OF "GUNN'S DOMESTIC MEDICINE."

WITH SUPPLEMENTARY TREATISES ON

Anatomy, Physiology and Hygiene,

ON

DOMESTIC AND SANITARY ECONOMY,

AND ON

PHYSICAL CULTURE AND DEVELOPMENT.

NEWLY ILLUSTRATED, AND RE-STEREOTYPED.

PUBLISHERS:

WILSTACH, BALDWIN & CO.,

141 AND 143 RACE STREET, CINCINNATI:

1880

SOLD TO SUBSCRIBERS ONLY.

This preparation is recommended as an admirable substitute for all the various salts, its pleasant acidity of taste and its effervescing character rendering it a very agreeable and refreshing drink.

Effervescing SOLUTION OF Citrate of Magnesia

DIRECTIONS.

As a cooling and laxative medicine, a tablespoon to a wineglassful every hour or two, until the desired effect is produced. As a cathartic for an adult the contents of one bottle, half of it at first, and the remainder in one or two hours. Keep the bottle corked in the intervals of taking.

W. F. HENRY & CO.,
Pharmacists,
BELLAIRE, OHIO.

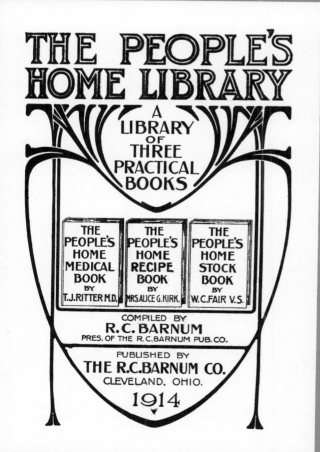

THE PEOPLE'S HOME LIBRARY

A LIBRARY OF THREE PRACTICAL BOOKS

| THE PEOPLE'S HOME MEDICAL BOOK BY T. J. RITTER M.D. | THE PEOPLE'S HOME RECIPE BOOK BY MRS. ALICE G. KIRK. | THE PEOPLE'S HOME STOCK BOOK BY W. C. FAIR V.S. |

COMPILED BY
R. C. BARNUM
PRES. OF THE R. C. BARNUM PUB. CO.

PUBLISHED BY
THE R. C. BARNUM CO.
CLEVELAND, OHIO.

1914

THE FAMILY DOCTOR,

OR THE

HOME BOOK

OF

HEALTH AND MEDICINE:

A POPULAR TREATISE

ON THE MEANS OF

AVOIDING AND CURING DISEASES,

AND OF PRESERVING THE

Health and Vigour of the Body

TO THE LATEST PERIOD;

INCLUDING AN ACCOUNT OF

THE NATURE AND PROPERTIES OF REMEDIES;

THE TREATMENT OF THE

DISEASES OF WOMEN AND CHILDREN,

AND THE MANAGEMENT OF

PREGNANCY AND PARTURITION.

BY A PHYSICIAN OF PHILADELPHIA.

NEW YORK AND AUBURN:
MILLER, ORTON & MULLIGAN.
NEW YORK: 25 PARK ROW—AUBURN: 107 GENESEE-ST.
1856.

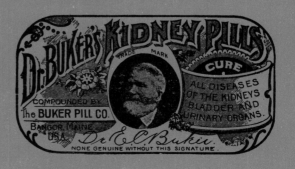

Dr. BUKER'S KIDNEY PILLS

TRADE MARK

CURE ALL DISEASES OF THE KIDNEYS BLADDER AND URINARY ORGANS.

COMPOUNDED BY The BUKER PILL CO.
BANGOR, MAINE USA.

NONE GENUINE WITHOUT THIS SIGNATURE.

DR. CHASE'S RECIPES;

OR,

INFORMATION FOR EVERYBODY:

AN INVALUABLE COLLECTION OF ABOUT EIGHT HUNDRED

 RACTICAL  ECIPES

FOR

Merchants, Grocers, Saloon-Keepers, Physicians, Druggists, Tanners, Shoemakers, Harness Makers, Painters, Jewelers, Blacksmiths, Tinners, Gunsmiths, Farriers, Barbers, Bakers, Dyers, Renovators, Farmers, and Families Generally

WITH

A Rational Treatment of Pleurisy, Inflammation of the Lungs, and other Inflammatory Diseases. and also for General Female Debility and Irregularities.

BY A. W. CHASE, M. D.

"WE LEARN TO LIVE, BY LIVING TO LEARN."

GREATLY ENLARGED AND IMPROVED BY THE PUBLISHER,

WHO HAS ADDED

Appendices to the Medical, Saloon, Farriers', Barbers' and Toilet, Bakers' and Cooking, Miscellaneous, and Coloring Departments, and also Several New Departments, viz.:

"Advice to Mothers," "Rules for the Preservation of Health," "Accidents and Emergencies," "Hints upon Etiquette and Personal Manners," "Hints on Housekeeping," "Amusements for the Young," and "Bee-Keeping."

ALL ARRANGED IN THEIR APPROPRIATE DEPARTMENTS, WITH A COPIOUS INDEX.

PUBLISHED BY R. A. BEAL,
ANN ARBOR, MICH. :
TO WHOM ALL ORDERS SHOULD BE ADDRESSED
1887.

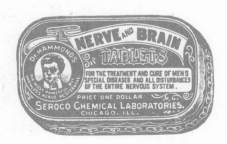

When man came first out of the hands of the Great Creator, clothed in body, as well as in soul, with immortality and incorruption, there was no place for physic, or the art of healing. As he knew no sin, so he knew no pain, no sickness, weakness, or bodily disorder. The habitation wherein the angelic mind, the Divine Particulae Aurae, abode, although originally formed of the dust of the earth, was liable to no decay. . . .

But since man rebelled against the Sovereign of heaven and earth, how entirely is the scene changed! The incorruptible frame hath put on corruption, the immortal hath put on mortality. The seeds of wickedness and pain, of sickness and death, are now lodged in our inmost substance; whence a thousand disorders continually spring, even without the aid of external violence. And how is the number of these increased by every thing round about us? The heavens, the earth, and all things contained therein, conspire to punish the rebels against their Creator. The sun and moon shed unwholesome influences from above; the earth exhales poisonous damps from beneath; the beasts of the field, the birds of the air, the fishes of the sea, are in a state of hostility; the air itself that surrounds us on every side, is replete with shafts of death; yea, the food we eat daily saps the foundation of that life which cannot be sustained without it. So has the Lord of All secured the execution of His decree—"Dust thou art, and unto dust shalt thou return."

But can nothing be found to lessen those inconveniences which cannot be wholly removed? To soften the evils of life, and prevent in part the sickness and pain to which we are continually exposed? That without question there may be One grand preventative of sickness of various kinds, seems intimated by the grand Author of Nature in the very sentence that entails death upon us,—"In the sweat of thy face shalt thou eat bread, till thou return to the ground." The power of exercise, both to preserve and restore health, is greater than can well be conceived; especially in those who add temperance thereto. . . .

It is probable Physic, as well as Religion, was in the first ages chiefly traditional; every father delivering down to his sons what he had in like manner received, concerning the manner of healing both outward hurts and the diseases incident to each climate, and the medicines which were of the greatest efficacy for the cure of each disorder. It is certain this is the method wherein the art of healing is preserved among the American Indians to this day. . . .

Hence it was, perhaps, that the ancients, not only of Greece and Rome, but even of barbarous nations, usually assigned physic a divine original. And indeed it was a natural thought, that He who had taught it to the very beasts and birds, the Cretan Stag, the Egyptian Ibis, could not be wanting to teach man. . . .

And has not the Author of Nature taught us the use of many other medicines by what is vulgarly termed accident? Thus, one walking some years since in a grove of pines, at a time when many in the neighboring towns were afflicted with a kind of new distemper—little sores in the inside of the mouth—a drop of natural gum fell from one of the trees on a book he was reading. This he took up, and thoughtlessly applied to one of those sore places. Finding the pain immediately cease, he applied it to another, which was also presently healed. The same remedy he afterwards imparted to others, and it did not fail to heal any that applied it. And doubtless numberless remedies have been thus casually discovered in every age and nation.

Thus far physic was wholly founded on experiment. . . . Thus, ancient men, having a little experience joined with common sense and common humanity, cured both themselves and neighbors of most of the distempers to which every nation was subject.

But in process of time, men of a philosophical turn were not satisfied with this. They began to enquire how they might account for

PREFACE
TO THE
Household Physician.

THIS book is written for the people. It is based on the assumption that every man—the mechanic, the farmer, and the day laborer, as well as the professional and business man—has a right to all the knowledge he is capable of acquiring, on all subjects, medicine not excepted. The book aims, therefore, to popularize and adapt to the many what has been claimed as belonging only to the few.

We do not hesitate to avow that our sympathies are with the great masses, who may be called the bone and muscle of the race. They are, in the main, more shrewd, more endowed with common sense, more simple and true in their natural instincts, and consequently less perverted, than many of those who claim more refinement and a higher place in the social scale.

"All men," says Hippocrates, one of the great fathers of medicine, "ought to be acquainted with the medical art. We believe that knowledge of medicine is the sister and companion of wisdom." Such knowledge would shield the many from the impositions of quackery. No one who reads this book thoroughly will be often imposed upon thereafter by quack nostrums, or quack doctors. Every man's physical organization is his own; and he is charged with the responsibility of taking care of it. To do this properly, he needs knowledge of it, and to withhold this from him is another form of the old oppression, which decreed knowledge and power to the few, and ignorance and obedience to the many.

In accordance with the design of the work, it has been written in plain, simple English, and brought within the comprehension of all who have medium powers of mind.

these things? How such medicines wrought such effects? . . . They explored the several kinds of animal and mineral, as well as vegetable substances. . . . Men of learning began to set experience aside—to build physic upon hypothesis—to form theories of diseases and their cure, and to substitute these in the place of experiments.

As theories increased, simple medicines were more and more disregarded and disused, till in a course of years the greater part of them

THE PRACTICAL
HOUSEHOLD PHYSICIAN.

A CYCLOPEDIA

OF

Family Medicine, Surgery, Nursing and Hygiene

FOR DAILY USE IN

THE PRESERVATION OF HEALTH AND CARE OF THE SICK AND INJURED.

CONTAINING A PLAIN DESCRIPTION OF THE PARTS OF THE HUMAN BODY AND THEIR USES; CHAPTERS ON "OUR HOMES," CLIMATE, FOOD AND DRINK, USE OF INTOXICANTS AND NARCOTICS; SPECIAL CHAPTERS GIVING IMPORTANT INFORMATION FOR EVERY WOMAN; WITH CLEAR AND FULL INFORMATION FOR ASSISTING THE SKILLFUL EFFORTS OF THE DOCTOR, AND FOR THE TREATMENT OF ACCIDENTS AND DISEASES. ARRANGED FOR READY REFERENCE TO ENABLE ONE TO DO INSTANTLY WHAT CAN AND OUGHT TO BE DONE IN EMERGENCIES TO RELIEVE SUFFERING OR SAVE LIFE.

BY

HENRY HARTSHORNE, A.M., M.D., LL.D.,

FORMERLY PROFESSOR OF HYGIENE IN THE UNIVERSITY OF PENNSYLVANIA, AND PROFESSOR OF PHYSIOLOGY AND DISEASES OF CHILDREN IN WOMAN'S MEDICAL COLLEGE OF PENNSYLVANIA; AUTHOR OF "OUR HOMES," "ESSENTIALS OF PRACTICAL MEDICINE," "A CONSPECTUS OF THE MEDICAL SCIENCES," EDITOR OF THE AMERICAN EDITION OF "REYNOLDS' SYSTEM OF MEDICINE," ETC., ETC.

WITH EIGHT COLORED PLATES AND NEARLY THREE HUNDRED WOOD-CUT ILLUSTRATIONS.

NEW AND REVISED EDITION.

JOHN C. WINSTON & CO.,
PHILADELPHIA, PA.; CHICAGO, ILLINOIS; SYRACUSE, N. Y.
1891.

---

were forgotten, at least in the politer nations. In the room of these, abundance of new ones were introduced, by reasoning, speculative men; and those more and more difficult to be applied, as being more remote from common observation. Hence, rules for the application of these and medical books, were immensely multiplied, till at length physic became an abstruse science, quite out of the reach of ordinary men.

Physicians now began to be in admiration, as persons who were something more than human. And profit attended employ as well as honor; so that they had now two weighty reasons for keeping the bulk of mankind at a distance, that they might not pry into the mysteries of the profession. To this end they increased those difficulties by design, which began in a manner by accident. . . .

Yet there have not been wanting from time to time, some lovers of mankind, who have endeavored, even contrary to their own interest, to reduce physic to its ancient standard. . . . So that every man of common sense, unless in some rare case, may prescribe either to himself or neighbor; and may be very secure from doing harm, even where he can do no good.

Even in the last age there was something of this kind done, particularly by the great and good Dr. Hydenham; and in the present, by his pupil, Dr. Dover, who has pointed out simple medicines for many diseases. . . .

Who would not wish to have a physician always in his house, and one that attends without fee or reward.

Is it enquired, but are there not books enough already on every part of the art of medicine? Yes, too many ten times over, considering how little to the purpose the far greater part of them speak. But besides this, they are too dear for poor men to buy, and too hard for plain men to understand.

Do you say, "But there are enough of those collections of receipts." Where? I have not seen one yet, either in our own or any other tongue, which contains only safe, and cheap, and easy medicines. In all that have yet fallen into my hands, I find many dear and many far-fetched medicines; besides many of so dangerous a kind as a prudent man would never meddle with. And against the greater part of these medicines there is a further objection—they consist of too many ingredients. . . .

MANNER OF USING THE MEDICINES

As to the manner of using the medicines here set down, I would advise, as soon as you know your distemper, which is very easy, unless in a complication of disorders, and then you would do well to apply to a physician that fears God. . . .

First—Use the first of the remedies for that disease which occurs in the ensuing collection, unless some other of them be easier to be had, and then it may do just as well.

Secondly—After a competent time, if it takes no effect, use the second, and the third, and so on. I have purposely set down, in most cases, several remedies for each disorder, not only because all are not equally easy to be procured at all times, and in all places, but likewise, because the medicine which cures one man will not always cure another of the same distemper. Nor will it cure the same man at all times. Therefore it was necessary to have a variety. However, I have subjoined the letter (I) to those medicines which some think infallible, (tried) to those which I have found to be of the greatest efficacy. I believe many others to be of equal virtue, but it has not laid in my way to make the trial. One I must aver from personal knowledge, grounded on a thousand experiments, to be far superior to all other medicines I have known—I mean electricity. . . .

Thirdly—Observe all the time the greatest exactness in your regimen or manner of living. Abstain from all mixed or high-seasoned food. Use plain diet easy of digestion, and this as sparingly as you can consistent with ease and strength.—Drink only water if it agrees with your stomach. Use as much exercise daily in the open air as you can, without weariness. Sup at six or seven on the lightest food; go to bed early, and rise betimes. To persevere with steadiness in this course, is often more than half the cure. Above all, add to the rest, for it is not labor lost, that old-fashioned medicine—*prayer;* and have faith in God, who "Killeth and maketh alive, who bringeth down to the grave and bringeth up."

For the sake of those who desire, through the blessing of God, to retain the health which they have recovered, I have added a few plain easy rules, briefly transcribed from Dr. Cheyne.

PLAIN EASY RULES

The air we breathe is of great consequence to our health. Those who have been long abroad in easterly or northerly winds should drink some warm pepper tea on going to bed, or a draught of toast and water.

Tender people should have those who lie with them, or are much about them, sound, sweet, and healthy.

Every one that would preserve health should be as clean and sweet as possible in their houses, clothes, and furniture.

The great rule of eating and drinking is to suit the quality and quantity of the food to the strength of the digestion; to take always such a sort and such a measure of food as sits light and easy on the stomach.

All pickled, or smoked, or salted food, and all high-seasoned, is unwholesome.

Nothing conduces more to health than abstinence and plain food, with due labor.

For studious persons, about eight ounces of animal food and twelve of vegetable, in twenty-four hours, is sufficient.

Water is the wholesomest of all drinks; it quickens the appetite and strengthens the digestion most.

Strong, and more especially spiritous liquors, are a certain, though slow, poison.

Experience shows there is very seldom any danger in leaving them off at once.

Strong liquors do not prevent the mischiefs of a surfeit, or carry it off so safely as water.

Malt liquors are extremely hurtful to tender persons.

Coffee and tea are extremely hurtful to persons who have weak nerves.

Figure 21.

Tender persons should eat very light suppers, and that two or three hours before going to bed.

Walking is the best exercise for those who are able to bear it; riding for those who are not. The open air, when the weather is fair, contributes much to the benefit of exercise.

We may strengthen any weak part of the body by constant exercise. Thus the lungs may be strengthened by loud speaking, or walking up an easy ascent; the digestion and the nerves by riding; the arms and hams by strong rubbing them daily.

The studious ought to have stated times for exercise, at least two or three hours a day; the one-half of this before dinner, the other before going to bed.

They should frequently shave, and frequently wash their feet.

Those who read or write much, should learn to do it standing; otherwise it will impair their health.

The fewer clothes any one uses by day or night, the hardier he will be.

Exercise, first, should always be on an empty stomach; secondly, should never be continued to weariness; thirdly, after it, we should take to cool by degrees, otherwise we shall catch cold.

The flesh brush is a most useful exercise, especially to strengthen any part that is weak.

Cold bathing is of great advantage to health; it prevents abundance of diseases. It promotes perspiration, helps the circulation of the blood, and prevents catching cold. . . .

AN EASY AND NATURAL METHOD OF CURING MOST DISEASES

 ABORTION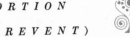

(TO PREVENT)

Women of a weak or relaxed habit should use solid food, avoiding great quantities of tea and other weak and watery liquors. They should go soon to bed and rise early, and take frequent exercise but avoid being overfatigued.

If of full habit, they ought to use a spare diet, and chiefly of the vegetable kind, avoiding strong liquors and everything that may tend to heat the body, or increase the quantity of blood.

In the first case, take daily half pint of decoction of Lignum Guaiacum; boiling an ounce of it in a quart of water for five minutes.

In the latter case, give half a drachm of powdered nitre in a cup of water-gruel, every five or six hours; in both cases she should sleep on a hard mattress with her head low, and be kept cool and quiet.

FOR AN AGUE

An ague is an intermitting fever, each fit of which is preceded by a cold shivering, and goes off in a sweat.

Go into the cold bath just before the cold fit.

Nothing tends more to prolong an ague than indulging a lazy indolent disposition. The patient ought therefore, between the fits, to take as much exercise as he can bear, and to use a light diet, and, for common drink, lemonade is the most proper.

When all other means fail, give blue vitrol, from one grain to two grains in the absence of the fit, and repeat it three or four times in twenty-four hours.

Or, take a handful of groundsel; shred it small, put it into a paper bag four inches square; pricking that side which is to be next the skin full of holes; cover this with a thin linen, and wear it on the pit of the stomach, renewing it two hours before the fit. (Tried.)

Or, apply to the stomach a large onion, slit.

Or, melt two pennyworth of frankincense, spread it on linen, grate a nutmeg upon it, cover it with linen, and hang this bag on the pit of the stomach. I have never yet known it fail.

Or, make six middling pills of cobwebs. Take one a little before the cold fit; two a little before the next fit, (suppose the next day;) the other three, if need be, a little before the third fit. This seldom fails.

Or, put a tea-spoonful of salt of tartar into a large glass of spring water, and drink it by

little and little; repeat the same dose the next two days before the time of the fit.

Or, two small tea-spoonsful of sal prunella an hour before the fit. It commonly cures in thrice taking. . . .

It is proper to take a gentle vomit, and sometimes a purge, before you use any of these medicines. If a vomit is taken two hours before the fit is expected, it generally prevents that fit, and sometimes cures an ague, especially in children. It is also proper to repeat the medicine (whatever it be) about a week after, in order to prevent a relapse. Do not take any purge soon after. The daily use of the flesh brush, and frequent cold bathing, are of great use to prevent relapses.

CANINE APPETITE

An insatiable desire of eating.

"If it be without vomiting, is often cured by a small bit of bread dipped in wine, and applied to the nostrils."

Dr. Scomberg

SPITTING OF BLOOD

Take a tea-cupful of stewing prunes at laying down for two or three nights. (Tried.)

Or, two spoonsful of juice of nettles every morning, and a large cup of decoction of nettles at night, for a week. (Tried.)

Or, three spoonsful of sage juice in a little honey. This presently stops either spitting or vomiting blood. (Tried.)

HARD BREASTS

Apply turnips roasted till soft, then mashed and mixed with a little oil of roses. Change this twice a day, keeping the breast very warm with flannel.

TO CURE BALDNESS

Rub the part morning and evening, with onions, till it is red, and rub it afterwards with honey.

Or, wash it with a decoction of boxwood. (Tried.)

Or, electrify it daily.

Dr. Fenner's Cough-Cold Syrup

This medicine contains of the best C. P. Grain **ALCOHOL 5½%** and other valuable ingredients.

Free from Opium, Morphine, or any Narcotic.

FOR COUGHS, COLDS, COLD IN THE HEAD, INFLUENZA, HOARSENESS.

DIRECTIONS

For Adults—1 teaspoonful every hour until relieved and then every two hours until a perfect cure is secured.

For Children—10 to 60 drops, according to age.

This Remedy, so pleasant to take that it is sought by children as well as by adults, is capable of great good to mankind. But like **Dr. Fenner's Golden Relief,** in order to secure the effects claimed for both remedies, they must be properly and persistently used, till the end sought is obtained.

Walking Colds

How long have you been walking about with your hard cold and cough? Why not part company with them? It will cost you only 50 cents, the price of a half size bottle of

Dr. Ayer's Cherry Pectoral

Your cough ceases, your cold disappears, your throat is strengthened, your lungs healed, and the danger from pneumonia slips by.

If your lungs are sore with a tight feeling in the chest, apply one of
Ayer's Cherry Pectoral Plasters
It draws out inflammation and quiets pain.

"Ayer's Cherry Pectoral was a favorite medicine in my father's home and the home of my grandfather. Recently a party of gentlemen were discussing the many cough medicines, and it was agreed by all present that Ayer's Cherry Pectoral was the only one that would check and absolutely cure an aggravated cough. C. E. GILBERT,
July 7, 1898. Pres. of Record Publishing Co., Austin, Texas.

"Long exposure to a heavy, cold rain resulted in a severe cold which prostrated me. I was unable to speak aloud and had a bad cough. I used no medicine except Dr. Ayer's Cherry Pectoral, and in less than a week's time I was completely cured." CALVIN TOBIAS,
May 3, 1898. Yellow Creek, Pa.

A BRUISE

Immediately apply treacle spread on brown paper. (Tried.)

Or, apply a plaster of chopped parsley mixed with butter.

Or, electrify the part. This is the quickest cure of all.

A COLD

Drink a pint of cold water lying down in bed. (Tried.)

Or, to one spoonful of oatmeal, and one spoonful of honey add a piece of butter the bigness of a nutmeg: pour on, gradually, near a pint of boiling water. Drink this lying down in bed.

A COLD IN THE HEAD

Pare very thin the yellow rind of an orange, roll it up inside out, and thrust a roll into each nostril.

BILIOUS CHOLIC

This is generally attended with vomiting a greenish or frothy matter, with feverish heat, violent thirst, a bitter taste in the mouth, and little and high colored urine.

Drink warm lemonade: I know nothing like it.

A COUGH

Every cough is a dry cough at first. As long as it continues so, it may be cured by chewing immediately after you cough, the quantity of a pepper corn of Peruvian bark. Swallow your spittle as long as it is bitter, and spit out the wood. If you cough again, do this again. It very seldom fails to cure any dry cough. I earnestly desire every one, who has any regard for his health, to try this within twenty-four hours after he perceives a cough.

Or, drink a pint of cold water lying down in bed. (Tried.)

Or, make a hole through a lemon and fill it with honey. Roast it and catch the juice. Take a tea-spoonful of this frequently. (Tried.)

TESTICLES INFLAMED

Boil bean flower in three parts of water, one part vinegar.

DEAFNESS WITH A HEADACHE AND BUZZING IN THE HEAD

Peel a clove of garlic, dip it in honey, and put it into your ear at night with a little black wool. Lie with that ear uppermost. Do this, if need be, eight or ten nights. (Tried.)

DROWNED

Rub the trunk of the body all over with salt. It frequently recovers them that seem dead.

THE FALLING SICKNESS

In the falling sickness, the patient falls to the ground either quite stiff or convulsed all over, utterly senseless, gnashing his teeth, and foaming at the mouth.

Be electrified. (Tried.)

Or, take a tea-spoonful of peony root, dried and grated fine, morning and evening for three months.

Or, half a pint of tar water, morning and evening, for three months.

Or, use an entire milk diet for three months. It seldom fails.

In the fit, blow up the nose a little powdered ginger. . . .

THE HEART BURNING

A sharp gnawing pain in the orifice of the stomach.

Drink a pint of cold water. (Tried.)

Or, drink slowly decoction of camomile flowers.

Or, eat four or five oysters.

Or, chew five or six pepper corns a little, then swallow them.

Or, chew fennel or parsley, and swallow your spittle.

LUNACY

Give decoctions of agrimony four times a day.

Or, rub the head several times a day with vinegar in which ground-ivy leaves have been infused.

Or, boil the juice of ground-ivy with sweet oil and white wine into an ointment. Shave the head, anoint it therewith, and chafe it every other day for three weeks. Bruise also the leaves and bind them on the head, and give three spoonsful of the juice, warm, every morning.

This generally cures melancholy.

RAGING MADNESS

Apply to the head cloths dipped in cold water.

Or, set the patient with his head under a great waterfall as long as his strength will bear, or pour cold water on his head out of a tea-kettle.

Or, let him eat nothing but apples for a month.

Or, nothing but bread and milk. (Tried.)

A RUPTURE IN CHILDREN

Boil a spoonful of egg-shells dried in an oven, and powdered, in three quarters of a pint of milk. Feed the child constantly with bread boiled in this milk.

A STITCH IN THE SIDE

Apply treacle spread on hot toast. (Tried.)

TO FASTEN THE TEETH

Put powdered alum, the quantity of a nutmeg, in a quart of spring water for twenty-four hours: then strain the water and gargle with it.

Or, gargle often with phyllera leaves boiled with a little alum in forge water.

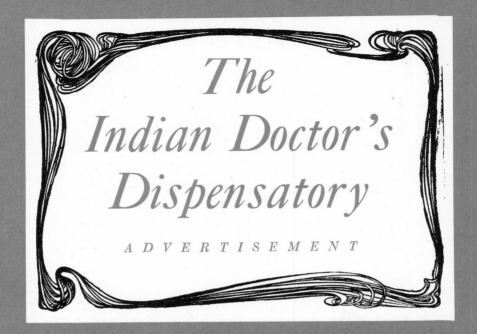

The Indian Doctor's Dispensatory

ADVERTISEMENT

THE AUTHOR would notify the purchaser that he puts the price of one dollar on this book of advice, well knowing that 75 cents would be enough for the common price of a book of its size. He is conscious that propriety, perspicuity and brevity will be found marked on every piece—and if so, the shorter the better.

But those who do not chuse to allow him 25 cents for his advice, may desist from the purchase. He conceives that these advices are calculated to assist every citizen in the preservation of his health, and his recovery if diseased; so that by attending to them, he may receive 30, 60, or an 100 fold for his dollar; by which he may also meet the wished for assistance set forth in simples and preparations, that will be in his own power.

Besides, if a physician must be employed, the boss, or head of the family, ought to know so much about the work he hires his artist to do, as to be able to estimate the value of it. He claims this 25 cents as a small compensation for the labor and observation of fifty years, without having made his labor an emolument of advantage heretofore. . . .

The author is well aware that the public mind has been long impressed with these ideas: viz. *"The natives of our own country are in possession of cures, simples, &c. that surpass what is used by our best practitioners."* He conceives this publication will gratify such generally, whose minds remain under such impressions. . . .

Something relating to the following work has been on my mind for twenty years past.

DR. SHOOP'S LABORATORY
FINEST IN AMERICA.

PREFACE

In my younger days I made a few memorandums and receipts; but finding as I advanced in reading a little on physic, and conversing with my friends who were physicians, that far the greatest part of them were trivial, I omitted making many more. However, having an insatiable taste and constant desire for relieving the afflicted and diseased, I have still been trying my hand from youth up, and I am now in my sixtieth year.

My father, old Hezekiah Smith, of Jersey, was always, since I could remember him, a *home old man*, or *Indian doctor*, with whom in my raising, I contracted ideas, practice and experience, that have never left me. . . .

About thirty years ago I called on old Dr. Wilkey, a German, who had been in the business of his profession, in the Flanders wars. He proposed to me to spend a few days with him, to instruct me in some knowledge which he had gained in his long life, and which he regretted should die with him: especially to make his *Leotrill*, a liquid which he prepared; for the obtaining of which he had paid a large sum in Flanders. With this medicine he made many of his cures, both in physic and surgery. With this, said he, "I can put a person in a complete salivation in ten minutes. I need only throw this with a syringe into any sore, ulcer, or wound, and it is fit at once for healing. Yes (said he) if there is a bullet lodged, it need scarcely ever be cut out; and a cancer in a woman's breast, I have never failed to cure with it." I only called to spend a few hours with this eminent old German, on my route from Virginia to Georgia, but have regretted, perhaps a thousand times, that I missed this great opportunity, so kindly proposed. I sometimes think of going to see his children (for he had some beautiful young folks, children by an English wife, when I was there) and try to obtain this Leotrill, and add it to my prescriptions.

There is an herb cultivated among the Ger-

THE
INDIAN DOCTOR'S
DISPENSATORY,

BEING

FATHER SMITH'S ADVICE

RESPECTING

DISEASES AND THEIR CURE;

CONSISTING OF PRESCRIPTIONS FOR

MANY COMPLAINTS:

AND A DESCRIPTION OF MEDICINES,

SIMPLE AND COMPOUND,

SHOWING THEIR VIRTUES AND HOW TO APPLY THEM.

DESIGNED FOR THE BENEFIT OF HIS CHILDREN, HIS FRIENDS AND THE PUBLIC, BUT MORE ESPECIALLY THE CITIZENS OF THE WESTERN PARTS OF THE UNITED STATES OF AMERICA.

BY PETER SMITH,
OF THE MIAMI COUNTRY.

Men seldom have wit enough to prize and take care of their health until they lose it—And Doctors often know not how to get their bread deservedly, until they have no teeth to chew it.

CINCINNATI:
PRINTED BY BROWNE AND LOOKER,
FOR THE AUTHOR.
1813.

mans, on the West side of the big Miami, I think it is in Montgomery county, particularly, I have been told, by the Dunkard preacher, Jacob Miller. This herb, I have full reason to believe, is an infallible cure for the bite of the mad dog, or hydrophobia. I have seen this herb in powder, and was assured that only this was used for several, man and beast, where no scruple could be entertained of their having been bitten with a mad dog, and nothing of the dire complaint was experienced; while these creatures to which it was omitted, fell victims. I cannot describe

MAN AND CHIEF. MEDICINE MAN.

One Bottle Cured Him.

I had chills and fever for years. Visited doctors in Boston and elsewhere, but got no relief, and was very much discouraged. I paid hundreds of dollars to the doctors without benefit, and then bought a bottle of Kickapoo Indian Sagwa for one dollar, and the second dose stopped the chills, one bottle effected a permanent cure.
MARTIN CONNELLY.
Worcester, Mass.

Chills Take Flight.

I have suffered three years from chills, was all worn out and discouraged. Doctors failed to relieve me. Took Kickapoo Indian Sagwa, and my chills have taken flight. I am cured. NEWTON MAYS.
Spring Hill, Kans.

Impure Blood.

The vital fluid which circulates through the body, giving it nourishment and strength, is of the highest importance. There cannot be a healthy condition of the body if the blood is impure. The germs of scrofula, salt rheum, and many other diseases, which sooner or later undermine the health, all arise from impure blood. To insure good health, this state of things must be changed; the blood must be cleansed from all impurities, and allowed free and unobstructed circulation through both veins and arteries. Kickapoo Indian Sagwa is the acknowledged Blood Renovator. Its equal cannot be found in all the science of medicine and chemistry. In all cases of blood disease, Sagwa works like magic.

A Great Sufferer.

I have been a great sufferer from eczema for the past five years, and have been treated by three different doctors, without receiving any benefit from them. Have now tried the Kickapoo Indian Sagwa in connection with the Kickapoo Indian Salve, and find they will do just what is claimed of them, that is, purify the blood and cure skin diseases. I have used the remedies for ten days and the eczema has nearly disappeared, and I earnestly recommend all those afflicted with any kind of skin disease to procure these great Indian Remedies at once. They will surely give relief in a short time.
MRS. C. W. LEIGHTON.
Gossville, N. H.

My Mother-in-law.

My mother-in-law, Mrs. Turbit, of Indiana, was paying us a visit last spring, and as she had a peculiar running sore just under the ear—that was called by doctors whom she consulted scrofula, erysipelas, and cancer—I requested her to try the Kickapoo Indian Remedies. She had not much faith, as so many doctors had failed to help her; nevertheless I got her a bottle of Indian Sagwa and a box of Indian Salve. She consented to give them a trial, and in just three days there was a marked improvement in her condition; in two weeks she was entirely well. The old sore healed, and save for a small scar it would be hard to tell it ever was there.
GEORGE RUSSELL,
Chief of Fire Department.
W. Bay City, Mich.

Scrofula.

In olden times of superstition this disease was believed to be cured by the patient being touched by the royal hand of the king. It was from this that the disease took the name of "king's evil." A terrible evil it is; and yet more terrible is the fact that in the veins of the majority of

Kickapoo Indian Sagwa cures Scrofula.

this herb, nor do I remember its name. I remember the dose is only what you may lift on the point of a case knife in powder. This is to be eaten on a piece of bread and butter, three mornings successively, and the cure is effected. . . .

If vouchers for the efficacy of my medicine herein described, may be wished for, I can observe that Mr. Edward Bartholomew, who lived in Philadelphia and kept the excise office in 1790, was one of my patients. He was a very fat man; one of his legs had been broken, which often inflamed, and appeared like mortifying. After he had given out applying to doctors, I undertook him; no cure, no pay. I saw him in Philadelphia, about fourteen years afterwards; he then gave me full credit for my applications, tho he had paid me in a few weeks after I first tried my means. His leg, when I first began with him, was as black as an old hat, and as big again as the other. My applications are described in Nos. 23 and 28.

Another voucher I will mention, is Mr. David Jones, a young Baptist minister, who lately lived with Dr. Samuel Jones, of Lower Dublin, Philadelphia country; who, residing a few years ago in the Miami county, I heard that he was sick, and went to see him. I found him attended by two doctors. His disorder was what I call the second grade of the bilious fever, attended with vomiting almost without intermission, which had then been for eight days. One of the doctors tarried with him, and I looked on, until the doctor and all present were convinced that he must die, and that quickly, unless something more effectual could take place. I then begged him of the doctor [as a patient].

I gave him my emetic No. 1, and tho' he had thrown every thing suddenly from his stomach before, this lay on for about twenty minutes; he then had three or four reaches, which were moderate, throwing up considerable bile, notwithstanding his violent vomiting before. At this time we thought that alarming symptoms plainly appeared of an approaching mortification; at least his breath, mouth plainly shewed a putrid state: But all yielded to application, which under God, effected a sudden cure. As soon as the above emetic had done, I began to apply No. 26 to overcome the cholic and spasmodic affections and No. 25, to act as a tonic, which succeeded so that in one hour he had manifest relief and ease. These two last numbers he continued to use, as directed in the present prescriptions; and in one week's time was able comfortably to ride about. He mended unusually fast, and became healthy and well; taking no other medicine. But he continued to take No. 25 three times a day, according to the prescription. . . .

In the winter of 1777, I inoculated about

130 persons for the small-pox. To the first parcel of 'them I gave calomel in the usual way, with jalap to work it off. The whole of them allowed to have the small-pox very favorably, so that my practise justified itself. But I observed that every one whose physic had worked him pretty well, as we say, had a sufficient portion of the small-pox; but on the contrary those whose physic had scarcely moved them, all had it very favorably; I then concluded that I would try Warner's pills No. 28. And living at my father's house at that time, I had plenty of them, where they were always kept. Accordingly I gave them to my next squad of small-pox patients which were about twenty. Observing the abstemious diet usual, I gave them nothing till about one day before I expected the fever: then I gave a small portion of the pills above named in such a manner as to purge very little if any, which is usually the case when they are given. But what was very special, there were scarcely any of them that were sick with the fever—and the small-pox scarcely enough to give any of them a receipt. Afterwards I proceeded with all the rest in the like manner, and with the same success; and of several families it might be said, they wanted two cooks for one nurse. . . .

If ever calomel has been given to advantage, I concluded it has been in the pleurisy; but I will venture to compare notes at any time with those who use calomel, and only let me have No. 2 or No. 3, there being no comparison between the success with which the latter is marked and the former, both as to certainty and speed of cure.

Not if we can do better without calomel than with it, both in debility and plethora, why should we not throw by the use of it? Especially considering that the unhappy sufferer may perhaps happen to take a drink of cool water, or otherwise transgress. I then conclude.

1. In bilious cases only, move the bile by taking No. 1, and then follow it with No. 4, or its preparations, or No. 5; then by some course keep up perspiration, and you need no calomel.

2. In plethoric and inflammatory cases, take No. 2 or 3, and bleed, if the pulse is high;

KICKAPOO
Cough • Cure.
----THE GREAT----
INDIAN VEGETABLE REMEDY
—FOR—
Coughs,
Colds,
Sore Throat,
Influenza, &c.

NO ONE NEED SUFFER LONG WITH A COUGH OR COLD IF THEY WILL ONLY TRY THIS POPULAR REMEDY.

Price, 50 cents per Bottle, 5 Bottles for $2.00.

For Sale by All Druggists.

bind to restore perspiration, then brace up a little (say by agrimoney tea) and you need not calomel.

I call myself an *Indian Doctor,* because I have incidentally obtained a knowledge of many of the simples used by the Indians; but chiefly because I have obtained my knowledge generally in the like manner that the Indians do.

I have indeed had the advantage in my early life of a slight classical education, and of reading some books on the medical business: such as Buchanan, Tissot, Sharp, Culpepper, and a little on anatomy, Smith on the nerves, Brown, &c. But I never pretended to live by my practice, I kept very little of the medicine of the shops; consequently my advices to my friends mostly were simples; and by this means I have by continued observations come to be of opinion, that our best medicines grow in the woods and gardens. I conceive, moreover, that my mind has providentially been led a step higher than the ancients or the Indians; their views being little more than *"This thing is good for that thing; this medicine will cure that complaint."* But it stands demonstrated to me, that there are but two radical disorders . . . consequently there need be only two classes of medicine.

In cases of debility, give No. 1 or No. 2, and then brace up, and correct the flatulence and spasms with No. 9, No. 25 and No. 26.

The cases of plethora and irritation are to be corrected on as simple and general a plan.

Now since I have adopted these views, I seldom feel at a loss to know what ails any patient, or what medicine is suitable to apply.

I have here prescribed many things, so that you may have a variety of choice.

Some cases, however, require a radical recruit of the iron property in the blood; and every thing will be in vain until that is done. Such I believe is consumption, derangement, &c. unto which stimulants should be applied; such as Nos. 2, 15, 16, No. 9 and 26, to take off the spasms and flatulence; but the radical cure should be attempted with No. 44.

I mention so many numbers not that they should all be used at once. Yet no one alone should be trusted to—and they may all or any of them be applied in their turns, should the first fail. . . .

My prescriptions in general I must leave to speak for themselves: I, however, feel a degree of satisfaction in thinking that herein I have in prospect the real benefit of my own children of their rising, numerous progeny and my fellow men in general, as to their bodily comfort in this life.

CHAPTER I

The *Doctrine of Respiration* I think somewhat important, because it will show the necessity of breathing good air.

An Indian, it is storied, when asked what he thought was the reason of the ebbing and flowing of the tide, made answer: "You know there is a great deal of odds between a big creature and a little one; a horse draws his breath a great deal slower than a mouse: the world is a big creature—he draws his breath only twice in the day and night; that makes the tide."

Now my intention is not to enquire about the tide, but to state to you how I think we draw our breath, or respire.

I consider the lungs to be the pump of life.— Fresh, cool air, drawn into the lungs, or lights, immediately is rarified by their heat, and is directly forced back again, in the same way that it was taken in; then we are by some means (voluntary or involuntary) disposed to fill ourselves again with fresh good air. Thus our respiration is carried on by the great author of existence, to whose praise we ought ever to be ready to say:

"His spirit moves our heaving lungs,
Or we should breathe no more,"

and however our lungs may act on the principles of the steam machine, and so operate from natural causes, we shall not always breathe.

Men have contrived to break nearly all God's appointments; but this *"It is appointed for all men once to die,"* has never been abro-

gated or defeated yet by any man. And we should always remember, when we are about to take medicine, *if the Lord will*, we shall do this or that with success; *if the Lord will*, I shall get well by this means or some other.

But to return to the breath—If the air be cool and clear it will always have elasticity, as it is called; it will swell and fly back again easily, when we receive it into our lungs.

If the air is any how nearly as warm as the lungs, I cannot see how we should breathe at all: it is necessary therefore for us to try to breathe good air, if we would wish to live.*

The motion and circulation of the blood is manifestly connected with our breathing. For every breath extends and contracts our lungs; and by this motion I conceive the valves of the heart are kept in operation; and every spring of the arteries and beating of the pulse are exactly in proportion to the operation of the lungs. When the breath is let out, the lungs are immediately, in their blood vessels, filled with blood; and when the breath is drawn in again, the blood in the lungs is forced out into the heart. That is, they say, "From the lungs when the air is inhaled, the blood is pressed into the left auricle of the heart, from thence to the left ventricle, thence to the aorta, and by it and its branches through the body to the capillary extremities of the arteries, through them into the veins, and by the veins to the right auricle of the heart, from thence into the right ventricle, from thence through the pulmonary arteries, at the time of respiration or exhaling the air from the lungs, into the lungs."

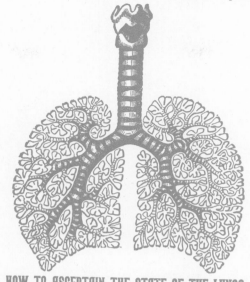

HOW TO ASCERTAIN THE STATE OF THE LUNGS.

Thus the lungs are alternately filling, first with blood, then with air, at every breath, the one pumping or working the other. By this circulation the blood runs its rounds, and is carried (at least some of it) to the extremities of the body in a few minutes; feeding our nerves, sinews and flesh as it passes on, and supplies and forces out that little juice through the pores of the skin, which we call perspiration and sweat.

From the blood vessels in the lungs is communicated a little stream of moisture, which grows into phlegm, and in a related state produces that matter which is raised and coughed up from the lungs.

Indeed I consider that this motion and circulation of air and blood is the true cause of heat being kept up in the body; and as the lungs have the most, and most violent

* In South Carolina I was once in company with old Dr. Dillihoo, who was noted for great skill and experience, having traveled into many parts of the world. In the course of our conversation, I asked him what he conceived the plague to be, which has been so much talked of in the world. He readily told me "that it was his opinion the plague is occasioned by an invisible insect. This insect, floating in the air, is taken in with the breath into the lungs, and there it either poisons, or propagates its kind, so as to produce that dreadful disease. This, he was confirmed, was likely to be the truth, from the experiments frequently made at Gibraltar. For there, said he, they of the garrison, when they fear the plague, have a way to elevate a piece of fresh meat, pretty high in the air; they put it up at night, and it comes down sound and sweet in the morning, they conclude there is no danger of the plague. But if the plague is in the air, the meat will be tainted and spoiled, and sometimes almost rotten.

"He was farther confirmed in his opinion of the insect, because in and about tobacco ware houses, the plague has never been known." I will remark, Now it is well known that tobacco will prevent moths from eating out woolen clothes, if we pack a little of it with them, that is, the moth cannot breed or exist, where there is a sufficient scent of the tobacco —this scent may be death to the invisible insect even after they are drawn in with the breath and fastened upon the lungs. This may account for tobacco being burned (as I have heard it is) in many old countries, on a chaffing dish in a room that the people of the house may take in the smoke plentifully with their breath, to preserve their health and prevent pestilential disorders. . . .

motion, they possess the greatest degree of heat of any part of the body, and even heat the blood.** And it is by this motion, together with some irregularities, that a fever takes place, producing a kind of electrical charge. When this is attended with too much bile, or an undue portion of the gall of the liver, then the fever is called a bilious fever, and always belongs to the diathesis of debility; and if the weakness is very prevalent, the nerves and tendons tremble and start, and the strength to speak or act be suspended, this is called a typhous or nervous fever.

But if there be a fullness of blood, a hard pulse, a fresh countenance, and an ability to speak and act with a degree of vigor or strength, then the fever may be called an inflammatory fever, and is exactly the opposite to the first mentioned. And your treatment must be accordingly. This belongs to the diathesis of plethora and irritation.

Here may we reflect on the balance of air and blood kept in motion to carry on life. For if the air and breath be suspended, how soon will death ensue; or if the blood be taken away, how soon will all vital motion cease.

** *The heat of the lungs and blood ought, I think, never to be suddenly checked or counteracted by cold: especially when the weather is hot, or when violent exercise has raised unusual heat in the lungs, and thro' the system. Then take care how you go into cold water, to swim, or even to wash—Remember that cold will coagulate and clot blood—and that very soon if its motion and circulation should be much or suddenly abated. Ah! how many have lost their lives, or their health, or become cripples for life, just by such folly!*

A large drink of cold water has often proved fatal when the lungs and blood have been so heated, for the reason before assigned.

Indeed in very hot weather, I think very cold water ought to be used with caution and in small quantities, at least until the stomach is moderately cooled by it. . . .

CHAPTER II

The diathesis of diseases, agreeable to Brown's Elements, I conceive to be the truth. I became somewhat acquainted with this system about 22 years ago.

Agreeable to that plan, there are but two kinds of diseases of the human body: consisting 1. in *Plethora* and *Irritation;* and 2. in *Debility, Weakness* and *Languor.*

Generally speaking, it is of importance for us to know to which of these an afflicted sufferer belongs. The cases I have compared to a lighted candle—if your candle burns strong and has a superfluous wick, then you may safely snuff it; but if it is dim, burns dull, and its wick is too short already, *you must beware of snuffing it,* lest you put it out. You had better pick open your wick, and gently feed the flame until you bring it to burn well.

Plethora and Irritation are not so critical. You may then bleed liberally; especially if the pulse is hard and high; No. 2 or No. 3 may then be given to great advantage. I have sometimes taken blood, and succeeded wonderfully, when mere stagnation had nearly prevented the pulse from beating at all.

But it is altogether critical in all cases of real debility to which belong all bilious cases, cramps, fits, hysterics, &c. Then blood ought ever cautiously to be let, if at all. And all diuretic and weakening medicines, should be very cautiously given, and sometimes carefully avoided. Your treatment should be strengthening and what is called tonic. Such is No. 1, No. 5, No. 9, &c. . . .

I acknowledge myself highly indebted to Brown for his doctrines of excitability, of predisposition of diseases, and observation on the pulse. The nature and use of opium and other stimulants, and his opinion concerning the consumption, and its being a curable disease.

But I conceive that after all, he has in a measure missed the radical cause of the consumption, and that mere stimulants will never effect the cure. But since I have buried two or three of my own family with that fatal disease, the iron doctrine has been strongly impressed on my mind. . . .

To Brown's opinion I assent in one thing more, for I am quite of his mind: to wit, *an old man ought never to marry a young woman.*

A word to the wise is enough.

* * *

CHAPTER III

Obstructed Perspiration I suppose to be the real first cause of half the diseases of the human body. In a state of oozing out of perspiration, or what is called moisture on the skin of a person, all over him, which it is allowed (if my recollection is correct) vents and discharges half or more of all that we eat and drink daily.

It would surprise you to see this floating all over you, in a state of health, like water over a piece of watered meadow.

This salutary perspiration is commonly obstructed and the skin becomes dry by what we commonly call catching cold. Its first symptoms are a stoppage of the nose, sneezing, and frequently a little dull headache.

But if the cold is suffered to continue, and the perspiration remains obstructed, the lungs will be soon affected. Or the headache will perhaps come violent. Or a lap or griping in the belly will most likely take place, and sometimes a violent vomiting with it; or a fever of some sort. The weak and the strong are all the subjects of this kind of the beginning of diseases.

All this evacuation is by the perspiration being obstructed, thrown back upon the blood and intestines. Now all this mischief may easily, or commonly be prevented if when the symptoms are first felt, or you have reason to think that you have taken cold, you will pursue the following directions.

Drink sage tea * copiously and go to bed—and drink it, hot or cold, but not very strong, until you bring yourself into a little sweat, then go to sleep and you may expect to wake up well. But if you have neglected a little too long, take a pill No. 26, and go to sleep but don't neglect the tea. If that do not cure you try No. 29, and some physic, perhaps such as No. 1, 2, or 5.

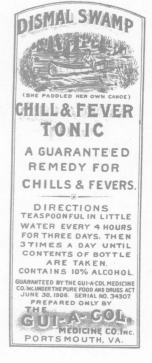

---

* *Or any other warming, sweating tea will do—such as pennyroyal, mint, sassafras, or dogwood buds.*

Ipecacuanha.

The home Ipecacuanha, or *Indian physic*, is an emetic, but commonly operates also as purge. It is always safe, if moderately taken. After discharging the bile, it leaves the stomach braced, so that in the lowest cases of debility, tonics (such as Columbo root or its preparations) may be taken after it to advantage. Contrary to other physics, I have found that weakly persons, who were of mere broken constitution, have become healthy and strong, only by taking this to vomit them on every occasion.

This is my great pioneer to clear the way for other medicine, in all cases of oppression in the breast, nausea, violent vomitings & fever in general. . . .

Ipecacuanha is a very bitter root. In a good bunch the green root will frequently be as big as a goose quill, is quirly and lumpy. The roots adhere in all sizes to a common root. The top and leaf resemble a bunch of close set briars, but smooth. The sprout for the new growth very much resemble the briar sprout. Many stalks grow to a good bunch two feet high, full of branches. On the top of which are very many light whitish blossoms. They issue in small nubs or squarish pods, about the size of a buckwheat grain. It grows plentifully in many of our mountains in America, and I believe may be cultivated in our gardens, any where in the United States.

I have raised by planting the sprouts in my garden to great advantage. I wish it to be planted in every man's garden; 'tis a great ornament—it will grow either from the seed or the sprouts. One hill from a single sprout, when three years old, I have found to make half a pound of dried root. What a pity this should be neglected—as it has been sufficiently proved to be fully equal if not superior to the imported Ipecacuanha of South America. It makes a most excellent and wholesome bitter when put in spirits.

The Scurvy Grass root is a special good purge. The stalk and leaf is rather of the flag kind, from six to ten inches long, has a small blue blossom on the top, issuing in a four-square pod, full of small seeds like tobacco seeds. The roots are as fine as Virginia snake root, of a pale yellow colour, and taste very hot and peppery, turning the lips and tongue yellow. It is found very plentifully in Virginia, and the southern states. And it is sometimes to be found in meadows, in Jersey, Pennsylvania and the Ohio states. The top is so hardy as to live thro the winter.

I have planted this in my garden for a number of years past, in the manner of chives, and from a single stool find it increase in two years to a bunch enough for several portions of physic. This can easily be procured from its spontaneous growth in the southern states. The green roots are to be made use of, as the dry will be purge. . . .

Its operation is tolerable quick, always safe, and if it fails working, it does not hurt.

This little native of the woods was shown to me by old Dr. Wilkey, of South Carolina, who highly commended it; saying that he had known more sudden and effectual reliefs from it, than from any other medicine.*. . .

It is to be noticed that if the skin is chafed with vinegar, and a small poultice of these roots applied, they will draw a good blister. When this is given as a purge, bracing medicine should follow it, such as No. 4, No. 5, or No. 9.

I have sometimes filled a phial with the roots, and then put on spirits, and given a teaspoonful at a time, where the system requires warming and stimulating.

The Devil's Nip, as it is shamefully called, grows about knee high, parting its stalk into three branches, on which are situate handsome oval pointed leaves; on a slender middle stem grows one handsome flower, resembling a lilly, some of which are white, and some of a pale pink color. The root . . . resembles the well known Indian turnip, but the root is more conical; its taste is too severe to be endured,

---

* *I remember that Dr. Wilkey related to me the following fact: said he—"I was one morning very early called to visit a woman who had taken a dose of corrosive sublimate (in mistake, thinking it was tartar emetic) when I came to her, her tongue was so swelled that she could not speak a word. I thought it was over with her, but I would try my little root (meaning the scurvy grass root). I prepared a decoction as soon as possible, and tho it was supposed she could not swallow, yet we tried one spoonful after another, and found it made way for itself—And what was surprising, she was so soon relieved, that on that very morning the woman fried pan-cakes for my breakfast."*

but not biting like the Indian turnip. It is said, that any person carrying a root or two, need never fear that any snake will bite him. A little of it put in the mouth of a snake, is instant death to him.—A German doctor used to give it to persons deranged and announced their cure by it. Its stimulant qualities are certainly rare.

The Red Lead Sear Cloth Salve: To prepare—take three half pints of Sweet Oil, or in case that cannot be had, take the like quantity of fresh butter when boiled and skimmed; one pint of Linseed oil: boil them in a skillet, so hot that it will burn a feather; then add one pound of pulverised Red Lead to be stirred gently into it, while hot, (but the oil must be somewhat cooled or it will foam and run over) until it becomes like soft wax.

This is to be spread on thin leather, and applied as a Sear Cloth or Plaster; which is not to be taken off, until it comes off of itself. If matter should gather in the sore, it must be let out by an awl through the plaster.

This plaster I have heard was formerly in the possession of a German whose name I do not recollect, who lived latterly in Kentucky. He performed many astonishing cures with it. I saw one of his patients, who had been wounded at the Germantown battle, 1777, in the Revolutionary war; one of his legs had been broken and shattered, while he was one of the forlorn party sent to tear down the fence and palings about Chew's house. He told me that due care had been taken in setting the bone, and to cure the humours, but all in vain, he had to endure grievous sores, every application being of little or no avail; until in about twenty years, he fortunately fell in with this German, who by the means of this plaster, cured his leg. It was then sound and well, when I had this story from his own mouth.

The Tooth-ache, to cure by Sympathy: The process—The patient is enjoined not to narrate what is done to him, or the Tooth-ache will return. (But a repetition will restore the cure.)

All the finger and toe nails are to be trimmed, the pieces off of each are to be laid on a rag or paper; to which also is to be laid a lock of hair taken from the head; then the gum of the tooth is to be gouged or pierced, to add some blood to the nails & hair; then the whole is to be wrapped together in the bank of some creek or gulley, at a place where no creature crosses. The operator may keep the putting away to himself, if he pleases.

Indians they say have queer notions. Hah! but I have tried this for perhaps fifteen years, on myself and many others, and seldom without immediate success. The tooth, it is believed when it becomes easy, will never ache again.—If the pain remains, chew root, No. 2, or No. 16.

An Antidote for Epidemic Diseases: Prepare you a few brimstone matches, and a bottle half full of spirits; light a match and thrust it into the mouth of the bottle, so as to fill the empty part with smoke. When the match is taken out, put your thumb on the mouth, and shake the spirits, to incorporate the smoke what they can. Do thus with several matches.

This I had from a very old man, when I was but a little boy. I remember he said, a dram of this rum will keep you from catching the Small-Pox or Measles: yes, if you will drink a dram of this in the morning, you may go safely where the plague is all day. But I rather suppose it had better be taken morning, noon and night.—I tried it myself before I had the Small-Pox.—

KEOKUK. MEDICINE MAN.

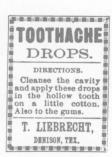

TONICS AND BITTERS

People placed great reliance on tonics and bitters to maintain health and to cure a truly remarkable range of maladies, as the Brown's Iron Bitters label (right) proclaims. The ingredients were never divulged, but most tonics relied upon alcohol or opium for their soothing effect.

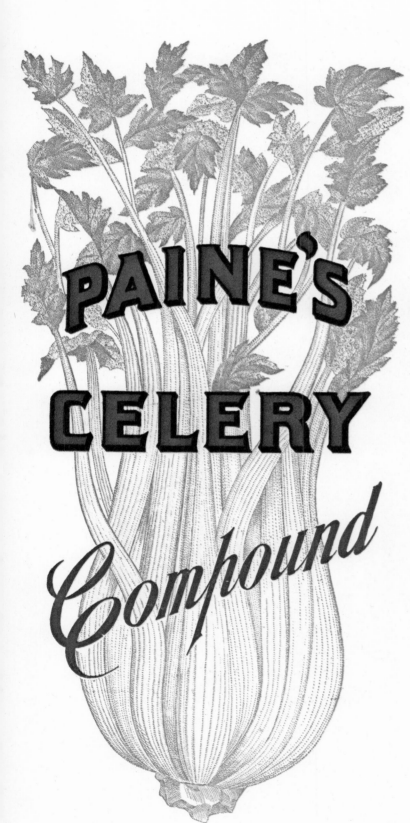

PAINE'S
CELERY
Compound

The Indian Doctor, Dr. John Williams' Last Legacy— A Useful Family Herbal

Tansy.

PREFACE

The author of this little book has a desire to leave something for the good of his fellow creature, and being sensible of soon retiring from time, and seeing no other opportunity to benefit the rising generation, hopes it will be kindly received, being a true and faithful statement of each medicine and cure. It has been carefully minuted according to his own knowledge, and not from hearsay. He has endeavoured to state the true nature and virtue of each vegetable; and they may be used with the greatest safety and advantage.

JOHN WILLIAMS

FOR THE KING'S EVIL

The King's Evil may be cured with a plant called King's Evil Weed. It grows in wild shady land, under almost all kinds of timber, and in the form of a plantain, but the leaves are smaller, and are spotted, green and white— a very beautiful plant. When it goes to seed, there comes up a stalk in the middle of the plant, six or eight inches high, and it bears the seed on the top of the stalk in a small bud.

Take this, root and branch, pound it soft, apply it to the tumor for a poultice or salve, and let the patient drink a tea made of the same for constant drink. If the tumor is broken open, simmer the root and leaf in sweet oil and mutton tallow, strain it off, and add to it beeswax and rosin, until hard enough for salve. Wash the sore with liquor made of the herb, boiled, and apply the salve.

FOR A FEVER SORE

Take the bark of Shrub Maple or Caveron Wood, boil it in fair water, wash the wound in it, and syringe with the same; take a parcel of the bark and a handful of blue flag root, boil them very strong, strain it off, boil it down to the consistence of salve, add to it a little beeswax and honey, mix it well together, while it is warm. Apply this for salve. It must be used two days, then for two days drink tar water, with which also the sore must be washed and syringed, and so continued.—Tar water is made thus: Put half a gallon of tar into a tub, pour on half a gallon of water, let it stand four days, then lay a piece of flannel cloth on the water to take up the oil, which is hurtful to the sore. . . .

TO CURE THE BITE OF ANY SNAKE

Take green hoarhound tops, pound them fine, press out the juice, let the patient drink a tablespoonful of the juice, morn, noon, and night, or three times in twenty-four hours; apply the pounded herbs to the bite, change the same twice a day. The patient may drink a spoonful of olive oil. This never fails.

FOR THE TOOTH ACHE, IF THE TOOTH BE HOLLOW

Take gum opium, camphor, and spirits of turpentine, equal parts, rub them in a mortar to a paste, dip lint in the paste, and put it in the hollow of the tooth every time after eating. Make use of this three or four days, and it will entirely cure the tooth from every aching.

THE BEST REMEDY FOR RATTLES IN CHILDREN

Take blood root, powder it, give the patient a small teaspoonful at a dose; if the first does not break the bladder in half an hour, repeat three times.—This has not been known to fail curing.

THE PIONEER OF PLASTER FAME.
TAKEN 1864.

REVOLUTION IN GRAPHICS

An outstanding effect of the Patent Medicine Era was
a revolution in the techniques and variety of
graphic-arts advertising. Even illogical or
far-fetched pictures or scenes were used with products,
as evidenced by the owl that Colburn associated with
its Phila. mustard. The technique in Carter's
ad is still used in children's puzzles.

CARTER'S LITTLE NERVE PILLS FOR THE NERVOUS & DYSPEPTIC

FIND—Cow, Owl, Fox, Frog, Parrot, Horse, Lizard, Goose, Man Smoking Pipe, Rooster Crowing, General Grant, Romeo and Juliet.

USE LUTTED'S COUGH DROPS.

RING'S VEGETABLE AMBROSIA FOR GRAY HAIR

TUBBS' UNIVERSAL PAIN ERADICATOR

ONE DOSE SMALL.

ECLECTRIC OIL

Dr. THOMAS.

WORTH ITS WEIGHT IN GOLD

The Great Internal and External Remedy

FOSTER, MILBURN & CO. Proprietors.

FOR A FEMALE WEAKNESS CALLED THE WHITE

Make a syrup of knotgrass tops and roots, yarrow tops and roots, plaintain tops and roots, hemp tops, of each one pound, bloodweed one pound. Boil them in six quarts of water, down to three quarts, strain it in, and add to it a pint of rum and two pounds of loaf sugar. Drink a small glass morning, noon, and night, fasting, or before eating.

FOR THE DIABETES

Take a deer's bladder, put it into a glass bottle that will hold a quart, hang it in the bottle by the neck by a thread, fill it up with good Madeira wine, and let it stand forty-eight hours, then drink three or four times a day, about half a gill at a time. If a deer's bladder is not to be had, a wether sheep's will answer.

PRESERVATIVE AGAINST ALL SORTS OF BILIOUS FEVERS

The fulness of bile is the cause of all sorts of fevers, and jaundice, bilious cholic, and cholera morbus. Physic often with blood root and mandrake roots mixed together, once a quarter, and make a small beer with elder roots, spruce boughs, burdock roots, hops, white ash bark, sarsaparilla roots and spikenard. Make a bitter with unicorn roots and bark, of white wood roots and the yellow dust of hops. If a family will continue this method, they will never be troubled with fevers.

FOR THE ASTHMA IN ADULTS

Take the liver of a wolf, one pound of sinical snake-root, one pound of spikenard root with the pith taken out, one pound of parsley root, one pound of liquorice distilled in two gallons of Sherry or Teneriffe wine. Draw off from the still one gallon—bottle it up. Half a tablespoonful is a dose to take morning, noon, and night, before eating.

CURE FOR OLD VENEREAL COMPLAINTS

Take a peck of black ash bark, boil it in a pailful of water, down to a quart, sweeten it with molasses; add to it a pint of rum. Drink half a pint at a time, morn and night. Or, take gamboge and gum aloes, equal parts, and make a pill as big as a small pea, fill it with molasses; two pills is a dose; continue taking the pill one week every night. Or, when the complaint is first taken, within ten or twelve days, make a pill of equal parts of pil-coche and calomel, pill it with molasses. Begin with one pill the first night, add one pill until it operates like a physic; then take them every night, and lessen one till all gone.

TO CURE A BREACH OR BURST IN THE BODY

Take four or five snails that crawl about on an old rotten wood; you may find them under loose bark that is moist, or on old logs or stumps. Collect a parcel of them, enough to cover the breach, lay them on a linen cloth, bind them on, and repeat it as often as the snails are dry. Let the patient drink turkey root, cinnamon, cloves and maise, made in tea, or steeped in wine, three or four times a day.

AN EXCELLENT PILL FOR THE HYSTERICS

Take a quantity of white root, otherwise called Canada root, boil it in fair water, when it is boiled very soft, strain out the roots and boil the liquor to the consistence of a thick paste, so that it may be pilled. Let the patient take two or three pills at a dose when the disorder is coming on.

FOR CHILDBED FEVERS

In childbed fevers take the rattle-snake's gall, five grains malitel, sweet balm tea once an hour until the fever abates, and every time the fever rises continue the same. Keep the body loose.

Passions

&

Sex

AT BED TIME I TAKE A PLEASANT HERB DRINK

SEARCH LIGHTS ON HEALTH

Light on Dark Corners.

A COMPLETE SEXUAL SCIENCE
—AND—
A GUIDE TO PURITY AND PHYSICAL MANHOOD.

Advice to Maiden, Wife, and Mother.

LOVE, COURTSHIP AND MARRIAGE.

BY

PROF. B. G. JEFFERIS, M. D., PH. D.,
CHICAGO, ILL.,
AND
J. L. NICHOLS, A. M.

EIGHTEENTH EDITION.

PUBLISHED BY

J. L. NICHOLS & CO.

NAPERVILLE, ILL. ———— TORONTO, ONT.

SOLD ONLY BY SUBSCRIPTION.

1897.

THE

MARRIAGE GUIDE,

OR

PHYSIOLOGICAL AND HYGIENIC INSTRUCTOR,

FOR THE MARRIED, OR THOSE INTENDING TO MARRY,

BOTH MALE AND FEMALE.

INCLUDING EVERYTHING RELATING TO THE PHILOSOPHY OF GENERATION, AND THE MUTUAL RELATIONS OF MAN AND WOMAN.

ILLUSTRATED BY
Numerous Engravings and Colored Plates, giving every necessary Anatomical detail.

BY DR. F. HOLLICK,
Author and Lecturer upon the Physiology and Derangements of the Generative System.

500th EDITION

REVISED, AND WITH NEW MATTER AND ILLUSTRATIONS.

NEW YORK:
EXCELSIOR PUBLISHING HOUSE,
29 AND 31 BEEKMAN STREET.

Although we ordinarily think of the Victorian Age
in the 1800's as being one of narrow-mindedness on the subject of sex,
the writings of that period on the subject are rather unusual.
There were many books devoted completely to what was called "the sexual science."
Every book of home medicine
had long passages discussing sexual organs, venereal illnesses, and deficiencies, some of
these writings being quite amusing.

Celibacy.　　139

Disadvantages of Celibacy.

Keeping Bachelor's Hall.

The old Bachelor sewing on his Button.

HEALTH A DUTY

Perhaps nothing will so much hasten the time when body and mind will both be adequately cared for, as a diffusion of the belief that the preservation of health is a duty. Few seem conscious that there is such a thing as physical morality.

Men's habitual words and acts imply that they are at liberty to treat their bodies as they please. Disorder entailed by disobedience to nature's dictates they regard as grievances, not as the effects of a conduct more or less flagitious. Though the evil consequences inflicted on their descendents and on future generations are often as great as those caused by crime, they do not think themselves in any degree criminal.

It is true that in the case of drunkenness the viciousness of a bodily transgression is recognized; but none appear to infer that if this bodily transgression is vicious, so, too, is every bodily transgression. The fact is, all breaches of the law of health are physical sins.

When this is generally seen, then, and perhaps not til then, will the physical training of the young receive all the attention it deserves.

Purity of life and thought should be taught in the home. It is the only safeguard of the young. Let parents wake up on this important subject.

THE POWER AND PECULIARITIES OF LOVE

LOVE IS A TONIC AND A REMEDY FOR DISEASE, MAKES PEOPLE LOOK YOUNGER, CREATES INDUSTRY, etc.

It is a physiological fact long demonstrated that persons possessing a loving disposition borrow less of the cares of life, and also live much longer than persons with a strong, narrow and selfish nature. Persons who love scenery, love domestic animals, show great attachment for all friends; love their home dearly and find interest and enchantment in almost everything, have qualities of mind and heart which indicate good health and a happy disposition.

Love strengthens health and disappointment cultivates disease. A person in love will invariably enjoy the best of health. Ninety-nine percent of our strong constitutioned men now in physical ruin, have wrecked themselves on the breakers of an unnatural love. Nothing but right love and a right marriage will restore them to health.

A woman is never so bright and full of health as when deeply in love. Many sickly and frail women are snatched from the clutches of some deadly disease and restored to health by falling in love.

It is a long established fact that married persons are healthier than unmarried persons, thus it proves that health and happiness belong to the home.

Love makes people look younger in years. Old maids and bachelors always look older than they are.

WHEN AND WHOM TO MARRY

Early Marriages: Women too early married always remain small in stature, weak, pale, emaciated, and more or less miserable.

If marriage is delayed too long in either sex, say from thirty to forty years, the offspring will often be puny and more liable to insanity, idiocy, and other maladies.

Puberty: This is the period when childhood passes from immaturity of the sexual func-

tions to maturity. Woman attains this state a year or two sooner than man. In the hotter climates the period of puberty is from twelve to fifteen years of age, while in cold climates, such as Russia, the United States, and Canada, puberty is frequently delayed until the seventeenth year.

Diseased Parents: No young man in the vigor of health should think for a moment of marrying a girl who has the impress of consumption or other disease already stamped upon her feeble constitution. On the other hand, no healthy, vigorous young woman ought to unite her destiny with a man, no matter how much she adored him, who is not healthy and able to brave the hardships of life.

126   *What Women Love in Men.*

What Women Love in Men.

1. Women naturally love courage, force and firmness in men. The ideal man in a woman's eye must be heroic and brave. Woman naturally despises a coward, and she has little or no respect for a bashful man.

2. Woman naturally loves her lord and master. Women who desperately object to be overruled, nevertheless admire men who overrule them, and few women would have any respect for a man whom they could completely rule and control.

3. Man is naturally the protector of woman; as the male wild animals of the forest protects the female, so it is natural for man to protect his wife and children, and therefore woman admires those qualities in a man which make him a protector.

4. Large Men.—Women naturally love men of strength, size and fine physique, a tall, large and strong man rather than a short, small and weak man. A woman always pities a weakly man, but rarely ever has any love for him.

5. Small and Weakly Men.—All men would be of good size in frame and flesh, were it not for the infirmities visited upon them by the indiscretion of parents and ancestors of generations before.

6. Youthful Sexual Excitement. — There are many children born healthy and vigorous who destroy the full vigor of their generative organs in youth by self-abuse, and if they survive and marry, their children will have small bones, small frames and sickly constitutions. It is therefore not strange that instinct should lead women to admire men not touched with these symptoms of physical debility.

7. Generosity. — Woman generally loves a generous man. Religion absorbs a great amount of money in temples, churches, ministerial salaries, etc., and ambition and appetite absorb countless millions, yet woman receives more gifts from man than all these combined; she

HOW TO WRITE A LOVE LETTER.

1. Love. — There is no greater or more profound reality than love. Why that reality should be obscured by mere sentimentalism, with all its train of absurdities is incomprehensible. There is no nobler possession than the love of another. There is no higher gift from one human being to another than love. The gift and the possession are true sanctifiers of life, and should be worn as precious jewels, without affectation and without bashfulness. For this reason there is nothing to be ashamed of in a love letter, provided it be sincere.

2. Forfeits. — No man need consider that he forfeits dignity if he speaks with his whole heart: no woman need fear she forfeits her womanly attributes if she responds as her heart bids her respond. "Perfect love casteth out fear" is as true now as when the maxim was first given to the world.

3. Telling Their Love. — The generality of the sex is, love to be loved ; how are they to know the fact that they

Marrying First Cousins is dangerous to offspring. The observation is universal, the children of married first cousins are too often idiots, insane, clump-footed, crippled, blind, or afflicted with diseases. First cousins are always sure to impart all the hereditary disease in both families to their children. If both are healthy there is less danger.

SEXUAL PROPRIETIES AND IMPROPRIETIES

To have offspring is not to be regarded as a luxury, but as a great primary necessity of health and happiness, of which every fully-developed man and woman should have a fair share.

Separate Beds: Many writers have vigorously championed as a reform the practice of separate beds for husband and wife. While we would not recommend such separation, it is no doubt very much better for both husband and wife, in case the wife is pregnant. In case of pregnancy it will add rest to the mother and add vigor to the unborn child. Sleeping together, however, is natural and cultivates true affection, and it is physiologically true that in very cold weather life is prolonged by husband and wife sleeping together.

Miscarriage: If a woman is liable to abortion or miscarriage, absolute abstinence is the only remedy. No sexual indulgence during pregnancy can be safely tolerated.

The best writers lay down the rule for the government of the marriage-bed, that sexual indulgence should only occur about once in a week or ten days, and this of course applies only to those who enjoy a fair degree of health. . . . Much pleasure is lost by excesses where much might be gained by temperance, giving rest to the organs for the accumulation of nervous force.

SMALL FAMILIES AND THE IMPROVEMENT OF THE RACE

Diseased people who are likely to beget only a sickly offspring may follow this course. It is not wise to rear too many children, nor is it wise to have too few.

Where one parent is consumptive and the other vigorous, the chances are just half as great that they will inherit physical weakness. If there is a scrofulous or consumptive taint in the blood, beware! Sickly children are no comfort to their parents, no real blessing. If such people marry, they had better, in most cases, avoid parentage.

Preventives: Remember that the thousands of preventives which are advertised in paper, private circulars, etc., are not only inefficient, unreliable and worthless, but positively dangerous, and the annual mortality of females in this country from this cause alone is truly horrifying. Study nature, for nature's laws alone guide you safely in the path of health and happiness.

Actual impotence during the period of manhood is a very rare complaint, and nature very unwillingly, and only after the absolute neglect of sanitary laws, gives up the power of reproduction.

When a single man fears that he is unable to fulfill the duties of marriage, he should not marry until his fear is dispelled. The suspicion of such a fear strongly tends to bring about the very weakness which he dreads. Go to a good physician (not to one of those quacks whose advertisements you see in the papers; they are invariably unreliable), and state the case fully and freely.

Excessive indulgences often enfeeble the powers and often result in impotence. Dissipated single men, professional libertines, and married men who are immoderate, often pay the penalty of their violations of the laws of nature, by losing their vital power. In such cases of excess there may be some temporary relief, but as age advances the effects of such indiscretion will become more and more manifest.

• Remedies in case of Impotence on account of Private diseases, or Masturbation, or other causes: First build up the body by taking some stimulating tonics. Constipation must be carefully avoided. If the kidneys do not work in good order, some remedy for their restoration must be taken. Take plenty of outdoor exercise, avoid horseback riding or heavy exhaustive work.

Food and Drinks which Weaken Desire: All kinds of food which cause dyspepsia, or bring on constipation, diarrhoea, or irritate the bowels, alcoholic beverages, or any indigestible compound, has the tendency to weaken the sexual power.

Coffee—Coffee drunk excessively causes a debilitating effect upon the sexual organs. The moderate use of coffee can be recommended, yet an excessive habit of drinking very strong coffee will sometimes wholly destroy vitality.

It is a hygienic and physiological fact that tobacco produces a sexual debility and those who suffer any weakness from that source should carefully avoid the weed in all its forms.

are loved unless they are told ? To write a sensible love letter requires more talent than to solve, with your pen, a profound problem in philosophy. Lovers must not then expect much from each other's epistles.

4. Confidential. — Ladies and gentlemen who correspond with each other should never be guilty of exposing any of the contents of any letters written expressing confidence, attachment or love. The man who confides in a lady and honors her with his confidence should be treated with perfect security and respect, and those who delight in showing their confidential letters to others are unworthy, heartless and unsafe companions.

5. Return of Letters. — If letters were written under circumstances which no longer exist and all confidential relations are at an end, then all letters should be promptly returned.

6. How to Begin a Love Letter. — How to begin a love letter has been no doubt the problem of lovers and suitors of all ages and nations. Fancy the youth of Young America with lifted pen, thinking how he shall address his beloved. Much depends upon this letter. What shall he say, and how shall he say it, is the great question. Perseverance, however, will solve the problem and determine results.

7. Forms of Beginning a Love Letter. — Never say, "My Dearest Nellie," "My Adored Nellie," or "My Darling Nellie," until Nellie has first called you "My Dear," or has given you to understand that such familiar terms are permissible. As a rule a gentleman will never err if he says "Dear Miss Nellie," and if the letters are cordially reciprocated the "Miss" may in time be omitted, or other familiar terms used instead. In addressing a widow "Dear Madam," or, "My Dear Madam," will be a proper form until sufficient intimacy will justify the use of other terms.

8. Respect. — A lady must always be treated with respectful delicacy, and a gentleman should never use the term "Dear" or "My Dear" under any circumstances unless he knows it is perfectly acceptable or a long and friendly acquaintance justifies it.

9. How to Finish a Letter. — A letter will be suggested by the remarks on how to begin one. "Yours respectfully," "Yours truly," "Yours sincerely," "Yours affectionately," "Yours ever affectionately," "Yours most affectionately," "Ever yours," "Ever your own," or "Yours," are all appropriate, each depending upon the beginning of the letter. It is difficult to see any phrase which could be added to them which would carry more meaning than they con-

Drugs Which Stimulate Desire: There are certain medicines which act locally on the membranes and organs of the male, and the papers are full of advertisement of "Lost Manhood Restored," etc., but in every case they are worthless or dangerous drugs and certain to lead to some painful malady or death. All these patent medicines should be carefully avoided. . . . Eating rye, corn, or graham bread, oatmeal, cracked wheat, plenty of fruit, etc. is a splendid medicine . . .

Drugs Which Moderate Desire: Among one of the most common domestic remedies is camphor. This has stood the test for ages. Small doses of half a grain in most instances diminishes the sensibility of the organs of sex . . . The safest drug among domestic remedies is a strong tea made out of hops. Salt-peter or nitrate of potash, taken in moderate quantities, are very good remedies.

"Over-indulgence in intercourse," says Dr. Hoff, "is sometimes the cause of barrenness; this is usually puzzling to the interested parties, inasmuch as the practices which, in their opinion, should be the source of a numerous progeny, have the very opposite effect. By greatly moderating their ardor, this defect may be remedied."

PRODUCING BOYS OR GIRLS AT WILL

Conception in the first half of the time between the menstrual periods produces females, and the males in the latter.

Where Did the Baby Come From?   303

WHERE DID THE BABY COME FROM?

———

Where did you come from, baby dear?
Out of the everywhere into here.

Where did you get the eyes so blue?
Out of the sky, as I came through.

Where did you get that little tear?
I found it waiting when I got here.

What makes your forehead so smooth and high?
A soft hand stroked it as I went by.

What makes your cheek like a warm, white rose?
I saw something better than anyone knows.

Whence that three-cornered smile of bliss?
Three angels gave me at once a kiss.

Where did you get this pretty ear?
God spoke, and it came out to hear.

Where did you get those arms and hands?
Love made itself into hooks and bands.

Feet, whence did you come, you darling things?
From the same box as the cherub's wings.

How did they all come just to be you?
God thought of me, and so I grew?

But how did you come to us, you dear?
God thought about you, and so I am here.
—GEORGE MACDONALD.

The most male power and passion creates boys; female, girls. This law probably causes those agricultural facts just cited thus: Conception right after menstruation gives girls, because the female is then the most impassioned; later, boys, because her wanted sexual warmth leaves him the most vigorous. Mere sexual excitement, a wild, fierce, furious rush of passion, is not only not sexual vigor, but in its inverse ratio; and a genuine insane fervor caused by weakness; just as a like nervous excitability indicates weak nerves instead of strong. Sexual power is deliberate, not wild, cool, not impetuous; while all false excitement diminishes effectiveness.

HEREDITY AND THE TRANSMISSION OF DISEASES

Bad Habits: It is known that a girl who marries the man with bad habits, is, in a measure, responsible for the evil tendencies which these habits have created in the children; and young people are constantly warned of the danger in marrying when they know they come from families troubled with chronic diseases or insanity. To be sure the warnings have had little effect thus far in preventing such marriages, and it is doubtful whether they will, unless the prophecy of an extremist writing for one of our periodicals comes to pass—that the time is not too far distant when such marriages will be a crime punishable by law.

Serious Consequences: The mother who has ruined her health by late hours, highly-spiced food, and general carelessness in regard to hygienic laws, and the father who is the slave of questionable habits, will be very sure to have children either mentally or morally inferior to what they might otherwise have had the right to expect. But the prenatal influe may be such that evils arising from such may be modified to a great degree.

Mental Derangements: Almost all forms of mental derangements are hereditary—one of the parents or near relation being afflicted. . . . In fact, all physical weakness is ingrafted in either parent, is transmitted from parents to offspring, and is often more strongly marked in the latter than in the former.

Marks and Deformities: Marks and deformities are transmissible from parents to offspring, equally with diseases and peculiar proclivities. Among such blemishes may be mentioned moles, hair-lips, deficient or supernumerary fingers, toes, and other characteristics. It is also asserted that dogs and cats that have accidentally lost their tails, bring forth similarly deformed. Blumenbach tells of a man, who had lost his little finger, having children with the same deformity.

EDUCATION OF THE CHILD IN THE WOMB

A lady once interviewed a prominent college president and asked him when the education of a child should begin. "Twenty-five years before it is born," was the prompt reply.

No better answer was ever given to that question. Every mother may well consider it.

The Unborn Child Affected by the Thoughts and the Surroundings of the Mother: That the child is affected in the womb of the mother, through the influences apparently connected with the objects by which she is surrounded, appears to have been well known in ancient days, as well as at the present time.

Evidences: Many evidences are found in ancient history, especially among the refined nations, showing that certain expedients were resorted to by which their females during the period of utero-gestation, were surrounded by the superior refinements of the age, with the hope of thus making upon them impressions which should have the effect of communicating certain desired qualities to the offspring. For this reason apartments were adorned with statuary and paintings, and special pains were taken not only to convey favorable impressions, but also to guard against unfavorable ones being made, upon the mind of the pregnant woman.

Hankering after Gin—A certain mother while pregnant, longed for gin, which could not be gotten; and her child cried incessantly for six weeks till gin was given it, which it eagerly clutched and drank with ravenous greediness, stopped crying and became healthy.

The Plastic Brain—The plastic brain of the foetus is prompt to receive all impressions. It retains them, and they become the characteristics of the child and the man. Low spirits, violent passions, irritability, frivolity, in the pregnant woman leave indelible marks on the unborn child.

A Historical Illustration—A woman rode side by side with her soldier husband, and witnessed the drilling of troops for battle. The scene inspired her with a deep longing to see a battle and share in the excitements of the conquerors. This was but a few months before her baby was born, and his name was Napoleon.

A Musician—The following was reported by Dr. F. W. Moffatt, in the mother's own language:—"When I was first pregnant, I wished my offspring to be a musician, so during the period of that pregnancy settled my whole mind on music and attended every musical entertainment I possibly could. I had my husband, who has a violin, to play for me by the hour. When the child was born, it was a girl, which grew and prospered and finally became an expert musician."

Caution—Any attempt on the part of the mother to destroy her child before birth is liable, if unsuccessful, to produce murderous tendencies. Even harboring murderous thoughts, whether toward her own child or not, might be followed by similar results.

SOLEMN LESSONS FOR PARENTS

Pregnant women should not be exposed to causes likely to distress or otherwise strongly impress their minds. A consistent life with worthy objects constantly kept in mind should be the aim of every expectant mother.

1. A woman bitten on the vulva by a dog, bore a child having a similar wound on the glans penis. The boy suffered from epilepsy, and when the fit came on, or during sleep, was frequently heard to cry out, "The dog bites me!"

2. A pregnant woman who was suddenly alarmed from seeing her husband come home with one side of his face swollen and distorted by a blow, bore a girl with a purple swelling upon the same side of her face.

JOAN OF ARC.

Solemn Lessons for Parents.

1. Excessive Pleasures and Pains.—A woman during her time of pregnancy should of all women be most carefully tended, and kept from violent and excessive pleasures and pains; and at that time she should cultivate gentleness, benevolence and kindness.

3. A pregnant woman who was forced to be present at the opening of a calf by a butcher, bore a child with all its bowels protruding from the abdomen. She was aware at the time of some going on within the womb.

4. A pregnant woman fell into a violent passion at not being able to procure a particular piece of meat of a butcher; she bled at the nose, and wiping the blood from her lips, bore a child wanting a lip.

6. A woman who had borne healthy children, became frightened by a beggar with a wooden leg and a stumped arm, who threatened to embrace her. Her next child had one stump leg and two stump arms.

Clean Houses—Keep your house clean and cool and well aired night and day. Your cellars cleared of all rubbish and whitewashed every spring, your drains cleaned with a strong solution of copper or chloride of lime, poured down once a week. Keep your gutters and yards clean and insist upon your neighbors doing the same.

Exercise—Children should have exercise in the house as well as outdoors, but should not be jolted and jumped and jarred in rough play, nor rudely rocked in the cradle, nor carelessly trundled over bumps in their carriages. They should not be held too much in the arms, but allowed to crawl and kick upon the floor and develop their limbs and muscles. A child should not be lifted by its arms, nor dragged along by one hand after it learns to take a few feeble steps, but when they do learn to walk steadily it is the best of all exercise, especially in the open air. Let the children as they grow older romp and play in the open air all they wish, girls as well as boys. Give the girls an even chance for health, while they are young at least, and don't mind about their complexion.

THINGS YOUNG WIVES SHOULD KNOW

THE PERIOD OF CONCEPTION

Woman's Courage—Courage is assigned to man—to woman it is due. Follow her steps from the time she enters the arena of married life, study each line—each shading and its effect—as though an artist with magic brush had depicted on canvas the hidden mysteries of life's various phases, and the result will be startling to those who have been but casual observers in the past. The courage and sublimity of woman's nature is inherent, descending through ages, thus becoming a fixed moral quantity of woman in her kind.

Courage Illustrated—Courage in woman is illustrated by the fortitude with which she bears her children, the cheerfulness with which she undertakes their moral and physical training, and the patience and perseverance she shows when called to tend by their sick-bed through the long, weary hours, days or weeks of their illness. All parents desire to bring into the world good, bright and healthy offspring without pain. Can this be accomplished? Propagating Likes—Sexual emotion is absolutely necessary to conception. The impress is made at the moment. Every quality of mind or body which is dominant then will undoubtedly determine the fate of the offspring. How imperatively necessary is it then, at that moment, to permit nothing but the most pleasant fancies to occupy the mind, namely, the thought of those actions and things which is most desirable to reappear in children.

WILL THE BABE BE BOY OR GIRL?

Function of the Ovary—The ovary is undoubtedly the predominant factor in this respect. The only means by which the determination of sex can be influenced is by the nutritional processes on the ovary. Disturbances in the ovary in this line, dating from fetal life, seem to determine a preponderance of male ova, while abundant normal nutritional processes favor the females.

We have observed in our experience, the evidence of nutritional disturbances, as a number of mothers of boys give birth to girls after symptoms of diabetes were first noticed.

Emotion and Secretion—Cases of this kind might be multiplied *ad libitum*, but such instances are not needed to demonstrate that the feelings influence every fibre of our frame. The soul pervades every element of our bodies, and "in every nerve it thrills with pleasure, or grows mad with pain." The direct influence of the immortal agent over the mortal organism is beautifully demonstrated by the effects of emotion on secretion.

CAN PARENTS CONTROL THE SEX OF THE CHILD

Interest in the Subject—The above subject has for a long time deeply interested the scientists, not only of Europe, but also our own country, and various experiments have been made to endeavor to found the same upon fact instead of theory.

Results of Investigation—These experiments were first made in the interest of science alone, but the raisers of cattle and horses, seeing an increase of gain to themselves, quickly took hold of the subject and have endeavored to reap the advantages therefrom.

The following results, which have been carefully kept record of, elucidate the following:

1st. *That the offspring of a cow or mare, if young, and the male older and in good health, was a male.*

2nd. *If the female is mature in age, healthy and strong, the male younger and deficient in copulative strength, the offspring was female.*

3rd. *That when both male and female were of mature age and healthy, the offspring was about equal, male or female.*

4th. *If the female is old, and the male young, the offspring will be male.*

5th. *If the male is old, with the female younger, the offspring will be female.*

6th. *If a female was ill fed or run down by labor, and the male well fed and in vigor; offspring, male.*

7th. *If the female was well fed and rested, and the male ill fed and worked; offspring, female.*

Conclusion—From the above we would draw the following conclusions. Men having physical and procreative propensities similar to animals, the genital function is first to feel disturbances of the nervous system, as the top of the tree first shows that the roots are not properly nourished. The function of generation being the last to be developed has nothing directly depending on or issuing from it, it is a twig and not a main branch, like the stomach and brain; it is a periodic function, capable of long intervals of inactivity, and the rest of the body cannot only survive.

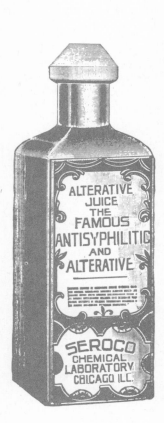

When a Male Child is Desired—The husband should partake of good substantial food. Exercise in open air; indulge in light literature; keep up a glow of spirits; abstain from indulgence for a short time previous to the procreative period. During this period the wife should abstain from animal foods, living mostly on vegetables and farinaceous articles of diet; exercise daily to almost fatigue, take the following treatment and pass a portion of her time with females older than herself. The following pill should be taken, one three times daily for several weeks:

Extract Hyosciamus .... ½ grain
    "   Valerian 1   "
    "   Sumbul 1   "
    "   Asafoetida 1   "

When a Female Child is Desired—Exactly the opposite course should be pursued—the woman should indulge in the most stimulating food—but should not indulge her passions, reserving her whole vigor for the desired time. The male should indulge in violent physical exercise to fatigue and morning and night take sitz baths of cold rock-salt water.

Care of the Passions—Abuse of the passions disturbs all the processes of life; a brutal kind of vigor in those who are reckless, but a soul that condemns its own conduct, is sure to produce disorders of the nervous system; the family of reflex center, the brain, the stomach, the genital system; between these, messengers of evil or of good are ever passing in sleeping and in working hours; to touch one is to touch all.

SEXUAL SCIENCE

ITS BEARING ON HEALTH

Life Propagation—The propagation of the human species is not committed to accident. Nor is it left to the caprice of the individual. It is made secure in a natural instinct which, with irrestible force and power, demands fulfillment. It is not only sensual pleasure that is found in the gratification of this natural impulse. There exists higher feelings of satisfaction in perpetuating one's own single, short and perishable existence by the transmission of one's mind and form to a new being.

Man Higher Than the Animal—In coarse, sensual love and in the lustful desire to satisfy this natural instinct, man stands on a level with the animal. But man has the power to raise himself to a height where this natural instinct no longer makes him a slave. Higher and nobler feelings are awakened, which, notwithstanding their sensual origin, lift him into a world of beauty, holiness and morality.

Holiness of Man's Instinct—On this height man overcomes his natural instinct. From an ever-flowing spring he draws material and inspiration for higher enjoyment, for more earnest work and for the reaching of the highest goal. The sexual feeling has been called the foundation for the development of the social feeling. In the words of a great student: "Were man to be robbed of the instinct of procreation and all that arises from it mentally, nearly all poetry and, perhaps, the entire moral sense as well, would be torn from his life."

The Power of Sexuality—Sexuality is the most powerful factor in individual and social existence. It is the strongest incentive man has to exert his strength and acquire property. It spurs him to the foundation of a home. By it are first awakened the feeling of love, first for one of the opposite sex, then for his offspring, and last, in a wider sense, for all humanity. Thus all morality and a great part of religion depend upon the existence of the sexual feeling.

Dangers Of the Sexual Life—Though the sexual life leads to the highest virtues and even to the sacrifice of self, yet in it lies a great danger. Unless properly checked it may degenerate into powerful passions and develop the gravest vices. When love is permitted to become an unbridled passion it is like a fire that burns and consumes everything. It is like a pit that swallows all—honor, fortune and happiness. . . .

Primitive People—Among very primitive people the satisfaction of the sexual appetite of man seems like that of the animal. Openness in the sexual act is not shunned. Men and women are not ashamed to go naked. Even to-day we see savages in this condition. The Australians and the Polynesians furnish good examples. It even exists in the United States of America, among the Malays of the Philippines.

The Female Common Property—Among these peoples the female is the common property of the male. She is for the time being the prize of the strongest. The men fight for the possession of the most beautiful of the opposite sex. A woman in such a country is a movable thing, a ware, an object of bargain and sale and gift. She is a thing to satisfy lust and to work.

Morality in Sexual Life—Morality in sexual life began when there appeared a feeling of shame in the manifestations of the natural instinct. Then arose modesty in the intercourse of the sexes. Efforts were made to conceal the part. "And they knew that they were naked."—Genesis, iii,7.

How to Perpetuate the Honey-Moon.

1. **Continue Your Courtship.**—Like causes produce like effects.

2. **Neglect of Your Companion.**—Do not assume a right to neglect your companion more after marriage than you did before.

3. **Secrets.**—Have no secrets that you keep from your companion. A third party is always disturbing.

4. **Avoid the Appearance of Evil.**—In matrimonial matters it is often that the mere appearance contains all the evil. Love, as soon as it rises above calculation and becomes love, is exacting. It gives all, and demands all.

5. **Once Married, Never Open Your Mind to Any Change.** If you keep the door of your purpose closed, evil or even desirable changes cannot make headway without help.

6. **Keep Step in Mental Development.**—A tree that grows for forty years may take all the sunlight from a tree that stops growing at twenty.

7. **Keep a Lively Interest in the Business of the home** Two that do not pull together, are weaker than either alone.

8. **Gauge Your Expenses by Your Revenues.**—Love must eat. The sheriff often levies on Cupid long before he takes away the old furniture.

9. **Start From Where Your Parents Started Rather than from Where They Now Are.**—Hollow and showy boarding often furnishes the too strong temptation, while the quietness of a humble home would cement the hearts beyond risk.

Modesty and Climate—The development of this degree of culture is favored by the coldness of the climate and the necessity for the complete protection of the body. Those who have investigated the primitive people have discovered that modesty appears among the northern races earlier than the southern.

Advance of Woman—The next stage in the development of culture in sexual life is noted when the female ceases to be a movable thing. She becomes a person. For a long time still she is placed far below the man socially. Yet the idea is developed that the right disposal of herself and her favors belong to her. She then becomes the object of the male's wooing. Feelings of morality begin to be added to the barbarous sensual feeling of sexual desire. Property in women ceases to exist. Individuals of the opposite sexes feel themselves drawn toward each other by their minds and appearances. They show love for each other only.

Foundation of Chastity—At this stage woman has a feeling that her charms belong only to the man of her choice, and she wishes to conceal them from others. Thus, by the side of modesty, are laid the foundations of chastity and faithfulness—as long as the bond of love lasts.

Woman as a Housewife—Woman attains this degree of social elevation earlier, when a tribe gives up its wandering life and settles down to a state of fixed habitation. For then man obtains a house and home, and the necessity arises for him to possess in woman a companion for the household—a housewife. Among the nations of the East, the Egyptians, the Israelites and the Greeks, early attained this stage of culture, and among those of the West the Germans were the first to elevate women.

Points of Female Esteem—Among all these races virginity, chastity, modesty and sexual faithfulness were held in great esteem. This was in marked contrast with other nations, which offer the female of the house to the guest for his sexual enjoyment.

Women in Japan—This stage in the culture of sexual morality is quite high. It appears much later than other forms of culture and civilization. This is seen in the Japanese, who are considered quite civilized and have accepted many of the modern improvements. In Japan it is the custom to marry a woman only after she has lived for a year in the tea-houses, which correspond with our houses of prostitution. To the Japanese the nakedness of women is nothing shocking. At all events, among them every unmarried woman can prostitute herself without lessening her value as a future wife. This is proof that with this remarkable people woman possesses no moral worth. She is valued in marriage only as a means of enjoyment, reproduction and work.

Bible Women—In Biblical times women occupied an inferior position to man. And even after Biblical times woman was still considered as an inferior creature. This may be due in part to the account in Genesis of the secondary creation of woman from the rib of man—Genesis, ii: 21 and 22: "And the Lord God caused a deep sleep to fall upon Adam, and he slept; and He took one of his ribs and closed up the flesh instead thereof; and the rib, which the Lord God had taken from man, made He a woman, and brought her unto the man." It was also due probably to her part in the fall of man and the consequent curse: "Thy will shall be thy husband, and he shall rule over thee," Genesis, iii: 16. Since the Fall, for which the Old Testament made woman responsible, became the foundation for the teachings of the Church, the wife's social position in the early centuries could but remain inferior.

State of Polygamy—Moreover, polygamy, is expressly recognized in the Old Testament—Deuteronomy, xxi: 15: "If a man have two wives, one beloved and the other hated." The value of each sex among the Jews is shown by Leviticus, xxvii: 3 and 4: "And thy estimation should be of the male from twenty years old even unto sixty years old, even thy estimation shall be fifty shekels of silver, after the shekel of the sanctuary; and if it be a female then thy estimation shall be thirty shekels." Even in the New Testament polygamy is not distinctly forbidden. The only passage in the Gospels favoring woman is that forbidding the putting away of a wife—Matthew xix: 9: "And I say unto you, whosoever shall put away his wife, except it be for fornication, and shall marry another, committeth adultery; and whoso marrieth her which is put away doth commit adultery."

THE PASSIONS

THEIR INFLUENCE ON HEALTH

There is no more interesting study than that of the passions. Of nothing do we think we know so much while in reality we know so little.

120 *Love.*

than they are. A flirting widow always looks younger than an old maid of like age.

12. Love renders women industrious and frugal, and a loving husband spends lavishly on a loved wife and children, though miserly towards others.

13. Love cultivates self-respect and produces beauty. Beauty in walk and beauty in looks; a girl in love is at her best; it brings out the finest traits of her character, she walks more erect and is more generous and forgiving; her voice is sweeter and she makes happy all about her. She works better, sings better and is better.

14. Now in conclusion, a love marriage is the best life insurance policy; it pays dividends every day, while every other insurance policy merely promises to pay after death. Remember that statistics demonstrate that married people outlive old maids and old bachelors by a goodly number of years and enjoy healthier and happier lives.

THE TURKISH WAY OF MAKING LOVE.

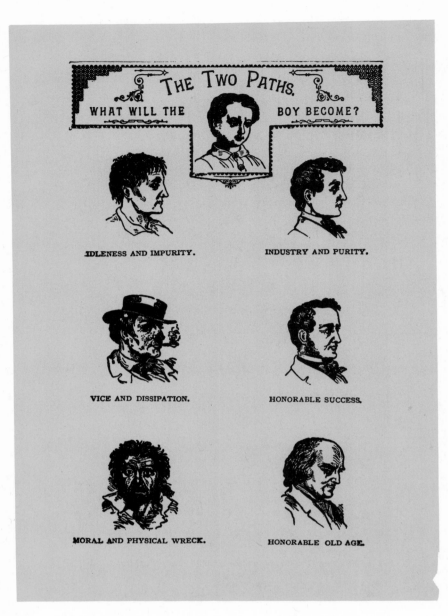

THE TWO PATHS.

WHAT WILL THE BOY BECOME?

IDLENESS AND IMPURITY.

INDUSTRY AND PURITY.

VICE AND DISSIPATION.

HONORABLE SUCCESS.

MORAL AND PHYSICAL WRECK.

HONORABLE OLD AGE.

drawn out with great pauses. The glands in the mouth may stop secreting and our mouth and throat become dry. The glands in the eye may secrete too much and the tears run down our cheeks.

DIFFERENT MANIFESTATIONS IN DIFFERENT PEOPLE—The passions often act differently upon different people. Every one of us, almost, has some peculiarity of expression. One person will laugh or act differently from his neighbor. He will redden or pale where others do not.

ANGER—Anger may throw one man in a violent passion, while it may make another merely frown and look stern. Joy may make one fairly intoxicated, while it may evoke almost no outward sign in another.

LOVE—Love, the strongest passion of all, will make one person the gentlest of creatures. It will make him think more of another. He will do anything for his beloved. His all he is willing to risk, even, his very life. Another will be made fierce by this same passion. Murderous thoughts will be aroused in his breast. He thinks of the welfare of no one, not even of the object of his love. He is willing to sacrifice the happiness, the honor, the life of another.

GRIEF—Grief will soften some people and harden others.

Every emotion, however, is shown by some sign, generally by the same actions in all, but occasionally by different expressions.

We love, we fear, we hate. We experience every passion and emotion. But have we ever stopped to think what are these passions that we are feeling every day?

THE INFLUENCE OF THE MIND ON THE BODY

We not only feel our passions, we act them. Every emotion has its outward manifestations.

A muscle may become stiff or lie limp. Our blood-vessels may constrict and make us pale or they may dilate and make us redden. The heart often beats more quickly or more slowly, and sometimes even stops for a time. Our breathing may be short and quick or long

THE BODILY FEELING THAT ACCOMPANIES EVERY PASSION

Every one of the actions is felt the same moment the emotion occurs. If the reader has never paid any attention to the matter he will be both interested and astonished to learn how many different bodily feelings he can detect in himself as present with every passion. He will be surprised to find out how for each emotion there is a different action or expression.

Of course a man can not stop in the middle of any passion to study what movements are taking place. But he can observe the more quiet states.

When worried by any slight trouble one will usually find that his brows are knitted.

When a person is embarrassed for the moment he feels something in his throat that makes him either swallow, clear his throat or give a slight cough.

When anyone is very much amused he will find it almost impossible to keep his features straight.

NO PASSION WITHOUT AN ACCOMPANYING ACTION

There can be no consciousness of any motion without an accompanying feeling.

Fear—What kind of an emotion of fear would be left if there were not present the feeling of quickened heart-beats or of shallow breathing, of goose-flesh, rising hair and queer empty feelings about the stomach?

Rage—Who can fancy the state of rage and picture no boiling in the chest, no flushing of the face, no quivering of the nostrils and no clenching of the teeth?

Tears—What would grief be without its tears, its sobs, its suffocation of the heart, its pang in the breast?

DIFFERENT EXPRESSIONS OF THE PASSION

As a rule, the same passion effects all men in the same way. There are exceptions, however.

We have all seen people dumb with joy instead of talking and shouting. We have seen how fright will cause the blood to rush into a man's head instead of driving it away. We have witnessed those who have met with losses running around in their grief, crying and lamenting instead of sitting down, bowed, and silent.

ARE THE PASSIONS FIRST FELT IN THE MIND OR IN THE BODY?

Let those who call this question silly pay attention to the following instances:

When we are reading or listening to a story

we are often surprised at the shiver that suddenly flows over our skin and at the heart's swellings and tears that sometimes unexpectedly excite us.

If we are walking in the woods and suddenly see a dark form, our heart stops beating and we catch our breath intently before we have time to form in our mind any idea of danger.

If we see anyone walking near a precipice we shudder and shrink back, although we know him to be safe and have in our mind no feeling of real danger.

An Illustrative Case—A writer tells of his

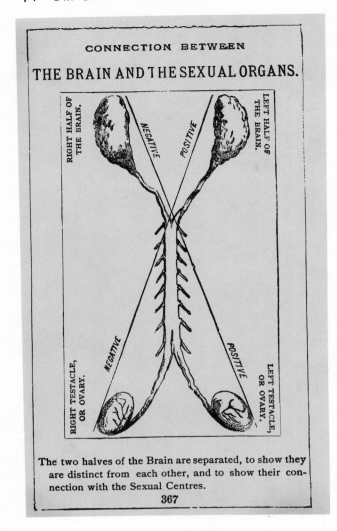

CONNECTION BETWEEN

THE BRAIN AND THE SEXUAL ORGANS.

RIGHT HALF OF THE BRAIN.

LEFT HALF OF THE BRAIN.

NEGATIVE

POSITIVE

NEGATIVE

POSITIVE

RIGHT TESTACLE, OR OVARY.

LEFT TESTACLE, OR OVARY.

The two halves of the Brain are separated, to show they are distinct from each other, and to show their connection with the Sexual Centres.

367

astonishment, when a boy of eight, at fainting at the sight of blood. He was watching a horse being bled. The blood was in a bucket with a stick in it.

Out of curiosity the boy picked up the stick and stirred the blood around and saw it drop from the end of the stick.

Suddenly the world grew black before his eyes, his ears began to buzz and he knew no more.

He had never heard that the sight of blood produced faintness and sickness, and he had no repugnance to it and no thought of danger from it. And even at his young age he could not help wondering how the mere presence of a pailful of red fluid could cause such violent effects in his body.

Fright—When a person jumps at a loud sound he says the noise frightened him. But

he never felt any real fear or thought there was any danger.

Many men can never grow used to standing beside a cannon when it is fired off, although they know perfectly well that there is no danger either to themselves or others. The mere sound is too much for them.

LIFE, MORALS AND HEALTH

AS AFFECTING

HEALTH

Problem of Life—The problem of life is the one great question that has puzzled all students since the time immemorial. And not only students. There is no one to whom the question has not arisen, "What is life and why are we here?" The philosopher, the theologian, the practical man of business and the pleasure-seeker all give different answers. But whether a man believes life here to be a preparation for another and better world, or whether he believes that the object of life is happiness, one thing must be recognized.

Life Duties—We are here on earth a race of human beings, with certain passions and certain feelings, and with bodies that must grow, develop and be propagated. As family beings we come in contact with our own flesh and blood, and with this relationship come certain duties. . . .

Duties in Reproduction—The duties concerned in reproduction must be thoroughly realized and appreciated if the strength and vigor of the race and nation is to be maintained.

Consequences of Neglect—Neglect of the first duty of man has caused the downfall of nations and the dwarfing and weakening of a once strong people.

Thoughtlessness in youth is responsible for untold misery.

Ignorance in young maidenhood has led to lives of unspeakable suffering.

Carelessness at important events claims more victims than all the wars.

Inexperience where experience is essential is responsible for many ruined constitutions and wrecked lives.

A medical work which does not give that

knowledge that will prevent disease and rear a healthy generation is not fulfilling its purpose.

The Great Law of Sex—Everything that has life, whether the smallest animal or the most modest flower, recognizes the distinction of sex. Not only in the animal kingdom, but even in the vegetable kingdom, is the law of gender obeyed.

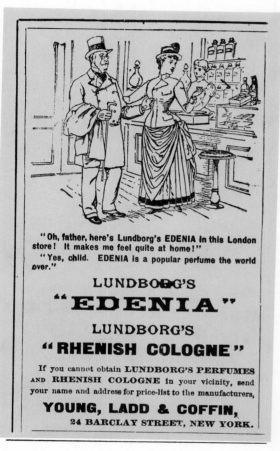

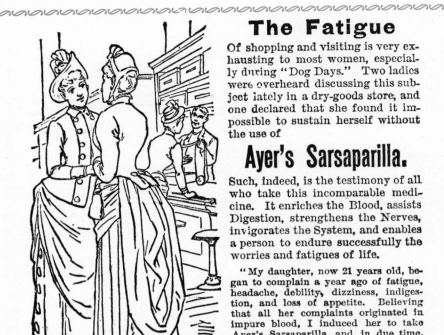

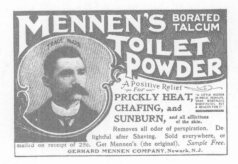

OUR grandmothers all knew the secret of beautiful complexions, and rosy cheeked country girls to this day go to the buttermilk pan for their beauty.

Buttermilk Toilet Soap

makes the face and hands as soft as velvet, whitens the skin and is the grandest complexion beautifier in the world.

Price, 25 cents. If your dealer does not keep it, send 12 cents for a full-size sample cake and souvenir.

COSMO COMPANY, Box 1108, Chicago, Ill.

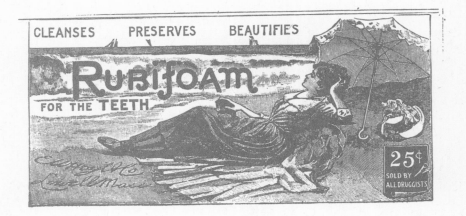

CLEANSES   PRESERVES   BEAUTIFIES

Rubifoam

FOR THE TEETH

25¢ SOLD BY ALL DRUGGISTS

Woodworth's Imperishable Perfumes:

TRIPLE EXTRACT FOR THE HANDKERCHIEF

BLUE LILIES

C. B. WOODWORTH & SONS, ROCHESTER, N.Y.

This picture shows two laundresses, one at work, the other not able to, because her hands are cracked and sore—she has been using soap containing too much alkali. Read Prof. Leed's report.

Gentlemen: The sample of "IVORY" Soap which you sent to me for analysis has been received, and you will find analysis herewith. The "IVORY" Soap, while strongly cleansing, leaves the skin soft and pleasant to the touch instead of harsh, uncomfortable, and liable to chap, as results from the use of many common laundry soaps, in which the ratio of uncombined to combined alkali is large. The percentage of uncombined fat in the "IVORY" is very small, hence the lather is clean, white and abundant, with entire absence of oil or grease. There are no injurious substances.

The above considerations show the "IVORY" to be a pure soap and excellent for laundry use.

Very Respectfully Yours,

LABORATORY OF CHEMISTRY, STEVENS INSTITUTE OF TECHNOLOGY, HOBOKEN, N. J.

ALBERT R. LEEDS, PH.D. PROFESSOR OF CHEMISTRY.

Plant Sexuality—The flower we see in the field has its pistil with its ovary and its stamens with their pollen. And not until the male element, the pollen, falls upon the female element, the pistil, can the seeds form in the ovary and burst forth to mature into another generation of plants. How eagerly does the pollen await the coming of the butterfly and bee to the flower on which it grows! And how tightly does it cling to its wing or foot until it is brushed off on the pistil of the next flower the insect visits! And even the tall, stately trees, whom no one would suspect of sexual desires, put threads or sails on their male blossom so that the wind will carry it to the female element of the nearest branch. The farmer would wait in vain for his corn ear if the dust from the waving tassels did not drop on the flowing silk below.

Animal Sexuality—In the animal kingdom how varied are the methods the male adopts to attract the female! The gay butterfly paints his wings in the brightest colors so he may attract a mate and so furnish future butterflies to beautify the fields. The cricket hidden among the tall grass can chirp and let his friends know where it can be found. The bird trills its sweetest notes to delight the female when hunting for a nestmate in spring. And so throughout the whole animal and vegetable world, even down to man. Adam would have been the only man in the world had Eve not been created. With man and woman in the world it was no longer necessary to rob either of a rib in order that the world might be populated.

Heredity Throughout Nature—How exact a copy of the parents is the offspring! The gardener never wonders, when he plants the seeds, what kind of flowers will spring up. The bulb he puts in the earth came from a lily and will bring forth a similar flower when it is grown. When the maple seed falls to the ground nothing but a maple tree will spring up. The farmer is never in doubt when he puts duck eggs or those of game under a white leghorn as to what will come out of the shell. The frog spawn will develop tadpoles, the shad eggs will turn into shad fish, and the offspring of the squirrel will resemble its parents.

Heredity in Man—And so with man. The

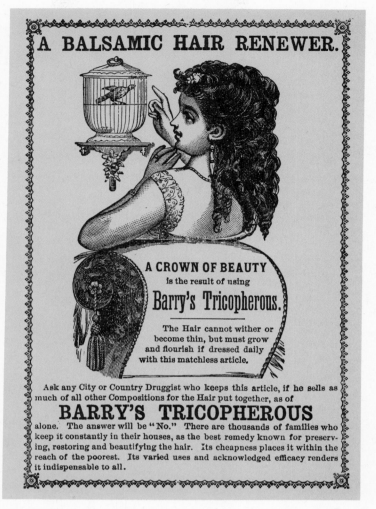

Indian squaw will have a papoose. The hot blood of the Spaniard will be seen in the Spanish babe, and the little Yankee baby will grow up cool and calculating.

Inheritable Traits and Diseases—Unfortunately, however, we can go much farther. The insane mother will bring to the world a feeble-minded child. An innocent babe will die of a horrible disease inherited from its father. The burglar will rear a youthful pickpocket. On the other hand, we may see a learned father enrich the world with a studious son. A robust woman often brings up a healthy babe. Truly is it a "visiting the iniquities of the fathers upon the children until the third and fourth-generations." There is no object in knowing about heredity unless we make proper application of our knowledge. The responsibility of bringing into the world a healthy, wise and moral generation rests on the fathers and mothers of the land. A proper appreciation of this would prevent much of the disease and misery that exists in the world.

The
Guide Board

THE

GUIDE-BOARD

TO

HEALTH, PEACE AND COMPETENCE;

OR,

THE ROAD TO HAPPY OLD AGE.

BY

W. W. HALL, M.D., NEW YORK,

AUTHOR OF "SOLDIER HEALTH," "SLEEP," "JOURNAL OF HEALTH," ETC., ETC.

Men consume too much food, and too little pure air;
They take too much medicine, and too little exercise.

SOLD ONLY BY SUBSCRIPTION.

SPRINGFIELD, MASS.:
D. E. FISK AND COMPANY.

PHILADELPHIA:
H. N. McKINNEY & CO., 16 NORTH SEVENTH STREET.

ST. LOUIS, MO.:
F. A. HUTCHINSON & CO., 502 NORTH SIXTH ST.

---

276   COMMON SENSE MEDICAL ADVISER.

Riding on Horseback is a fine exercise for both sexes. It promotes digestion, improves the circulation, and expands and develops the respiratory organs. The pure, fresh air, pleasant scenery, and pleasurable excitement, impart renewed vigor to the equestrian. In the Southern States it is a universal accomplishment, and children are taught to ride as well as to walk.

Fig. 112.

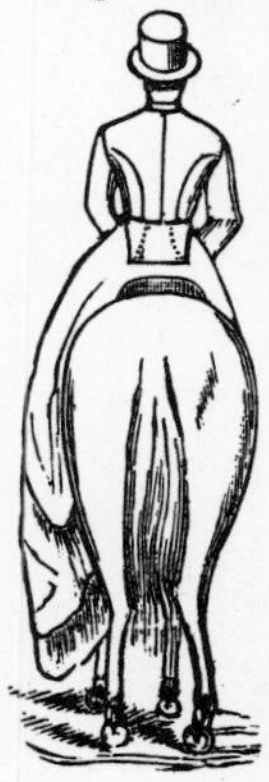

Dancing. Notwithstanding the fact that dancing has been perverted to the basest purposes, has been made the fruitful source of dissipation, and has often laid the foundation for disease, it is yet capable of being made to minister to health and happiness. As a means of physical culture, it favors the development of the muscular system, and promotes health and cheerfulness. When practiced for this purpose, Jacques terms it "the best of all in-door exercises, as it brings to bear upon the physical system a great number of energizing and harmonious influences."

D. E. FISK & COMPANY,

SPRINGFIELD, MASS.:

H. N. McKINNEY & COMPANY,

16 North Seventh Street,

PHILADELPHIA, PA.

PUBLISHERS OF

THE 'GUIDE BOARD TO HEALTH,'

AND

"FUN BETTER THAN PHYSIC,"

By Dr. W. W. HALL.

The "Guide Board" is sold ONLY by Canvassing Agents.

Agents of *many years' experience* find our works as

ACCEPTABLE, CHEAP, AND RAPID SELLING

as any in the field.

Persons wishing to engage permanently, professional men, and students during their vacations, or any one, male or female, will find it to their interest to apply for terms and territory, before engaging elsewhere.

We do not advertise that Agents can make twenty or thirty dollars a day, (for that we do not believe,) but with diligence, and courtesy to the public, we think Agents can do as well with our publications as with any, and we shall continue to issue new works to supply the demand.

We pay *liberal Premiums* to any one sending us Agents.

Two books of the 1800's had great influence in the United States.
Although medical in character, they were not
actually home medicine books.
Most of the books published and sold
as Home Medical books were written by medical men
in such a manner as to be used only in cases of emergencies.
Each disease was listed with its symptoms and treatment
in hope that the sick would benefit.
However, Dr. W. W. Hall of New York City had his own inimitable
way of writing health books in the form of short essays on
various topics of health.
There was a great deal of interest in his books
when they were published 100 years ago because they were different.
Yet pick them up today and they are still fascinating.
The reason? They are still different.
The ideas expressed by Dr. Hall made for
unusual reading then and they still do.
One of his most popular books was The Guide Board
written in 1869.
Some of the ideas might today be considered a little strange.

The Guide Board

PREFACE

The first and immediate aim of the good and great physician, is to restore his patient to health in the shortest time, with the smallest amount of medicine, and with the least discomfort practicable. When this is accom-

plished, he has a more elevated ambition; an object noble and still more human presses upon his attention—THE PREVENTION OF ALL DISEASES. It is hard enough to get along in this world when a man is well; but to have to make a living under the depressing influence of sickness, and pain, and suffering, is worse than having to climb a steep clay bank in wet weather. Old age is comfortless enough of itself; but to be old, and full of aches and pain, and gout and rheumatism is dreadful to think of. To prevent the young from getting sick, to enable all to grow old gracefully, with a heart full of the milk of human kindness, a genial smile and a pleasant word for everybody, and to go down to the grave "like a shock of corn fully ripe in his season," —these are the main objects of this book.

BRANDY AND THROAT DISEASE

In several instances persons have applied to me who had been advised to take brandy freely for a throat affection. None but an ignorant man, or a drunkard, would give such advice; it is warranted by no one principle in medicine, reason, or common sense. The throat is inflamed, the brandy inflames the whole body, and the throat affection, being least urgent from its being scattered over a smaller surface, is less felt, and the excitement of the liquor gives a general feeling of wellness, until the system becomes accustomed to the stimulus, and then the throat, body, and the man all the more speedily go to ruin together.

I have in my mind, while writing these lines, the melancholy history of two young men, one from Kentucky and the other from Missouri, who were advised to drink brandy freely three times a day, for a throat complaint; one of them, within a year, became a confirmed drunkard, and lost his property, and will leave an interesting family in want within another year; the other was one of the most high-minded, honorable young men I have lately known; he was the only son of a widow, and she was rich; *within six months* he became a regular toper, lost his business, spent all his money, and left secretly for California, many thousands of dollars in debt.

MORAL CAUSES OF CHOLERA

The "London Christian Times" suggests that moral causes have much to do in engendering this disease, and that moral remedies may go far to alleviate or cure it.

The filthy, low-lying regions, says the "Times", where the disease presents itself with most inveteracy, are also the regions of coarse, imbruted vice. Self-indulgence in sordid and unwholesome luxuries undermine the constitu-

The Story of Sexual Abuse is plainly told by the downcast countenance, the inability to look a person fairly in the face, the peculiar lifting of the upper lip and the furtive glance of the eye. The state of the mind and of the nervous system corroborates this evidence, for there seems to be a desire to escape from conversation and to elude society.. The mind seems engrossed and abstracted, the individual appears absorbed in a constant meditation, he is forgetful and loses nearly all interest in the ordinary affairs of life. The whole appearance of a patient, suffering from spermatorrhea, is perfectly understood by the experienced physician, for the facial expressions, state of mind, and movements of the body, all unconsciously betray, and unitedly proclaim his condition.

tion. Perseverance in such indulgence, for a series of generations, debilitates a race. The harassment and anxiety attendant upon precarious and dishonest means of obtaining a livelihood, shake terribly such enfeebled constitutions.

Vicious indulgence and sordid habits, by demoralizing a large proportion of the lower classes, are the real cause of predisposition to a new and awful form of the disease. The filth and squalor are merely the external indications of this internal rottenness. When a large portion of any community has been thus predisposed, disease catches around it like wildfire, and even those who have kept themselves above the general degradation are not exempted from its visitations. The honest poor are by their poverty brought into contagious proximity to the class prepared for sickness. The wealthy are brought into contact with the infected stratum of society by business relations. Let the whole truth be told: the vicious and the unreflecting of the wealthier class expose themselves to contagion by visiting infected dens in search of illicit pleasure. Nay, more; the anxious, mammon-hunting, voluptuous habits of the wealthy predispose them to contagion. . . .

MONEY A MEDICINE

Prosperity is the best pill; it wakes up the failing pulses of life, and renovates the whole machinery of man. Take two poor men who are equally ill, to whom exercise is alike applicable: Condemn one to the unendurable drudgery of walking a mile thrice, daily, to a certain post, and when he gets there to turn round and walk back again; and let another spend an equal time in collecting bills, or obtaining subscriptions at a percentage which clears him ten dollars a day, if he is diligent; it is easy to conjecture which of the two will convalesce the more rapidly. One thing I am certain of: making money helps *me* amazingly; it is the elixir of mind and body both. This idea of the hygienic value of money on men is strikingly illustrated in the report of M. Vellerme, Secretary of the Poor Law Commissioners in Havre, where the average age of the rich is twelve years greater than that of the poor.

> 1088 prosperous persons died at an average of 42 years
>
> 4791 middling class persons died at an average age of 29 years
>
> 19848 poor persons died at an average age of 20 years

Therefore, as it is easier to take money than to take pills, I advise my readers, one and all, as a means of long life, to get rich by practising industry and honorable economy.

SUDDEN DEATH

The chances of escaping sudden death are nearly two to one in favor of women. Death always begins at the head, the heart, or the lungs; therefore,—

1. Keep the head cool by taking the world easy.

2. Keep the lungs breathing deeply and fully about seventeen times a minute, by cultivating alacrity in all the bodily movements.

3. Keep the heart beating about sixty-eight times a minute; that is, let the pulse beat four times while the lungs breathe once; by eating temperately, sleeping fully and soundly, exercising moderately, and avoiding all temporary excitants, mental or liquid.

HOW TO BE HAPPY

That is the question. Reader, I have seen a great deal, and felt more; have talked and travelled, and enjoyed, and suffered with all sorts of people; have wandered much, and staid at home more; have been on the sea, and in it, and under it; have been laughed at, shot at, quarrelled at, praised, blamed, abused; have been blown at, and blown up; have had much, and had little,—so much as to enjoy nothing, so little that I would have enjoyed a crust of bread; because the ship went to the bottom with everything in it, leaving me to float to a sandbank. And then, again, I have wandered over the earth, and under it, and through it,—its caves, and its dungeons and darkness,—after stalagmites, and stalactites, and specimens of black rocks and white ones, blue stones and gray; lived for months on desert islands, just for the purpose of picking up new shells on the beach, which the tide of night never failed to leave behind it. In those bygone days, when I had the three great requisites of an enjoying traveller, to wit, plenty of time, plenty of patience, and plenty of money, so, if the coach turned over and smashed up, I could afford to wait until another could be had, or if the ship went to the bottom instead of its destined port, it was just the same to me; because if I was not at one place I was another, and there was always some strange rock to look at, some quiet "dip," that set me calculating how many horse power it required to make that rock just turn so, and all the million inquiries which geology, astronomy, conchology, and a dozen other dry names suggested, which not only had the effect to keep me from fretting, but kept me in an interested humor,—well, in all these different situations, and as many more, I have found out, among others, three things:—

1. *That man out of money cannot be happy.*

2. *That a man out of health cannot be happy.*

3. *That a man without a wife cannot be happy.*

Therefore I have come to the conclusion, that the best way to be happy is to take care of your health, keep out of debt, and get a wife.

EARLY MARRIAGES

Early marriages—by which we mean under twenty-three for the woman, and under twenty-eight for the man—are the misfortune and calamity of those who contract them. The constitution of the woman is prematurely taxed by early child-bearing, and is broken down before she is thirty-five, the age in which she ought to be in all the glory of matronly beauty, or social and domestic influence and power and enjoyment. But instead of this, in what condition does "thirty-five" find the great majority of American women?—thin, pale, wasted, hollow cheeks, sunken and dark-circled eyes, no strength, no power of endurance, with a complication of peculiar ailments, which, while they baffle medical skill, irritate the body, and leave the mind habitually fretful and complaining.

The influence which these things have on the manly ambitions of the husband is disastrous; his solicitude and sympathy for his suffering wife waste the mental power which ought to have been put forth on his business; his time is diverted, whilst the reckless waste of servants unlooked after, and that unavoidable wreck and ruin to house and furniture and clothing, which is an inseparable attendant on every wifeless family,—these things, we say, soon begin to have a depressing effect on the energies of the young father and husband, who is too often driven into do-nothing indulgence, into reckless shifts, or into the forgetfulness of habitual drunkenness. . . .

Do not marry under twenty-eight for yourself, nor under twenty-three for your wife; and remember, too, that the best dowry a woman can bring you is a sound constitution; it is worth more to you than "a fortune," while its moral and physical effect on the future health and happiness of the children who may be born to you cannot be measured by any array of dollars.

BATHING

Once a week is often enough for a decent white man to wash himself all over; and whether in summer or winter, that ought to be done with soap, warm water, and a hog's hair brush, in a room showing at least seventy degrees Fahrenheit. If a man is a pig in his nature, then no amount of washing will keep him clean, inside or out. Such a one needs a bath every time he turns round.

Baths should be taken early in the morning,

for it is then that the system possesses the power of reaction in the highest degree. Any kind of bath is dangerous soon after a meal, or soon after fatiguing exercise. No man or woman should take a bath at the close of the day, unless by the advice of the family physician. Many a man, in attempting to cheat his doctor out of a fee, has cheated himself out of his life; ay, it is done every day.

The safest mode of a cold bath is a plunge into a river; the safest time is instantly after getting up. The necessary effort of swimming to shore compels a reaction, and the effect is delightful.

The best, safest, cheapest, and most universally accessible mode of keeping the surface of the body clean, besides the once-a-week washing up with soap, warm water, and hog's hair brush, is as follows:—

Soon as you get out of bed in the morning wash your face, hands, neck, and breast; then, into the same basin of water, put both feet at once, for about a minute, rubbing them briskly all the time; then, with the towel which has been dampened by wiping the face, feet, etc., wipe the whole body well, fast and hard, mouth shut, breast projecting. Let the whole thing be done within five minutes.

ODORIFEROUS FEET

That an odor issues from every person, peculiar to himself, is proven by the fact that the dog can find his master, although out of sight; but this emanation from the body is so ethereal, generally, that the human sense of smell cannot distinguish it. In very rare instances the calamity may be inherited, or may arise from a scrofulous constitution. At the same time, it is true, that in almost every case, bad-smelling feet, or person, arises from old perspiration in a decaying condition. There is no special odor to the perspiration from the hands. It is because they are constantly exposed to the air, and are frequently washed and ventilated and so with the face. It is from the feet, always covered, from the arm-pits, seldom washed; and from the groins, always in a perspiring condition, that fetid odors come. The remedy, then, is the plentiful and frequent application of soap and hot water, twice a day, as long as needed. They may not avail sometimes, especially with men, for many keep their boots on the whole day; the perspiration of the feet condenses on them, decomposes, and the gas given out is absorbed by the leather, and remains permanently. In such cases, not only is the strictest personal cleanliness necessary, the toes and nails being very particularly attended to, but shoes should be worn to allow of a more free escape of gases; they should be changed every day; and when not on the feet, should be exposed to the outdoor air, so as to have the most thorough ventilation.

SLEEPING TOGETHER

If a man were to see a quarter of an inch of worm put in his cup of coffee, he could not drink it, because he knows that the whole cup would be impregnated. If a very small amount of some virulent poison be introduced into a glass of water, the drinking of it might not produce instant death, but that would not prove that it was not hurtful, only that there was not enough of it to cause a destructive result immediately.

We sicken at the thought of taking the breath of another the moment it leaves the mouth, but that breath mingles with the air about the bed in which two persons lay; and it is rebreathed, but not the less offensive is it in reality, on account of the dilution, except that it is not taken in its concentrated form; but each breath makes it more concentrated. One sleeper corrupts the atmosphere of the room by his own breathing, but when two persons are breathing at the same time, twelve or fourteen times in each minute, in each minute extracting all the nutriment from a gallon of air, the deterioration must be rapid indeed, especially in a small and close room. A bird cannot live without a large supply of pure air. A canary bird, hung up in a curtained bedstead where two persons slept, died before the morning.

Many infants are found dead in bed, and it is attributed to having been overlaid by the parents; but the idea that any person could lay still for a moment on a baby, or anything else of the same size, is absurd. Death was caused by the want of pure air . . .

The most destructive typhoid and putrid fevers are known to arise directly from a number of persons living in the same small room.

Those who can afford it, should therefore arrange to have each member of the family sleep in a separate bed. If persons must sleep in the same bed, they should be about the same age, and in good health. If the health be much unequal, both will suffer, but the healthier one the most, the invalid suffering for want of entirely pure air.

So many cases are mentioned in standard medical works, where healthy, robust infants and larger children have dwindled away, and died in a few months from sleeping with grandparents, or other old persons, that it is useless to cite special instances in proof.

OUR DAUGHTERS

Our daughters are the hope of our country's future. Their physical, moral, and domestic education are of an importance which no array of figures can express, which multitudes of ponderous tomes could not adequately portray.

As is the mother, so is the man, if she be a woman of physical vigor, a high guarantee is given of healthy children. If her moral character is pure, formed in the mould of Bible piety, we may anticipate for her offspring lives of the self-same piety, with its benevolent influences spreading far and wide from all their habitations.

If the mother, in her domestic relations, be a pattern for all that is cleanly and systematic, and punctual and prompt and persevering, with womanly dignity and lovingness pervading all, then may we look for every son of such a woman to be a man of mark for his time, and every daughter to become a wife well worthy of a king.

When such destinies hang upon the future of our daughters, ought they to be hurried from a loving mother's side at seventeen, at fifteen, at twelve, to the purchased care of a governess? to the herded tuition of fashionable boarding-schools, where glitter and superficiality and empty show predominate; where nothing that is radically useful and good is thorough; where associations are inevitable with the children of the parvenu, as well as with the scion of the decayed aristocrat, thus exposing the pure heart to the withering and corrupting examples of mere pretence and of baseless pride?

The theatre, the ball-room, the sea-shore, or the spa, are these the schools to mould aright the character of the girls who are to be the mothers of the next generation? Is the heterogeneous weekly newspaper, the trashy monthly, the "last novel," be it from whom it may,—are these suitable textbooks to form the principles of her who is soon to become the wife, the mother, the matron?

We trust these suggestive inquiries will arrest the attention, and command the mature reflection of every parent.

OUR DAUGHTERS RUINED

A young lady in good health was sent to a distant city, to finish her education in a boarding-school of considerable note. In one month she returned, suffering from general debility, dizziness, neuralgic pains, and headache.

It must be a very telling process, which, in a single month, transforms a rollicking, romping, ruddy-faced girl of sixteen to a pale, weakly, failing invalid. It is not often done so quickly; but, in the course of a boarding school

education, it is done thousands of times. Public thanks are due to a correspondent of the "Buffalo Medical Journal," for the pains he took to ferret out the facts of the daily routine of the establishment, the proprietors of which so richly merit the reprobation of the whole community, both for their recklessness of human health and their ignorance of physiological law. Said an accomplished lady to us, not long since, "My only daughter is made a wreck of,—she lost her mind at that wretched school!"

At this model establishment, where the daughters of the rich, and of the aspiring are prepared for the grave every year, twelve hours are devoted to study out of the twenty-four, when five should be the utmost limit. Two hours are allowed for exercise; three for eating; seven hours for sleep.

Plenty of time allowed to eat themselves to death, at the expense of stinting them to the smallest amount of time for renovating the brain, the very fountain of life, upon whose healthful and vigorous action depends the ability of advantageous mental culture and physical energy. . . .

UNTIMELY EXERCISE

A brisk walk, in a cool, bracing atmosphere, is a luxury, provided it be taken under proper circumstances. Sidney Smith made a great mistake when he said that a public speaker would never break down if he would walk a dozen miles before speaking. He might not break down, in one sense of the word; for there would be nothing to break. He would have no strength, and there would be no elevation to tumble from, because his speech would be as flat as cold soup. The less a man exercises before a morning's sermon or speech the better. The vital energy should not be expanded on the muscles, but on the brain. To speak with freshness, and with a vigor which shall carry all before it, a man should neither sing, talk, nor walk before speaking.

A DANGEROUS CURIOSITY

It is the most natural thing in the world, when you have gone to bed, to get up, run to the window, hoist it and look out, at an alarm

Dangers in Children Sleeping Together and too Close Physical Contact

By M. LOUBET, Former President of France, and now one of the Foremost Child Culturists of Europe

PROFESSOR PINARD said not long ago:
"The milk and heart of a mother cannot be replaced."
"Your children should sleep alone," I say in another motto. I have already told how the late Casimir-Perier discovered worthy occupation for ex-presidents in championing the physique of French children; how his mantle fell on me, who, in turn, discovered the giant organization, ready made, of the French Mutual Benefit Societies. Puericulturists and mutualists are practically one. They are tremendously in earnest, doing vast good.

"Respect the child's privacy!" I say.

The mottoes come to the same thing—a mystery. It may be had both in sleep or waking. It is overwhelmingly in evidence among the very young in boarding schools that receive boys even at the age of seven! They enter plump, rosy, hearty; they quit pale, overtrained and lacking the vitality of youth that bubbles over.

"They are growing," used to be the explanation; but men like Paul Bourget have shown it to be a boarding-school phenomenon, and the puericulturists have found its cause is never-ceasing human contact.

"The little fellows are never an hour alone," says Prof. Pinard. "Their play and leisure are programmed and supervised; no lonely strolls, no dreaming; all is done in groups of boys, accompanied by an under-teacher. Studying must be in common; no boy can go off and read alone. Their privacy is not respected. The boys sleep in dormitories; even their repose must be amid a tornado of human vibrations."

Is it vibrations? This is one theory. Or do stronger boys absorb the vitality of the weak? This is the vampire theory.

But the fact is that children living in their families have an instinct to escape from the "tornado" when wise parents let them.

Watch your little boy or girl. If they are really free, you will discover they take daily rests from "human" contact.

This we know: uninterrupted human contact is a bad condition. Certain children need a longer daily rest from it than others.

Here we grope in the dark. Robust little girls and boys may have nerves that put up a weak defense against the danger, while intense and wiry children, though physically mediocre, seem actually to fatten on the oozing vitality of their playmates.

The child, fleeing for rest in the country, will take to the garden, woods or meadow—alone, or in little groups that do not hurt each other. Put two other children into the group, and you may find them all coming back in bad shape.

Respect the child's privacy. Too often we call the poor, little, solitary seekers of repose "morbid." The child that roams off alone is looked upon as "peculiar," when it blindly seeks to save its vital forces!

In cities the child's refuge is its bedroom. Every child, when it is possible, should have its own exclusive bedroom, its "den," its own private place, its refuge, pure and cool, from the bombardments of alien vitalities.

How Vitality is Sapped.

For six months once I slept on a good bed in a library workroom, and I know the truth. All day long that room was tingling with the vitality of two hard workers and two strong loafers. We even ate in that library workroom. At bedtime I threw open wide the windows, cooled it, purified it as I could. My bed was perfect and the room was large, yet no one will know how abominably ill I slept those six months. No opening of windows could chase out the clinging aura.

If the aura of the absent can cling to a room, what shall we think of the present? Lucky children who can each have his exclusive bedroom! It may be little; that is nothing. It is sweet, pure, cool repose. Here, lying eight, ten hours each day alone, the child recuperates from the mysterious ill of over-contact with its kind.

There are two kinds of sleep. Prof. Vaschide's long-continued, scientific studies of the question show that solitary sleep alone is truly reparative and reposeful. The child who sleeps in the room with grown people, the child who must sleep with other children, has a sleep that is more superficial, less continuous.

All the functions of the organism, such as the beating of the heart, blood pressure, respiratory movements, production of heat, automatically slackened during solitary sleep, undergo notable perturbations as to rhythm and constancy in sleep that is troubled by human contact. Sleep under human contact attains the depth of solitary sleep only in cases of exhaustion. The pupil of the eye, contracted in normal solitary sleep, is much less so in deep sleep under human contact; while the maximum depth of the latter is attained much more slowly.

Even husband and wife do ill to sleep together in the cities of our present-day civilization.

The common nuptial sleep is an old habit. But old habits have no sacred claims when the conditions change. Our forefathers and mothers were much more thick-skinned, less spiritual, less sensitive to outside influences, more grasping of their own, than are our city dwellers. In the dry cold of Canada such an intense oxygen-burning of fatty food goes on in the bodies of the lusty "habitants," that they sleep quite harmlessly packed together in an overheated, oxygenless atmosphere that gives headache to the casual visitor for twenty-four hours later. In a similar manner, our sleeping-together ancestors had hardier organisms—physical, nervous, psychical—defending themselves against what are, to us, the very real ills—though mysterious—of sleep under human contact.

The mere fact that husband and wife seem to get used to sleeping together proves little.

Habit relatively increases the duration of contact-sleep, though it is never really equal to that of solitary sleep; and the increase calls for months and even years of habit. Contact-sleep has the more logical dreams; the awakening is more rapid and the beginning of sleep more sudden; but it differs from solitary sleep, and even the married adults who "get used" to it complain at length of sensations of fatigue which they attribute to a hundred other causes.

If such may be the ills of adults bound together by sacred affinities, what must not be feared for tender children sleeping side by side with adults or with children even hardier or more intense than they?

It matters little—until the cause be discovered—whether we call it bombardment by n-rays, or human-electric emanations, or the clinging aura, or the vampire temperament that takes up vitalities in contact with it. The important thing is to protect the little ones against it.

Respect the child's privacy! One of the crying ills of the world, from workingman up to the easy line, is the crowding of the family into a relatively small apartment. Better run cots nightly into dining-room and parlor than to force the little ones to sleep together, or, far worse, with adults!

of fire or any unusual noise or clamor going on outside. A lady was roused from her sleep by a cry of "Fire!" Her chamber was as bright almost as day when she opened her eyes. She went to the window, and soon saw that it was her husband's cotton factory. She felt on the instant a shock at the pit of her stomach; the result was a painful disease, which troubled her for the remainder of her life, a period of nearly fifteen years.

A young lady, just budding into womanhood, was called by the sound of midnight music to the window, and in her undress leaned her arm on the cold sill; the next day she had an attack of inflammation of the lungs which nearly killed her. She eventually recovered, only to be the victim of a life-long asthma, the horrible suffering from the oft-repeated attacks of which, during now these twenty years, is the painful penalty to be paid over and over again as long as life lasts.

A letter just received from a successful banker, who has been an invalid for five years, every now and then spitting blood by the pint, with a harassing cough which makes every night and morning a purgatory, states that the immediate cause of all his sufferings, and the final blasting of life's prospects, was his getting up on a cool night to look out of his chamber window, his body being in a perspiration at the time. That sturdy old Trojan, Dr. Johnson, used to say, that "mankind did not so much require instructing as reminding"; hence the present reminder, that it is dangerous for people to be poking their nightcaps out of windows after nightfall. . . .

PRECAUTIONS

Never sleep in a room where there is any green paper on the walls, as this color is made of arsenic or lead; the former is by far the most dangerous, being Scheele's green, and is known positively by a drop of muriatic acid on the green leaving it white.

White glazed visiting-cards contain sugar of lead, and will poison a child who is tempted to chew them from the slight sweetish taste.

Green glazed cards, used for concert-tickets, are still more poisonous; a single one of them contains a grain and a half of arsenic, enough to kill a child.

Never put a pin in the mouth or between the teeth, for a single instant, because a sudden effort to laugh or speak may convey it to the throat, or lungs, or stomach, causing death in a few minutes, or requiring the windpipe to be cut open to get it out; if it has passed into the stomach, it may, as it has done, cause years of suffering, ceasing only when it has made its way out of the body through the walls of the abdomen or other portion of the system.

It is best to have no button, or string about any garment worn during the night. A long loose night-gown is the best thing to sleep in. Many a man has facilitated an attack of apoplexy by buttoning his shirt-collar.

If you wake up of a cold night, and find yourself very restless, get out of bed, and standing on a piece of carpet or cloth of any kind, spend five or ten minutes in rubbing the whole body vigorously and rapidly with the hands, having previously thrown the bed-clothing towards the foot of the bed so as to air both bed and body.

If you find that you have inadvertently eaten too much, instead of taking something to settle the stomach, thus adding to the load under which it already labors, take a continuous walk, with just enough activity to keep up a very slight moisture or perspiration on the skin, and do not stop until entirely relieved, but end your exercise in a warm room, so as to cool off very slowly. . . .

Riding against a cold wind, immediately after singing or speaking in public is suicide.

Many public speakers have been disabled for life by speaking under a hoarseness of voice. . . .

Never go to bed with cold feet, if you want to sleep well.

If a person faints, place him instantly flat on a bed, or floor, or earth, on his back, and quietly let him alone at least for ten minutes; if it is simply a fainting-fit, the blood, flowing on a level, will more speedily equalize itself throughout the system; cold water dashed in the face, or a sitting-position are unnecessary and pernicious.

Never blow your nose, nor spit the product of a cough, nor throw a fruit peel, on the sidewalk.

HEALTHFUL OBSERVANCES

To eat when you do not feel like it, is brutal; nay, this is slander on the lower animals, they do not so debase themselves.

Do not enter a sick-chamber on an empty stomach; nor remain as a watcher or nurse until you feel almost exhausted; nor sit between the patient and the fire; nor in the direction of a current of air from the patient towards yourself; nor eat or drink anything after being in a sick-room until you have rinsed your mouth thoroughly.

Do not sleep in any garment worn during the day. . . .

Some of the most painful "stomach-aches" are occasioned by indigestion; this generates wind, and hence distention. It is often promptly remedied by kneading the abdomen with the ball of the hand, skin to skin, from one side to another, from the lower edge of the ribs downwards, because the accumulated air is forced on and outwards along the alimentary canal.

In going into a colder atmosphere, keep the mouth closed, and walk with a rapidity sufficient to keep off a feeling of chilliness.

The "night-sweats" of disease come on towards daylight; their deathly clamminess and coldness is greatly modified by sleeping in a single, loose, long woolen shirt.

The man or woman who drinks a cup of strong tea or coffee, or other stimulant, in order to aid in the better performance of any work or duty, public or private, is foolish, because it is to the body and brain an expenditure of what is not yet got; it is using power in advance, and this can never be done, even once, with impunity.

The less a man drinks of anything in hot weather the better, for the more we drink the more we want to drink, until even ice-water palls and becomes of a metallic taste; hence the longer you can put off drinking cold water on the morning of a hot day, the better will you feel at night.

Drinking largely at meals, even of cold water or simple teas, is a mere habit, and is always hurtful. No one should drink, at any one meal more than a quarter of a pint of any liquid, even of cold water, for it always re-tards, impairs, and interferes with a healthful digestion.

If you sleep at all in the daytime, it will interfere with the soundness of your sleep at night; much less, if the nap be taken in the forenoon.

A short nap in the daytime may be necessary to some. Let it not exceed ten minutes; to this end sleep with the forehead resting on a chair-back or edge of the table.

Never swallow an atom of food while in a passion, or if under any great mental excitement, whether of a depressing or elevating character; brutes won't do it.

HEALTH AT HOME

Health is Wealth: Health is one of the foundation pillars of happiness in the home. It is a condition of the best instruction and the best education. It is an essential preliminary to the best success in the best work, and to the highest attainment in the widest usefulness. Without it there is sadness at the hearthstone, silence and sorrow, instead of cheerful words and happy hearts.

What are fortunes and honors in the absence of the future health and vigor of our loved ones? What is home itself, where disease abides as a permanent visitor, and poisons every perfume with a malarious infection?

PREVENTION OF DISEASE

Early and Strange Notions of Disease: It was supposed formerly that diseases were caused by the evil spirits or demons which are supposed to have entered the body and deranged its action. Hence it was said of the dumb that they had a "dumb evil." Incantations, exorcisms, etc., were constantly resorted to in order to drive them out. It was thought by others that diseases came arbitrarily, or as a special visitation of an overruling power, and hence they were to be removed by fasting and prayer.

Many Diseases May be Avoided: A proper knowledge and observance of hygienic laws would greatly lessen the number of such diseases as pneumonia, consumption, catarrh, gout, rheumatism, scrofula, dyspepsia, etc. It is a lamentable fact that in densely populated cities nearly one half of the children die before they are five years old. Every physiologist knows that at least nine tenths of these lives could be saved by an observance of the laws of health. Professor Bennet, of Edinburgh, estimated that 100,000 persons die annually in Scotland from diseases easily preventable, and the same testimony could be obtained from the medical profession in this and other countries.

FOOD AND HEALTH

ONIONS—Few people dream of the many virtues of onions. Lung and liver complaints are certainly benefited, often cured, by a free consumption of onions, either cooked or raw. Colds yield to them like magic. Don't be afraid of them. Taken at night all offense will be wanting by morning, and the good effects will amply compensate for the trifling annoyance. Taken regularly, they greatly promote the health of the lungs and the digestive organs. An extract made by boiling down the juice of onions to a syrup, and taken as a medicine, answers the purpose very well, but fried, roasted, or boiled onions are better. . . .

TOMATOES—The tomato is one of the most healthful as well as the most relished of all vegetables. Its qualities do not depend on the mode of preparation for the table; it may be eaten thrice a day, cold or hot, cooked or raw, alone or with salt or pepper or vinegar, or altogether, to a like advantage, and to the utmost that can be taken with an appetite. Its excellence arises from its slight acidity, and the seeds which it contains. The acidity refreshes and tones up the system in the same manner as fruits, while the seeds act as a mechanical, gently irritant to the inner coating of the bowels, causing them to throw out a very large amount of fluid matter, and thus keeping them free. The tomato is also very nutritious.

FRUIT SAVES DOCTOR'S BILLS—An experienced physician in the West writes as follows: "My bills are cut down in families in proportion as they eat fresh fruit. Strawberries, currants, and tomatoes are better medicine than calomel, or jalap, and 'rather better to take.' Apples freely eaten do the

work of vermifuge or lozenges. Every fruit or berry has its mission to man hidden away within it. Therefore, set out a strawberry bed, if you haven't one. . . . Plant currants. A fresh cutting will grow if you but stick it in the ground. Border the fence with raspberries. Walk around your place during the early spring days, and make a mental inventory of every spot where you can stick in a fruit tree or a berry bush. Plant something."

EVIL OF RAPID EATING—Eat slowly, thoroughly masticating your food. Rapid eating is one of our national evils and is the chief cause of dyspepsia. Every year its slain are counted by thousands. The saliva does not flow too rapidly to mix with the food to promote digestions, and the coarse pieces swallowed resist the action of the digestive fluid. The fluid washed down with drinks which dilute the gastric juice and hinder its work will not supply the place of the saliva. Failing to get the taste of the food by rapid mastication, we think it insipid, and hence use condiments which over-stimulate the digestive organs. In these ways, the system is overworked, and the tone of the stomach being affected, a foundation is laid for dyspepsia.

LOSS OF APPETITE, AND HOW TO RECOVER IT—The appetite is often lost through excessive use of stimulants, food taken too hot, sedentary occupation, liver disorder, and want of change of air. To ascertain and remove the cause is the first duty. Exercise, change of air, and diet will generally prove sufficient to recover the appetite. Children, if they have plenty of outdoor exercise, are regular in their habits, and eat only plain, nourishing food, will seldom, if ever, complain of a lack of appetite.

BEST TIMES FOR MEALS—*Breakfast* should be eaten as soon as possible after rising. If not convenient to eat at once, a single cup of warm wheat or corn, coffee or chocolate, with plenty of milk, will remove the feeling of languor and faintness for an hour or more.

Dinner should be eaten late in the afternoon or early in the evening. It is the principal meal of the day, and, to be enjoyed as well as digested, admits of neither hurry nor interference. The work of the day should be over; and

a long rest should follow before bed-time. Eat no late suppers.

Luncheon in the middle of the day is the meal most abused. It is rarely that sufficient time is taken for it. This meal should consist of substantial food, but light in quantity. The pressure of work at midday is so great that the digestive organs should not be heavily taxed at that time.

ICE WATER HINDERS DIGESTION— Cold water is a less rapid solvent than warm water, as cold air is a better preservative than warm air. So ice water taken into the stomach chills the coats and contents of that organ, and thus suddenly checks and hinders the digestion of the food.

TEA AND COFFEE AND HEALTH

TEA AND DIGESTION—Tea possesses an active principle called *theine*. It contains tannin, which, if the tea is strong, coagulates the albumen of the food—actually *tans* it—and thus delays digestion.

TEA DRINKING AND SICK-HEAD-ACHE; AN ILLUSTRATION—I have advised all patients consulting me the last two years, for sick-headache, to abandon at once, and wholly the use of tea, of any and all kinds. It has been difficult, though, to induce any to do so, the hold which habits had upon them being so strong, and utterly impossible to persuade others to make the sacrifice.

Of the few who have complied with my request there were three men past middle age, and otherwise tolerably healthy, but who were among those the worst afflicted with this malady of any that I have ever met. One of these was upward of sixty-years of age, and had suffered his entire lifetime, or from his earliest recollection, with sick-headache, frequently as often as every week, and sometimes for two days at a time. Prescribed for him several times, but with no other result than to partially relieve the severity of the attacks—did not break in at all upon the frequency of their recurrence—so finally prevailed upon him, two years ago last spring, to abstain from the use of tea.

As he lived out of the city I never learned the result until three or four months since, when I one day met him upon the street, and he remarked, "Well, doctor, I got rid of my sick-headaches by stopping tea." He further said that his pain was much greater than common for a few days after leaving it off, but he then went much longer than usual before another attack, which was also less severe, and after two or three such recurrences, each at longer intervals and in less violence, they disappeared entirely. And that of late he had tried to use tea again, but even when taken weak it brought on the former symptoms.

COFFEE AS A BEVERAGE—Coffee, though of a taste little allied to tea, derives its efficiency in precisely the same manner and from nearly the same substances. Its value and effects in the system are therefore the same as those above stated. Yet it must be generally conceded that a free coffee drinker will almost invariably complain of biliousness and present a cadaverous appearance. For working people, as a rule, coffee will seldom produce this effect; but for all persons of sedentary habits, who take but little exercise, coffee is not to be recommended. In the case of coffee, as in that of tea, *it should not be drunk strong, except as a medicine.* As a rule, coffee is less harmful than tea.

THE AIR WE BREATHE

EVIL EFFECT OF BREATHING RE-SPIRED AIR—If we take back into our lungs that which has been expelled, we soon feel the effect. The muscles after a time become inactive, the blood stagnates, the heart acts slowly, the food is undigested, the brain is clogged. The constant breathing of even the slightly impure air of our houses cannot but tend to undermine the health. The blood is not purified, and is in a condition to receive the seeds of disease at any time. The system uninspired by the energizing oxygen is sensitive to cold. The pale cheek, the lusterless eye, the languid step, speak too plainly of oxygen starvation.

The foul air which passes off from the lungs and the pores of the skin does not fall to the floor, but diffuses itself through the surrounding atmosphere. A single breath will to a trifling extent taint the air of a whole room.

AIR IN SICK ROOMS—Fresh air is one of the most important and difficult things to obtain and retain in a sick room. The following simple arrangement will remedy the evil of foul gas, generated by burning a kerosene lamp all night in a nursery or sick room:—

Take a raisin box or other suitably sized box that will contain the lamp when set up on end. Place the lamp in the box, outside the window, with the open side facing the room. When there are blinds, the box can be attached to each by leaving them a little open, and fastening with a cord; or the lamp box can be nailed to the window casing in a permanent manner. The lamp burns quite as well outside, and a decided improvement of the air in the room is experienced.

BAD AIR IN SCHOOL AND LECTURE ROOMS—Our school rooms, heated by furnaces or red hot stoves, often have no means of ventilation, or, if provided, these are seldom used. Pupils starved by scanty lung food (and we might add brain food) are listless and dull. This process goes on from year to year, and the weakened and poisoned body at last succumbs to disease, and a "mysterious Providence" is charged with sickness and death. The voice of nature, as well as nature's God, cries aloud, "Do thyself no harm!" Those who violate the God-given laws of life and health may expect the penalty. Whatsoever we sow we shall inevitably reap. If we sow the seeds of disease, we must reap sickness and death. To breathe the atmosphere of many school houses, lecture rooms, and theaters, is to breathe the atmosphere of death.

FOUL AIR IN CHURCHES—We sit in our churches, from which the air and light of heaven have been excluded six days out of seven, and, though, ventilated as well as heated for the seventh, we bewail our listlessness and want of interest in the life-giving Gospel, and we charge it either to the preacher or our own depravity, when the fact is, no temporary ventilation can take from the carbonic-impregnated crypts and walls the depravity which has there fixed its abode. The foul air left by the congregation on Sunday is often shut up during the week and heated for the next Lord's day, when the people assemble, to be re-breathed as polluted atmospheres.

CARE OF THE HAIR

WHY LADIES ARE NOT BALD—Ladies, notwithstanding they wear long hair, which is more likely to fall out, seldom are bald-headed. Their heads are not kept covered indoors, and when out-doors, they are not closely covered. In sleeping none should confine the hair in a close night-cap.

SUDDEN CHANGES IN THE COLOR OF THE HAIR—Sudden and severe frights have sometimes so affected the nerves connected with the papillae at the roots of the hair, as to produce instantaneous changes in the color of the hair. A German medical magazine, now before us, reports two recent cases.

A REMARKABLE CASE IN BERLIN—A physician of Berlin, a strong, healthy, and less than middle-aged man, sent his wife and one daughter to spend last summer at a watering place. The day that he expected a letter informing him of their arrival, there came one saying that his daughter had been taken sick very suddenly, and was already dead. The shock was terrible, and instantly his hair became entirely gray. He had to visit some patients that same afternoon, and they scarcely recognized him. Their peculiar actions revealed the change to him.

UTILITY OF BEARDS—A recent writer in one of our standard magazines strongly puts the case as follows: There are more solid inducements for wearing the beard than the mere improvement of a man's personal appearance, and the cultivation of such an aid to the every-day diplomacy of life. Nature combining, as she never fails to do, the useful with the ornamental, provides us with a far better respirator than science could ever make, and one that is never so hideous to wear as that black seal upon the face that looks like a passport to the realms of suffering and death. The hair of the moustache not only absorbs the moisture and miasma of the fogs, but it strains the air from the dust and soot of our great cities. It acts, also in the most scientific manner, by taking

Per Bottle 57c.

Fig. 91.

heat from the warm breath as it leaves the chest, and supplying it to the cold air taken in. It is not only a respirator, but, with the beard entire, we are provided with a comforter as well; and these are never left at home, like umbrellas, and all such appliances, whenever they are wanted.

BATHING AND HEALTH

BATHING IN ANCIENT TIMES—In the early ages among all the leading nations of the East, bathing was one of the most flourishing institutions. The baths were celebrated for their magnificence. They often formed parts of buildings of vast extent and grandeur, termed Gymnasia, and were large enough to accommodate several thousand persons at the same time. In these baths was centered all that was elaborate in workmanship, elegant in design, and beautiful in art. Nothing was thought too grand or magnificent for their decoration. Precious gems and metals, and the finest works of the painter and sculptor, were to be found within their walls. The great hall of the bath was generally ornamented with statues of Hercules, Hygeia and Aesculapius.

THE BATH A PUBLIC BENEFIT—A great bath in every town in the country, sustained at the public expense, and under capable and accredited supervision, would be of inestimable hygienic value to the people at large. The benefit of thorough bathing would not only be felt in our families, but in business, in our legislative halls, and throughout society generally. Physiology and Hygiene are subjects foreign to the great masses of our people. The rich as well as the poor are ignorant of them. They are thought to be only fit subjects for doctors, and fortunate it is for the profession that they think so, for a large part of their revenue is derived from the ignorance of the people on these subjects. One of the greatest hygienic influences we can bring to bear upon the public health and the advancement of our physical condition, is cleanliness. To be poor is no disgrace; to be unclean is a shame and a crime. If we allow the skin to become filthy, its proper action is interfered with, thereby affecting the whole system, and often causing dangerous disease.

WHAT SLEEP WILL CURE—The cry for rest has always been louder than the cry for food. Not that it is more important, but it is often harder to get. The best rest comes from sound sleep. Of two men or women, otherwise equal, the one who sleeps the best will be the most devotional, healthy, and efficient. Sleep will do much to cure irritability of temper, peevishness, uneasiness. It will cure insanity. It will build up and make strong a weary body. It will do much to cure dyspepsia, particularly that variety known as nervous dyspepsia. It will relieve the languor and prostration felt by consumptives. It will cure hypochondria. It will cure the headache. It will cure neuralgia. It will cure a broken spirit. It will help cure sorrow.

WHY HIGH PILLOWS ARE INJURIOUS—It is often a question among people who are unacquainted with anatomy and physiology, whether lying with head exalted or on a level with the body is more unwholesome. Most, consulting their own case on this point, argue in favor of that which they prefer. Now, although many delight in bolstering up their heads at night, and sleep soundly without injury, yet it is a dangerous habit. The vessels in which the blood passes from the heart to the head are always lessened in their cavities when the head is resting in bed higher than the body; therefore, in all diseases attended with fever, the head should be pretty nearly on a level with the body; and people ought to accustom themselves to sleep thus and avoid danger.

EVIL EFFECTS OF SLEEPING EXCLUSIVELY ON ONE SIDE—The question is often put to physicians, "Why is my head lopsided or larger on one side?" It may be accounted for by always lying on one side. Young mothers are apt to place the child always in one position when putting it to bed, and the skull being soft and thin, the brain grows most on the under side, and finally assumes permanently this irregular and uneven shape. In cholera times, or when the bowels are cold, constipated, and inactive, it is well to lie on the breast, and thus keep the bowels warm.

THE CAUSE OF NIGHTMARE—Nightmare is caused by remaining so long in one position that the blood ceases to circulate. How hard we try to run in our sleep, sometimes, to get out of the way of some terrible danger! It does such a person no good to ask what's the matter. Don't waste time in asking a question but give relief to the sleeper by an instantaneous shake, or even a touch of the body, which breaks the dreadful spell in an instant, because it sets the blood going toward the heart.

EVIL OF INSUFFICIENT CLOTHING—One of the great evils induced by fashion is the unequal distribution of clothing upon the person. One part over-clothed, and another not half clad, is a very common condition, especially among women and children. Women are governed by fashion, children are governed by women, and it is the great resource of fashion to produce new effects by piling on the textures, now here and now there, and by leaving other parts exposed. If the declared purpose were to induce disease, no surer or more effectual way could be found to do it than this. The derangement of the circulation is direct and immediate; its healthy equilibrium is destroyed, the thinly-dressed parts lose their blood to the more vascular, and internal derangements give rise to various chronic bodily ailments.

A lady in New York has just died from consumption produced by a cold which she caught by crossing to and from the different hotels at Saratoga, in the evening, in thin satin slippers and low-necked evening dress, and nothing over her shoulders.

NEWSPAPERS AS PROTECTORS FROM COLD—A newspaper, folded several times and laid across the chest during a cold walk or ride, is a most excellent protector. If the bed-clothing is not sufficiently warm, especially at hotels, two or three large newspapers spread on the bed between the blankets will secure a comfortable night, as far as cold is concerned. A thin shawl may be made warm by folding a paper inside it. The paper is impervious to the wind and cold air from outside, and prevents the rapid escape of the warm air beneath it. If you suffer from cold feet on a journey, fold a piece of newspaper over your stocking; this is better than rubber.

MUFFLING THE THROAT—There is nothing that makes the throat delicate and sensitive more than muffling it closely in wraps of woolen and fur. The rule is, that the neck should be kept as cool as comfort will allow.

Tight collars frequently cause diseases of the throat and lungs. The neck should be dressed lightly. From the many movements which are made by the larynx in speaking, it is inferred that it is a matter of great importance that the neck in health should always be loosely dressed. Tight cravats are sure to obstruct the proper function of this organ, and bring on irritation, which may lead to bronchitis or consumption. An eminent physician, who devotes his whole attention to the throat and lungs, says that about three fourths of all throat diseases would get well by wearing very loose collars, and no neck-tie at all. He also adds: "If you have a disease of the throat, let nature do the curing, and the physician just as little as possible."

A CONTRACTED WAIST

A NATURAL WAIST.

POISONOUS CLOTHING—Dress goods of woolen, silk, and cotton, have been found to contain arsenic in dangerous quantities; so, also, gentlemen's underclothing, hat linings, and the linings of boots and shoes. Professor Nichols of the Massachusetts Institute of Technology, reports the examination of a lady's dress which contained eight grains of arsenic to the square foot. In Troy, New York, lately, the death of a child was attributed to arsenic sucked from a veil which had been thrown over the child's crib to keep off flies.

INJURIOUS DRESS OF MANY SCHOOL-GIRLS—A gifted female writer in an article in one of our educational journals, discussing the prospects of the success of girls in our public schools and seminaries, says: "By means of corsets, band, or belt, her liver is divided into an upper and lower section; the one forced up, to crowd the heart, lungs, and stomach; the other down, to find room as it can, where there is no room for it. Every vital organ is displaced or cramped. Blockades are estab-

lished by tight shoes, tight gloves, tight garters, tight corsets, or still more murderous tight skirt-bands; and there the blood must run, by extra pumping, every time it passes from the heart to the extremities or back. . . . To study in such a costume is to burn the candle at both ends—but the spirit of the age is upon her; the ages to come press on her; study she must and die she must.

MISSOURI JOURNAL—A young lady of our acquaintance called on one of our physicians the other day to prescribe for a rush of blood to the head. "I have been doctoring myself," said the languid fair one, with a smile to the kind M.D., while he was feeling her pulse. "Why, I have taken Brandreth's Pills, Parr's Pills, Strangburg's Pills, Sand's Sarsaparilla, Jayne's Expectorant, used Sherman's Lozenges and Plaster, and—"

"My heaven! madam," interrupted the astonished doctor, "all those do your complaint no good!"

"No! Then what shall I take?" pettishly inquired the patient.

"Take," exclaimed the doctor, eyeing her from head to foot; "take!" exclaimed he, after a moment's reflection, "why—madam—take—take off your corsets!"

It is needless for us to state that she is still suffering from the disease.

T O B A C C O   A N D   H E A L T H

EFFECTS OF TOBACCO ON THE SYSTEM—Some years ago, the French government directed the Academy of Medicine to inquire into the influence of Tobacco on the human system. The report of the commission appointed by the Academy states that a large number of the diseases of the nervous system and of the heart, noticed in the cases of those affected with paralysis or insanity, were to be regarded as the sequence of excessive indulgence in the use of this article. The report also stated that tobacco seems primarily to act upon the organic nervous system, depressing the faculties, and influencing the nutrition of the body, the circulation of the blood, and the number of red corpuscles in the blood. Attention was also called to the bad digestion, benumbed intelligence, and clouded memory of those who use tobacco to excess.

Dr. Gibbons says: "Tobacco impairs digestion, poisons the blood, depresses the vital powers, causes the limbs to tremble, and weakens and otherwise disorders the heart.". . .

Dr. Hassock makes the use of tobacco one cause of "the alarming frequency of apoplexy, palsy, epilepsy, and other diseases of the nervous system."

Another result of the habit is the creation of a thirst, of which Dr. Rush says: "It cannot be allayed by water, for no sedative, or even insipid liquor, will be relished after the mouth and throat have been exposed to the stimulants of the smoke or the use of tobacco."

CLIMATE AND HEALTH

TIME REQUIRED FOR A COMPLETE CHANGE OF BODY—We have noted in a previous chapter the fact that our bodies are continually wasting away, and that by food and drink they are as constantly repaired. We lose the fleshly particles of our bodies once a year, and the bones in seven years. Hence, in seven years we have possessed seven bodies of flesh and blood, and one frame of bone. We have not now a particle of flesh and bones we had seven years ago. The water we have drunk, the flesh and vegetable we have eaten, being made of the component parts of our bodies, cause us to hanker and long for the same substances of which our bodies are composed. Like substances in us call for like substances without to supply the waste of the system.

EFFECTS OF DRY AND MOIST CLIMATES—It is not generally known, but it is nevertheless true, that a pure moderately dry air generally produces a great mental sprightliness, especially with full-blooded persons. A cloudy and moist atmosphere, on the other hand, produces mental relaxation, and with many, melancholy. This explains why suicides so often happen when the sky is overcast. The depressed mental state is thus further enhanced. Villeneuve reports that of every ten suicides which were committed in Paris during two years, nine take place in the rainy season. The influence of the climate is also well exemplified in the case of mountaineers. They are quicker, more active, and excitable.

It is also well known that the inhabitants

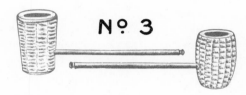
under a preponderating clear sky possess more talent for art, while those under a gloomy sky have more propensity for speculation and thought.

CAUTION IN CARRYING LEAD PENCILS—There is often danger in carrying lead pencils in the pocket. Several cases of death are recorded of persons who were pierced by pencils carried in the pocket. We should be careful to place the pencil or other sharp instrument, in such a way in the pocket as to provide against such danger.

ORANGE PEEL POISONOUS—Fatal consequences may follow the swallowing of the rind of oranges. The oil of the rind is highly

PRESERVES AND BEAUTIFIES THE COMPLEXION.
IMPARTS A PERFECTLY NATURAL APPEARANCE
TO THE SKIN IF BETTER RESULTS ARE WANTED.
TRY HITE'S MAGIC CREAM.

PREPARED BY
J. F. HITE,
OWENSBORO, WHOLESALE DRUGGIST, KENTUCKY.

What is more desirable than a Refined Complexion? For it use

POZZONI'S COMPLEXION POWDER

acrid, and adds greatly to the noxious quality of the indigestible mass.

Quite recently a child something over a year old was attacked with violent dysenteric symptoms, for which no cause could be assigned. The attack came on during the passage of a steamer from San Diego. The symptoms were so identical with those which arise from poisoning by orange peel, that the physician inquired particularly if the child had had an opportunity of getting this substance in its mouth. He was informed that it had been playing with an orange, and nibbling at it, just before the attack of the disease. The discharges from the bowels were frequent, and consisted of blood and mucus. After a week of severe enteric inflammation the child died. . . .

CARE CONCERNING POISONOUS CANDIES—In no class of articles intended for consumption is the use of poisons so free as in candies and confections. Arsenate of copper, copperas, white lead and litharge (or red lead) and the aniline colors, red, green, or blue, and other poisons, mineral and vegetable, are frequently employed in the manufacture of candies. There are confectioners who do not use dangerous drugs, or who use them so sparingly that they work no immediate appreciable harm to the consumer; but others are neither so scrupulous nor so well informed about the real nature of the poisons which impart the desired vividness of color or fineness of flavor to their products. Bright, highly-colored, handsome candies always sell better than dull, plain varieties. . . .

DANGER OF GREEN-COLORED MATERIALS—In the use of green papers, tarlatans, artificial flowers, and other green-colored materials, great care and discrimination should be exercised, as the color frequently contains arsenic in the form of the brilliant, but very poisonous, arsenate of copper, known as Schiele's Schweinfurt, and Paris Green. Such paper is sold in many stores for ornamental purposes, and even used in wrapping candies, and for Kindergarten material and toys. These colors and materials containing them, among which are green wall-paper and window-shades, and the bright green tarlatans and crepes used for evening dresses, etc., are not only dangerous in the hands of children, lest they may get particles of the poisonous color into their mouth or inhale its dust, but also from the comparatively large amount of arsenic they contain, and by the fact that the color is slowly decomposed by moisture and heat, and passes poisonous arsenious gases into the air. . . .

COLGATE & CO'S PERFUMERY.

Cashmere Bouquet Extract FOR THE HANDKERCHIEF,

Cashmere Bouquet Sachet Powder,

Cashmere Bouquet Toilet Soap.

COLGATE & CO'S

name and trade mark on all their goods guarantee the highest quality.

It is far more agreeable to keep the skin in a healthy condition than to be obliged to heal and mollify it when rough and irritated. Witch Cream is a delightful lotion for the lady's toilet table, for the gentlemen's shaving table, and for the baby's toilet basket. More could not be said to prove its delicacy and efficiency.

Witch Cream

For sale by Druggists, 50 and 25 cent bottles.
Small size by mail, 35c. Sample by mail, 10c.
C. H. & J. Price, Salem, Mass.

EATING, SLEEPING, AND SPEAKING— Simple Precautions—Never eat hurriedly, because it causes indigestion.

Never dine in excitement, because the blood is called to the brain which ought to aid digestion.

Never swallow food without thorough chewing, because it brings on dyspepsia.

Never eat when you do not want it, because when you shall want you cannot eat.

Never sleep with your mouth open, because the air breathed with carbonic acid disturbs the mucous membranes.

Never go to rest without washing the hands and face, because more dirt accumulates on the skin in the day than in the night, and is re-absorbed during the night.

Never begin a journey until breakfast is eaten.

Never speak under a hoarseness, especially if it requires an effort, or painful feeling.

DANGER FROM COSMETICS—Ladies who use cosmetics to give an artificial whiteness and softness to their complexions, will do well to read a little pamphlet published by Dr. Lewis A. Sayre of New York, describing three cases of lead palsy which have come under his notice. In these three cases the disease was clearly attributable to the lead, which is an essential ingredient in nearly all the nostrums sold under the names of "Bloom of Youth," "Beautifying Lotion," and the Like. . . .

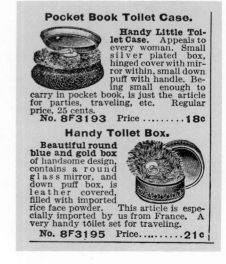

Health and Disease

In the latter part of the 1800's a book was written by Dr. Edward B. Foote. Called Plain Home Talk, it was about the "Human System—the Habits of Men and Women—The Causes and Prevention of Disease—Our Sexual Relations and Social Natures, embracing Medical Common Sense, etc." This book differed from its contemporaries in that the readers were told to write to Dr. Foote if they had any problem and he would be glad to answer them immediately. Also the readers were invited to visit Dr. Foote's office in the Murray Hill section of New York City. The author also included testimonials that he purportedly received from his satisfied patients.

He wrote another book called Health and Disease several years later which actually was a repeat of Plain Home Talk but with different testimonials.

Outwardly these books seemed to be books for treatment of the ill at home without the aid of the doctor. Actually the doctor was very much in evidence. The patient would write to the doctor if the ordinary treatments did not work and although there was no charge for the advice, Dr. Foote would then recommend certain medicines and treatments which the patient was obligated to pay for. Dr. Foote also advertised various appliances to be used which could only be bought through him.

His medications were not of the patent medicine type that could be found in almost any drug store and they were not mentioned in the book. Dr. Foote was primarily interested in letters from readers because then he could make his pitch—and obtain sales.

Housewares and Domestic Products

The same outlets that advertised and promoted patent medicines also touted housewares and even support garments—and did so as colorfully and imaginatively as any root tonic ad. Often corsets were advertised in media that on other pages denounced them as a menace to health.

PLAIN
HOME TALK

ABOUT THE

HUMAN SYSTEM—THE HABITS OF MEN AND WOMEN—THE CAUSES AND
PREVENTION OF DISEASE—OUR SEXUAL RELATIONS
AND SOCIAL NATURES.

EMBRACING

MEDICAL COMMON SENSE

APPLIED TO

CAUSES, PREVENTION, AND CURE OF CHRONIC DISEASES—THE NATURAL
RELATIONS OF MEN AND WOMEN TO EACH OTHER—SOCIETY
—LOVE—MARRIAGE—PARENTAGE—ETC., ETC.

BY

EDWARD B. FOOTE, M.D.,

AUTHOR OF MEDICAL COMMON SENSE; SCIENCE IN STORY, AND VARIOUS
PUBLICATIONS: ON THE PHYSICAL IMPROVEMENT OF HUMANITY;
PHYSIOLOGICAL MARRIAGE; CROUP; RUPTURE AND HERNIA;
DEFECTIVE VISION; A STEP BACKWARDS, ETC., ETC.

EMBELLISHED WITH TWO HUNDRED ILLUSTRATIONS.

New York:

MURRAY HILL PUBLISHING COMPANY, 129 E. 28TH ST.,
CHARLES NOBLE, 312 STRAND, LONDON, ENGLAND,
GUSTAV NEY, BERLIN, PRUSSIA.
1891.

Ladies Should be Allowed to Pop the Question.

What! solicit gentlemen to marry them? Certainly!—why not? Have not ladies preferences which they have a *natural* right to indicate as well as gentlemen? Is there any good reason why ladies should not have the privilege to choose, as well as refuse?

YOUNG REBELS OF THE YEAR 1900 AGAINST OLD KING CUSTOM.

Fig. 79.

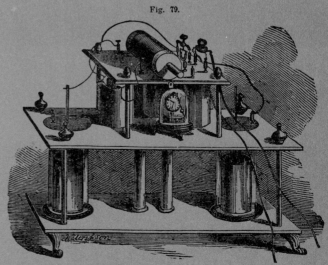

DR. FOOTE'S MAGNETIC ELECTROMOTOR.

DR. FOOTE'S NEW BOOK

ON

HEALTH AND DISEASE,

WITH RECIPES,

Including Sexology.

*Treating of the Human System in Health and Disease, of
Hygiene and Sanitation—Causes, Prevention and Home
Treatment of Chronic Diseases, including Private
Words for Men and Women, and*

250 Practical Prescriptions.

BY

EDWARD B. FOOTE, M.D.,

*Author of Plain Home Talk, Science in Story, and numerous monographs on the
Human Temperaments, Improvement of Humanity, Causes of Insanity,
Disease and Death, Continence, Divorce, etc., etc.*

———

Revised and Enlarged by the Author in 1900.

———

NEW YORK:

MURRAY HILL PUBLISHING COMPANY, 129 EAST 28TH ST.
1904.

Ignorance.

Fig. 8.

Trying to lift himself over
the fence by the straps of
his boots.

Violating the Moral Nature.

Fig. 9.

A man who has nearly worn
himself out in the service of
the devil.

REMEDIES FOR CHILDREN

Children were used in ads partly for their sentimental appeal and partly because certain nostrums had been prepared especially for their needs. Dr. Hand lists on the back of a trading card a number of disorders of children for which he claimed cures and Vegetine implies by its picture that its 'purifier' was good for young blood. Whatever Tarrant's Seltzer Apperient might have been, it seems to have produced a peculiar-looking child.

PREFACE

"Common Sense," I am aware, is quoted at a discount; especially by the medical profession, which proverbially ignores every thing that has not the mixed odor of incomprehensibility and antiquity. Medical works are generally a heterogeneous compound of vague ideas and jaw-breaking words, in which the dead languages are largely employed to treat of living subjects. Orthodoxy in medicine consists in walking in the beaten paths of Aesculapian ancestors, and looking with grave contempt on all who essay to cut out new paths for themselves. Progress is supposed to be possible in every thing except medicine; but in this science, which all admit has room for improvement, the epithet of "Quack" is applied to every medical discoverer. I trust I may prove worthy of the denunciations of the bigoted.

It was with the foregoing preface that the author, about twelve years ago, issued a medical work bearing the title of *Medical Common Sense*—a book of about 300 pages, and somewhat less than 100 illustrations. When that volume first made its appearance, some of my prudent friends shook their grave heads, and predicted for the author pecuniary failure and professional disgrace. Like those of many other prophets, their predictions proved to be only croakings, and the expected martyr soon found himself surrounded by hosts of new friends and swarms of new patients. While awaiting the popular verdict, after the first issue, one of the oldest and most noted clergymen of New York called at my office for the avowed purpose of assuring me how much he was pleased with the publication, and his appreciation possessed greater value to me because he had studied medicine in his youthful days, with the view of fitting himself for practice. He pronounced "Medical Common Sense" a refreshing contribution to medical literature, and expressed a hope that it would obtain a large circulation. I breathed easier, for the splendid physique, generous countenance, cultivated manner, and commanding presence of the first juror gave to his encouraging words the color and impressiveness of authority, and I almost felt as if the popular verdict had already been rendered; nor was this feeling delusive, for as the book continued to circulate, letters came in daily, like the droppings of the ballots on election day, from intelligent men and women in all parts of the country, thanking me for the information I had presented in language which could be comprehended by the masses of the people. The appreciation of the latter has been attested by the fact that over two hundred and fifty thousand copies have been sold.

My correspondence with the people has often exceeded one hundred letters per day, and the personal experiences and observations which have been confided to me by these numerous correspondents have enabled me to form some idea of the popular needs, and to supply, still further, that physiological instruction which is so greatly wanted to make mankind healthy and happy. . . . For the adult, this work contains information which no man or woman can afford to do without, when it may be obtained at a price comparatively so trifling. If the physiological deductions and social views of the author are dissented from, the valuable facts upon which they are based remain, and the reader is at liberty to use them to sustain opinions and suggestions which he may adjudge more acceptable to the popular mind. Anything, every thing—that the human family may grow wiser and happier.

E.B.F.

READ WHAT PHYSICIANS, CLERGYMEN, EDITORS AND PEOPLE GENERALLY THINK OF PLAIN TALK AND MEDICAL COMMON SENSE

DEAR SIR: I was in Bristol a few days ago, and when at a bookstall, I saw your remarkable book entitled "Plain Home Talk." I began to read, but could not put down the book till it was read through. Although a hard student for fifty years, I have met with much that was new, startling, and very instructive. If every adult in the civilized world could understand, and follow out your views, in a few generations there would be a world of physical, intellectual, and moral giants. Your work is priceless in value and calculated to regenerate society.

If there is anything you think I should like to have in tract-form, please send it. I have lately retired from practice, and am ready for anything in advance. Believe me, fraternally yours, S. EADON, M.A., M.D., PH.D., F.S.A., GRAD. OF MED. OF EDINBURGH, GLASGOW, AND ABERDEEN

Philadelphia, Pa., January 16, 1884
DEAR SIR: I have carefully read your book "Plain Home Talk and Medical Common Sense," and as I am myself a physician, and also have given a good deal of attention to social science and kindred studies, I feel competent to judge of it. I was strongly prejudiced against all publications of the kind I thought this to be. But now I must, as an honest man, say to you that your book is an able, honest, and truthful presentation of facts and theories, and calculated to do much good. I thank you for it. You may use this letter, as I mean what I say and am not ashamed to say it.

Your obedient servant,
LOUIS SEYMOUR

Pastor's Study, *Howellville, Pa.*
June 8, 1887
DR. E. B. FOOTE—DEAR SIR:
I have just finished reading your book, "Plain Home Talk," etc., with much pleasure. It is a book that should be in every American home.

I am yours fraternally,
REV. LEWIS R. HARLEY

Cerro Gordo, Ark., February 6,
DR. E. B. FOOTE—DEAR SIR:
For some weeks past I have devoted a considerable portion of my time to the reading of your "Plain Home Talk and Medical Common sense," which I have found to be of great benefit to me. I am a beginner in the study of medicine, and am devoting all the time I can on such works as yours, which I think are of much more benefit than many old text-books which have been offered me by old practitioners. Your work is so plainly and yet so artistically framed that it is perfect fit for all, and, indeed, if it was but known and read by everyone as it should be, there is no doubt that every man would be his own doctor. . . .
Yours with very great respect,
WM. J. SCOTT

READ WHAT ONE OF OUR LEADING NEWSPAPERS SAYS REGARDING OUR PUBLISHING HOUSE, AND OF THE AUTHOR OF PLAIN HOME TALK

We trust our vanity may be pardoned if we obtrude in these pages a notice of ourselves which will be read with no less interest by the friends of our author. It may inspire the confidence of agents in us, and the confidence of the sick in Dr. Foote. The following is from the NEW YORK INDEPENDENT:

Among the many successful enterprises in our metropolis may be mentioned that of the MURRAY HILL PUBLISHING COMPANY, whose office and publishing rooms are at 129 East 28th Street. This company was organized mainly for the purpose of publishing the medical and reformatory works written by that eminently successful physician, E. B. FOOTE, M.D. author of *Medical Common Sense,* a work widely known in this and foreign countries, it having reached a sale of 250,000 copies. This work was revised and enlarged a few years ago, and reissued under the title of *Plain Home Talk and Medical Common Sense,* a valuable work of over 900 pages and 200 illustrations. The work, so revised and enlarged, has also sold to the extent of nearly one hundred thousand copies, and has been favorably noticed by the leading papers of the country.

DR. FOOTE possesses the happy faculty of conveying information relating to the physical well-being of people in such a plain way that he has succeeded in interesting thousands of those who have hardly heretofore given a serious thought to such matters. His *Plain Home Talk* is filled with interesting facts and suggestions to the sick, which has been derived from over twenty years of experience in the treatment of all forms of chronic disease. His elegantly fitted offices at his residence, 120 Lexington Avenue, are daily thronged with patients from all parts of the country, who bear witness to his uniformly successful treatment of their various ailments.

We are disinclined to omit in this connection a brief description of DR. FOOTE'S establishment. The laboratory in which the medicines are prepared occupies the upper floor, consisting of three rooms, fitted up with all the conveniences and appliances of a first-class laboratory. One of these rooms, where considerable heat is employed, is made thoroughly fireproof by about six inches of Portland Cement upon its floor and walls. Here are many thousands of dollars' worth of various kinds of medicinal roots and plants, from which, under the personal supervision of the Doctor, competent assistants prepare the medicines for use. No mercurial or injurious drugs are allowed to enter this laboratory, and

The floor below the laboratory is occupied

the greatest pains are taken to exclude everything excepting the purest and best products of the botanical kingdom. The laboratory is connected with the sub-basement of the building by a large hydraulic elevator.

The floor below the laboratory is occupied by the stenographers, or short-hand writers, who are employed in attending, under the direct dictation of the Doctor, to the immense correspondence, which often exceeds one hundred letters per day. In no other way could one brain and one pair of hands attend to so many professional letters. The Doctor has originated and perfected a series of questions relating to the physical conditions of invalids. These questions are so thorough and complete that when they are answered by patients at a distance, the Doctor is able to make a complete diagnosis and prescribe for his patients with about the same facility that he could do were they present. The questions are furnished to all applicants by mail or otherwise. By the aid of such perfected questions and ingenious registers for booking all cases, he is now successfully treating patients in all parts of this country and many in Europe, Asia and the West Indies. The immense sale of his works, treating directly of disease and how to avoid it has made his name almost a household word. On the first floor are the spacious and elegantly furnished offices, occupying four rooms where DOCTOR FOOTE personally superintends the reception and consultation of his patients, assisted by two physicians. Here may be seen patients who have travelled long distances to avail themselves of the Doctor's well-known skill and experience. The fact that no charge is made for consultations in person or by letter greatly increases the labor of conducting such an establishment. But this rule was adopted by the Doctor at the outset of his practice and he proposes to adhere to it in spite of the extra work it entails. Two large rooms in the basement are occupied for smaller publications, packing rooms, etc., while in the sub-basement is a carpenter's shop, wherein are manufactured the wooden boxes used in sending away medicines. . . .

"THE MURRAY HILL PUBLISHING COMPANY," says the INDEPENDENT in conclusion, "conducts its business on the subscription plan mainly, and its agents may be found in almost every neighborhood, while other publishers in London and Berlin pursue a similar plan in the sale of the Doctor's publications abroad."

CHAPTER I
DISEASE AND ITS CAUSES

Our planet with each revolution carries a huge load of human suffering, a large portion of which arises from disease. We see this enemy in the cradle, distorting the features and bedimming the eyes of innocent babes. Too often it carries its little victims to the burial-ground, bathed with the tears of mothers. We see it in youthhood, arresting the physical development of young men and young women; consigning them to premature graves, or moving them like sickly shadows through years of hapless life. It rudely grasps people in the prime of life, and hurries them away from the fields of useful labor to wearisome chambers, where the mind, which has been schooled to activity, becomes a dangerous ally to the enemy by chafing and fretting in its imprisonment. It lays violent hands on our gray-haired fathers and mothers, who yesterday greeted us with a smile, animation, and elasticity of youth, but who to-day go groping about with rounded shoulders and trembling steps. At last, it arrests the physical functions, the outer shell returns to its original dust, and the inner, living body, enters the new life, where—may we hope—this fearful disturber of our comfort and happiness is refused admission.

THE CAUSES OF DISEASE

Disease of every character, except that which may be induced by poison or by accident of body or limb, originates in a derangement of the circulation of vital electricity, disturbance of the mind, or an abnormal condition of the blood. Wherever it begins, unless speedily checked, the whole system is soon convulsed in its grasp, because of the close relationship existing between the various organs of the body. . . .

Large quantities of animal electricity are also generated by the alkalies and acids of the animal organisms. The mucous membranes, or linings of the cavities, are continually excreting a semi-fluid called alkali, and the serous membranes, or outer coverings of the same, an aqueous or watery fluid, called acid, and according to the testimony of Dr. Bird, if these fluids are so placed as to be connected by parietes of an animal membrane, or a porous diaphragm, a current of electricity is evolved.

Hence, we find that not only are our stomachs generating electricity, but we are inhaling it by our lungs, and our pores, and the external or serous, and internal or mucous surfaces, united as they are natural parietes and porous diaphragms, are producing it in large quantities. As it is produced, or enters the system, it is so modified as to be made fit for the uses of the body.

The brain is as industriously distributing this vital electricity through the system, as the heart is circulating the blood, and too much, or too little, given to any particular organ, produces diseases therein. The complete withdrawal of nervo-electricity from any part paralyzes it, so that it has neither sense or motion. . . .

MAGNETIC EXERCISE.

THE GERM THEORY

What is the germ theory? It is the doctrine that disease is communicated to the human system by minute animal organisms generally known under the name of bacteria, which are found in great abundance in both air and water. The reader will be interested . . . that the theory of the cause of disease, as given in the beginning of this chapter, is not the least affected by more recent discoveries. . . .

CHAPTER II
THE CAUSES OF NERVOUS DERANGEMENTS AND AFFECTIONS OF THE BLOOD

. . . A large proportion of all the evils . . . really spring from one common root—ignorance. Errors in eating, drinking, sleeping, dressing, ventilation, sexual isolation, sexual association, medicating, etc., the bad habits of childhood and of adult age, may be traced directly to ignorance. It casts a black shadow over every hearth-stone—it makes a dark corner in every institution of learning. . . .

There are two kinds of ignorance—real and wilful. The latter is the outgrowth of the former. No sane person will voluntarily sacrifice health through wilful ignorance, unless that wilful ignorance is plumbly backed by some of the genuine article. . . . A person may shut his eyes to a disagreeable truth—resolve within himself that he will not see it, and impatiently trample it under his feet, and yet, did he fully comprehend the consequences, he would desist from his folly. . . . A thoughtless young woman may dress imprudently to attend a fashionable ball, covering but partially, or leaving completely exposed, portions of her person which she habitually wraps in flannels or furs. She is told of the danger, but laughingly retorts, "I know it, but I am bound to have a good time." . . .

Real ignorance is the fearful enemy of mankind. Let us commence at the very beginning of the human being. How many know the essential conditions to bring into the world a healthy child? A man and woman love each other, or think they do, or they do not, but it is expedient to marry, and they do marry. The next thing you hear is, that the wife is pregnant. How did she become so? Accidentally, probably, for nearly all children are the accidents of gratified passion, instead of the products of willing parents who premeditated and prepared themselves for so important a work. . . . Many a child has been conceived when its father was lounging about home on account of sickness, and to-day suffers physically, and perhaps mentally, from the effects of that paternal illness. There are thousands of children to-day with disordered nervous and vascular systems who are so because they were conceived at the "making up" of quarrelsome progenitors. Many a child is the offspring of a rape, perpetrated by a brutal husband upon an unwilling wife, and this offspring goes through life with a weakly nervous system as a consequence. . . .

The coyness of young people of both sexes, but especially of young women, in attending to the "calls of nature," are fruitful sources of nervous and blood derangements. Children are brought up to regard the necessary attentions to the bladder and bowels as something so indelicate as to require the greatest privacy, so much so, that when places constructed for such purposes are not entirely shielded from observation, a young man, or a young woman, will go all day, or possibly for several days, without attending to two very important functions with any degree of regularity. The results are, the blood becomes poisoned by the retention and absorption of waste matters, the nervous energies of the liver, bowels, kidneys, and bladder become paralyzed, and if the victim be a female, the pressure of water in the bladder in front, of the excrementitious matters of the bowels above and behind, displaces that sensitive organ, the womb, and then follow all sorts of ills to make life wretched.

The Food We Eat—Considering the fact that man is omnivorous, and almost as much so as the pig, and that he eats about eight hundred pounds of food, exclusive of fluids, annually, it ought to surprise no one when I say that many derangements of the blood arise from the use of improper food. . . .

Keep Flies off Your Food—It is to be admitted that this cannot always be effectually

Fig. 17.

THE UNHEALTHY PAIR.

Fig. 18.

SHEEP—WHOLESOME TO THE EYE AND WHOLESOME TO THE STOMACH.

done. During the warm weather the fly is omnipresent. He is ready to dip his unclean proboscis into everything. He creeps over your pies and cakes, and inspects every fresh loaf of bread; he takes a plunge into your soup, and a swim in your milk; he probes your butter to see if it is pure or only oleomargarine; all this and more he performs after a clumsy fashion, unless you faithfully employ the wire-gauze covers to be found at the house-furnishing stores for table use. . . . Protect yourselves by screens in your windows, screen doors, and wire covers on your tables. By all means keep flies from contaminating your food by every device you can conveniently employ. . . .

Grease is supplied quite too abundantly for the table to preserve the purity of blood. Weak stomachs call loudly for reform in this particular, while strong ones faithfully perform their work of sending the offending substances to the vascular system, to feed or create humors. Fat is not digested in the stomach, but simply melted and absorbed into the blood. A certain amount is necessary to nourish the brain, and save the wear and tear of the nervous system; but fatty meats and rich gravies are positively injurious. Dead Animal fats are non-conductors of electricity, and their presence in large quantities in the stomach tends to resist the pneumogastric nerve, and to impair digestion.

Fig. 40.

BAD POSITION IN SITTING.

Bad Habits of Children and Youth—A great error is generally committed by parents in sending their children to school at an age so tender that the development of the mental faculties seriously interferes with the vigorous formation of their physical parts. A child of three or four years of age, seated on a bench in school is no more in his place than a twelve-year old boy would be on the judge's bench in a Court of Chancery. . . . Children should be kept out of school, and allowed to dig play-houses in the sand, play horse with strings, jump ropes, and roll hoops until their little limbs become hard and chests broad, and, too, until they evince some desire for study. If this desire is manifested before the age of five or six, it should not be discouraged. . . . We once had in the United States Senate a man who was taught his alphabet by his wife after marriage. We have had, at least, two Presidents of the United States who hardly saw the inside of a school-room before they became old enough to work and pay for their own education. . . .

Fig. 39.

THE LITTLE BAREFOOTED CANDY-EATER.

Masturbation, or self-pollution, is a prevalent vice among both children and youth. The amative passions prematurely developed by stimulating diet, importune gratification which cannot be granted in the manner prescribed by Nature, because marriage is an institution available for adults. Ignorant of the physiological effects of resorting to artificial means, and goaded to desperation by the perusal of popular romances, the unsophisticated youth falls an easy victim to a habit which taps the very fountains of nervovitality, and drains from the blood all its purest and most strengthening qualities. . . .

Social Magnetism Versus Sexual Isolation—Some of my readers who have given little or no attention to the subject of animal magnetism, personal magnetism, individual electricity, etc., as it is variously denominated, will be startled at the above heading, in the chapter giving some of the principal causes of blood and nervous derangements. . . . There are two classes, however, of both sexes, who will instinctively comprehend the subject under consideration before reading anything more than the caption. One is composed of girls and boys, and women and men, who possess fine sympathetic organizations, easily affected by atmospheric changes, or by social or domestic discord, and whose condition in life has been such as to cause them to live more or less isolated from those of their opposite sex. The other embraces warm-blooded, affectionate impulsive people of both sexes, who have been compelled by various circumstances to live in sexual isolation. Both of these classes will understand me, and say AMEN, when I place sexual starvation among the principal derangements of the nervous and vascular systems. . . .

Prostitution—It is sickening to reflect that in civilized countries there exists, to an extent even greater than in the vast domain, where the ethics of civilization are not taught, a class of women who, for a sum of money varying from twenty-five cents to $100, will put themselves in sexual contact with men for whom they entertain no sentiment of love, no sense of physical attraction, and toward whom they, in many cases, feel an aversion if not disgust.

Fig. 58.

THE INNOCENT GIRL CHANGED
BY HARDSHIP AND VICE.

It is also humiliating to all who are working for, and have faith in, the ultimate moral and physical regeneration of the human race, that the amative passions of men can be so morbid as to lead them for one moment to value the indulgence of this nature which can be purchased like a paper of tobacco or a glass of rum; . . .

Mental qualities are undoubtedly catching, so to speak, and the more so when the association is so intimate as it is between two persons uniting in the sexual relation. Therefore, the patron of the harlot is not only in danger of contracting a hideous blood malady or nervous affection, but he takes on more or less of the mental degradation and reckless nature of his companion in vice, and what is more, he may take upon himself the possible villainous magnetism and criminal nature of the man who preceded him as a patron . . .

Wealth—Wealth, with its attendant dissipation, is a prolific source of nervous derangements and blood impurities. . . . That some of the indigent among us die of scanty food is undoubtedly true; but vastly more die from eating too much than from eating too little; vastly more from excess than from starvation. . . . Our daughters are oftener brought to the grave by their rich attire, than our beggars by their nakedness. So the poor are often overworked; but they suffer less than many among the rich who have no work to do nor interesting object to fill up life; to satisfy the infinite craving of man for action. . . .

Melancholy— . . . Melancholy seriously disturbs the circulation of the nervo-electric forces, and causes an undue consumption of the latter in the brain. Melancholy people are almost invariably dyspeptic, because a full supply of the electric element is withheld from the pneumo-gastric nerve, which conveys from the brain the force that gives tone and activity to the digestive organs. Despondency, in fact, affects all the organs of the system on the same principle; the brain consuming, in its excitement, more than its natural allowance of nervo-electricity, and as a consequence, withholding the vital element from the organs which are dependent upon it for healthful action.

Cheerfulness should be cultivated by every

Fig. 51.

THE ISOLATED GIRL.

one. It is an antidote for many ills; and a laugh is of immense value, physiologically. It produces an electric effect throughout the whole system. . . .

CHAPTER III
PREVENTION OF DISEASE

How to Have Healthy Babies—Now, certainly, an argument is not necessary here to show that we should devote as much attention to the proper propagation of children as we do to the breeding of calves and colts. . . .

HOW TO HAVE HEALTHY BABIES.   223

preserve tranquillity of mind and vigor of body to this woman, who is freighted with a germ which is developing the soul and body of a new human being. Critical period! How greatly it decides, and, too, how early, whether the earthly existence of the future man or woman shall be happy or miserable.—Shall the fœtus of to-day wish twenty or fifty years hence that it had never been born? The friends of the pregnant woman, and those of all who surround her, should be united to prevent this. She may maintain her physical health by seeking for residence such locations as are proverbially healthful; living and sleeping in well-ventilated rooms; carefully watching diet—eating only those things which seem to agree with stomach and mind; avoiding excessive and irregular eating; exercising daily in the open air without reference to the criticism of Mrs. Grundy on one corner, or the smoking loafer on the other; observing habits of personal cleanliness; and, in brief, by patient, constant watchfulness, doing every thing within her power to promote a feeling of health, and avoiding every thing which in any way produces the contrary effect. Mental tranquillity may be maintained by carefully keeping up the physical health; by association with those who are cheerful and entertaining; by reading books and newspapers of an interesting and elevating character; by doing acts of

Fig. 65.

A CLUSTER OF BABIES.

No. 1 represents poor scrofulous little Job—the offspring of parents who ought not to have had children. No. 2 represents suffering John—the offspring of parents in an unhealthy condition. No. 3 is fretful Peter—the child of fretful, bad tempered parentage. No. 4 is poor Benny—the child of sensuality, liquor, and tobacco. No. 5 is healthy Charley—the fortunate offspring of healthy and intelligent parents.

—People who are physically infirm should not have children while such infirmities exist, because they are almost certain to transmit them to the offspring, and the combined infirmities of each parent (when both are diseased) frequently result in most lamentable consequences to the innocent victims of this indiscretion. . . .

—People claiming entire immunity from disease, have seasons of feeling less vigorous and vivacious than others, and unfortunately for offspring, coition is sometimes resorted to at such periods, by way of experiment, to see if better feeling may not be induced. If more convenient, a glass of wine, beer, or other stimulant, or a narcotic is taken for the purpose; but if the drug fails, the exhilarating delirium of sexual excitement is sought; and if offspring is produced, it not only receives at the moment of conception the organic impression of the physical derangements leading to the momentary depression of the parent, but probably also the embryonic formation of vitiated appetite and passion.

Sleep—Nearly everyone who is not a baby sleeps too little. . . . Many do not seem to know the value of sleep. They overlook the fact that it is the season of vital recuperation; that while the body is recumbent, the eyes closed, and the faculties at rest, repairs go on which are no less necessary for the duration of life, than for the health of every individual . . . . Insanity often results from the want of sleep.

Cleanliness—Insomuch as uncleanliness is the parent of epidemics and the nesting places of microbes, so is cleanliness a preventive of disease. Many do not know, while others who do, overlook the fact, that the skin is full of little sewers, called pores, through which are emptied out from the blood five-sevenths of all its impurities. . . . When the skin is neglected, these tubes, or pores become literally dammed up, and if nature cannot force a passage through them for disposing of effete matters, her next attempt is to throw them out in the form of pimples, ulcers, or boils. If this effort is not successful, they remain in the circulation, poisoning the blood and making that fluid, which should be the dispenser of health, the fountain of corruption and disease.

CHAPTER IV
COMMON-SENSE REMEDIES

Vegetable Medicines—The trees, shrubs, flowers, and plants, I contend, possess, in a refined form all the medicinal properties of the mineral kingdom. Their numerous and far-reaching roots span rocks, ramify in various strata of soil, and extract from good old mother earth her hidden medicinal treasures, which are transposed to regions of air, light, and heat, where chemical changes are effected which at once deprive them of their grosser characteristics, and render them far more efficacious and harmless, as antidotes for human infirmities, than they can possibly be made in the laboratory of the most skilful chemist. . . .

The brute creation is more enlightened to-day in materia medica than those physicians who resort to the mineral kingdom for medicines. When the horse feels unwell, he eats dock and other herbs, if he can get them and recovers. The cat, subject to fits, eats catnip herb, and observe the delight which she manifests in rolling on it, snuffing its aroma, and finally eating it. Naturalists say that the fox, rabbit, and many other animals keep themselves from madness by the use of the medicinal plants with which their wild abodes are surrounded; . . .

Psychic Medicine—All successful physicians cannot fail to have observed how much easier it is to cure a patient when they themselves feel complete confidence that a cure is to be realized; it is as when you are on a yacht with both wind and tide in your favor. . . . There are wonderful powers in the human mind, and we have only to educate ourselves in the art of employing them. . . . The healing art was never more progressive in America than when there was the utmost freedom in medicine. Progress is only possible in freedom. In the ranks of mental healers and Christian Scientists their own idealism is the stumbling block.

Therapeutic Electricity—It is generally conceded by the medical profession and the public at large to-day that electricity may be advantageously employed in the treatment of disease. . . . To-day there is hardly an edu-

Fig. 52.

SOCIAL MAGNETISM.

cated member of the profession who will deny its virtue if intelligently employed. . . .

It is the interruption or partial withdrawal of the nervo-electric circulation, which causes what we term "nervous diseases"; and there are more affections of this character than were ever dreamed of in the allopathic philosophy. . . . In diseased lungs and shortness of breath, there is frequently an interruption of the nervo-electric circulation, and hence the value of electrical remedies of some sort, in addition to internal medical treatment, in the cure of many cases of pulmonary disease.

. . . I meet with very few diseases than can be cured by electricity, galvanism, or electro-magnetism alone. . . . Recourse must be had to mild medication. . . .

Animal Magnetism—"Hypnotism" is popular! They (learned professors) are not disposed to award due honor to Mesmer by calling it Mesmerism. . . .

Whatever differences exist in the minds of medical men as to just what causes mesmeric phenomena, all now recognize and believe in them, and the employment of mesmerism or hypnotism is recommended in many cases of nervous disease.

Water—In all ages of the world, and in all nations, civilized and barbarous, water has been held in high estimation as a remedial agent.

At the present time, sanitariums have entirely taken the place of what used to be called "water-cures" in this country.

—Water possesses a great amount of electricity. If the blood of an individual contains its natural supply of iron, it attracts the electricity from the water, thereby rendering the body of the invalid in an electrically positive condition compared with the atmosphere. As soon, then, as the application has been made, an active radiation of electricity from the system takes place, which accelerates the escape of effete matter, and renders the pores, skin, and other organs more active. . . .

CHAPTER VI
PRIVATE WORDS FOR WOMEN

I want the attention and candid consideration of my female readers to what I have to say regarding the common affections of the amative and procreative organs of their sex. It will not do to pass this subject over as too vulgar or indelicate for investigation. If it be pretended by any woman that she places no value whatever on the enjoyment which may be derived from the reasonable use of healthy procreative organs, she will not certainly be ashamed to admit that phsyical health is a blessing, and that disease, whether in the head, stomach, or the organs of generation, is an evil which should employ her faculties of reason to avoid. If the subject is delicate, the complex sexual organism is also delicate, and a vast amount of human suffering, not only to women themselves, but to posterity, results from a foolish squeamishness on the part of many females, old and young, who shut their eyes upon everything calculated to teach them how to preserve the strength and healthfulness of the organs peculiar to their sex. . . .

—Corsets or waist-bands, even if only moderately tight, are liable to have three bad effects: 1st, binding especially at waist-bands, and slowing the function of stomach and liver; 2d, pressing downward the contents of abdomen upon the pelvic organs, inducing pelvic disorders; and 3d, restricting the motion of the chest and its contents the lungs. . . .

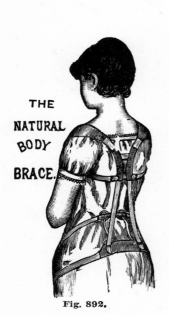

THE NATURAL BODY BRACE.

Fig. 892.

Besides the general causes of diseases of women, heretofore described, there are others more directly affecting the generative organs. The contagious venereal diseases are too often responsible for not only acute affections, but also those of long standing. That mischievous systemic poison, syphilis, does more general than local damage to health and displays its ravages from head to toe, in brain, nerve, skin and bone. . . .

CHAPTER VIII
PRIVATE WORDS FOR MEN

As a rule, men know more of women than they do of themselves, and I will venture the prediction that a majority of them will read the chapter "Private Words for Women" before reading this one, which is especially intended for them. Still it may be said that they are generally better informed on the structure of the male organism, than the women are on the anatomy and physiology of the female body. The ignorance of men, however, in regard to themselves is highly discreditable when their advantages for information are taken into account. . . . I trust every male reader will carefully look over and digest all I have to present in this chapter, for by doing so he will better comprehend the complexity of his sexual organs and probably be induced to take better care of them. . . .

CHAPTER IX
IMPOTENCY

This term may be properly applied to that inactivity of the organ of amativeness, or that interruption of its nervous or electrical organs, which paralyzes the erectile tissues or muscle of the latter. . . .

Now, then in my opinion, when the organ of amativeness is cut off from proper electrical communication with the erectile tissue and muscles, so that the erection and proper action of the procreative organs are imperfect, the disease may be properly termed impotency, whether the person so affected be female or male. The disease, whether it exists in one sex or the other, is identical in its nature and effects. . . .

The conditions necessary to a full and satisfactory accomplishment of the generative act are so numerous and so complicated that there may be many causes of failure. The erectile function is dependent upon the mental as well as upon the physical state, and upon the cooperation of both. . . .

The state of mind has much to do with sexual potency. All through the animal kingdom both males and females are acted upon by what are called "secondary sexual characteristics," which become most prominent and attractive during certain seasons. These appeal to all the senses—sight, sound, smell, taste, and touch.—In mankind there are not only many such secondary influences, but also more subtle psychical attractions that might be called "tertiary," and these count for more with women than with men.—The apathetic wife may paralyze the potency of the husband. . . . On the other hand men, should remember . . . that they may be repelled by an unclean (tobacco) mouth, an unpleasant (alcoholic) breath, soiled hands, or a careless word. . . .

—Opium habitués and inveterate users of tobacco may lose their sexual power from the depressing effects of these drugs upon the sexual system, and excessive use of beer may put either a temporary or permanent quietus on desire or capacity. . . .

C H A P T E R   X I I

T R E A T M E N T   O F

D I S E A S E

Evidences of the Curability of Chronic Diseases

In presenting the following evidences of the curability of chronic diseases, the author begs the indulgence of his readers while offering a few explanations:

1st—These evidences are presented for the two-fold purpose of showing what can be accomplished by what has been termed "Common Sense Remedies." . . .

2d—The signatures of the writers are omitted from the extracts of letters in compliance with a standing promise, made at the very beginning of my practice, and repeated in every edition of this book, that the names of all correspondents and patients should in no case be mentioned without their declared consent. . . .

3d—As it has been contrary to my practice to ask testimonials, and with few exceptions to accept and publish them when proffered, the following are wholly from patients at a distance who have consulted me. . . .

4th—An extract detached from the body of a letter is often less expressive of satisfaction and gratitude than the letter would be if presented in full; but room can only be spared for a brief quotation from each. . . .

5th—Nevertheless, these testimonials are of more value than they would be if they were obtained by solicitation, because, as they now appear, they possess the spontaneous acknowledgements of grateful patients who have been benefited or cured.

CASE 73,212—Catarrh of Long Standing in a Woman Sixty-Nine Years of Age, Whose General Health was Much Impaired.

She writes from Cambridgeport, Mass: "Yours of October 27th is at hand. I have often thought I would write to you, acknowledging the wonderful cure I received from your skilful treatment. I think I can safely say that I am entirely cured of that terrible trouble for which you treated me. When I last wrote you I was improving slowly, but had not fully recovered, when in March, my husband died. So you see that I have been all broken up since, and more than that, had lost your address. Since then I have buried three sisters and a sister's husband. At the present time I am quite well."

CASE 100,120—Incipient Consumption in a Young Woman Whose Parents and Two Sisters Died of This Disease.

She writes from Worcester County, Mass., October 9th, as follows: "In reply to your letter I am happy to say that at the present time I am enjoying perfect health, thanks to your treatment, and rest and care of myself on my own part. I am feeling better at the present time than I have for years."

CASE 92,162—Catarrh Affecting Nasal Passages, Throat, and Bronchi; Neurasthenia, and Rheumatism of Long Standing.

A middle-aged man writes from Fort Walla Walla, State of Washington, as follows: "Your kind letter and medicine of last month came duly to hand. I do not think that I will need more medicine as I feel better now than I did for ten years. In fact I am a different man, see things in a different light, all owing to your treatment. I shall take your advice in regard to marrying very soon. You have in nine months accomplished what others failed in for three years, and whenever I get the opportunity will not fail to advise others, and tell them what you have done for me. Nine months ago Life was a burden to me and I did not care how soon it should end; now everything is changed; I feel like a young man of twenty. . . .

CASE 61,010—Bad Fistula in a Scrofulous Woman suffering From Dyspepsia, Constipation, etc.

She writes from Berkeley County, W.Va.: "I think I have good news to tell you this time. My health has improved more since I last wrote you than it has in the same length of time since I have been under your treatment. I weighed 135 pounds two months ago, and still improve rapidly. My cheeks are as rosy as can be, and I never felt so fresh and buoyant as now. That fistula on the left side has all been healed since November. The one on the right side has been healed since May. . . .

CASE 46,246—Bright's Disease, Showing Dropsy, Advanced Symptoms, Cured.

Patient writes: "I am still in good health; no change for the worse that I am conscious of. In July last I passed a very rigid examination for admittance to the American Legion of Honor, an organization incorporated for a system of life insurance. All I can remember of the condition of the urine was 'specific gravity, 1020 alkaline.' You may gather something from that as to what the condition was. Wishing you continued success in your profession, and a long and happy life, I am," etc.

CASE 42,143—Spermatorrhoea.

An officer in the English Navy writes from Davenport, England: "I received your letter some months ago, and you requested me to write you after finishing a course of remedies. I finished them about the end of February and was married the 21st of last month. I might say that they made me a changed man. I am strong and vigorous and look the picture of health, and I live according to your suggestions in your valuable book."

CASE 102,095—Self-Abuse, Much Nervous Depression, Dyspepsia, and Constipation.

A gentleman approaching 30 years of age, after four months' treatment, writes from Akron, Ohio: "Your letter of the 25th of July duly received. I know it has been some time since I wrote you last, but I intended to use all the medicine before making my final report. I have some tablets of No. 4 left yet. I can say that my condition has much improved under your care, and do not think I will need any more medicine. The pimples are much better, and I have good control of my sexual organs."

CASE 87,077—Barrenness and Dysmenorrhoea, Dyspepsia and Catarrh. No Children, Though Married Six Years.

A lady writes from Illinois: "I received a letter from you some time ago. I was not at home at the time as I had left for Buffalo where I visited five weeks with my parents. I intended writing you, but since we have had baby I don't get much time to do anything outside of my general work. Baby was born March 15th. I was sick five days before baby was born. She was very weak and weighed but three pounds. She is a lovely baby now and we are proud of her; also of you, Doctor, for we would not have had our darling had it not been for you. We are indeed very grateful to you. Baby being a girl robbed her of your name; we named her Vivian. I had baby's picture taken when six months old and we will send you one so you can see for yourself how rapidly she has improved. She weighed twenty-three pounds when six months old. . . ."

CASE 67,219—Syphilis (secondary) with Marked Constitutional Disturbance.

A gentleman writes after seven months' treatment from Brooklyn, N.Y.: "From the day I commenced your treatment I saw no traces of my disease. I have increased since then from 138 to 198 pounds, and to-day am as big and strong as an ox. My brother whom you treated has died, but I think had he stayed with you that he would have been all right."

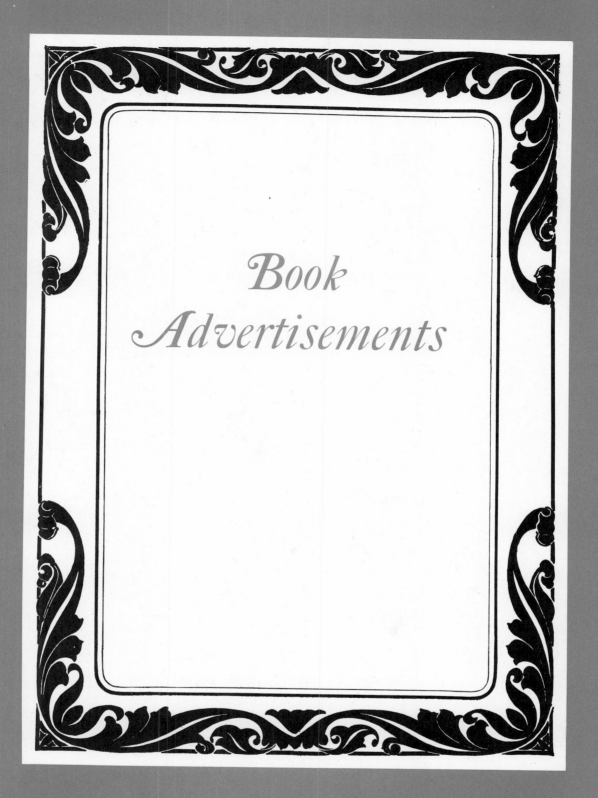

Book
Advertisements

*In the nineteenth century,
the publishing of various types of home medicine books
was big business and the competition
for the sale of these volumes was very keen.
As a result, the advertisements were lavish and eye-catching.
Most of the books were offered on subscription only,
rather than being sold in book-shops.
When a title was advertised in a magazine, a newspaper,
or the back of another book,
the publisher always asked for agents to represent him.
It would seem that agents did not do too badly
at making quick, and multiple, sales.*

Proprietary drugs are those drugs advertised directly to the public. Most people referred to the proprietaries as "patent medicines," believing them to have the approval of the United States Patent Office. This was, in general, not so. (The name derived not from the Patent Office, but from the practice European rulers had of issuing royal "patents" to favorite medicine makers.)

Some of the proprietary drugs sold today have been around since the turn of the century—or longer. Examples include Lydia E. Pinkham's "Vegetable Compound," Dr. Kilmer's "Swamp Root," Listerine, and several others. Sometimes the companies changed the formula under the trademark, but very often not. Until early in this century, any drug, no matter how worthless or outrageously adulterated, could be placed on the market; any statement, no matter how fantastic, could be made about it; and any ingredient, no matter how habit-forming or lethal, could be put in it with no mention made on the label. In 1906, the first Pure Food and Drug Act required that narcotics (but not poisons) be listed on labels, but even then, little was done to prevent the sale of such products.

The patent medicines bottled in Colonial America were similar to those brewed in England and just as worthless. But the American dealers expanded their sales by setting up a system of selling their products through traveling agents. These peddlers were to be seen throughout rural America from Colonial days until the end of the 19th century. During that period, the country had hundreds of traveling medicine showmen who specialized in removing tapeworms, restoring hair, and selling curative herbs. They entertained the people with juggling, magic, songs and comedy. There were always musicians or Indians as part of the show. When people gathered round the wagon, the "professor" would come forth and talk to the people about their health. Then there would be some sort of contest to draw the crowd together and focus on the grand finale to the medicine show: the product.

At the turn of the century, the manufacturers of patent medicines claimed practically anything for their wares. Most of the medicines, of course, were completely worthless.

The women of America have bought more Lydia E. Pinkham's Vegetable Compound than any other tonic, as well as Lydia Pinkham's Tablets. To this day, the Vegetable Compound is sold, but it has changed with the times. In 1880, the label said that it was good for all female ailments and the falling of the womb, as well as for all weaknesses of the generative organs of either sex. The tablets were advertised for the woman who "Can't Give Your Husband Real Companionship." The

BRINGS
HEALTH and BEAUTY.

label now says that the product relieves certain symptoms connected with change of life and distresses of monthly periods, and is effective as a uterine sedative.

Many patent medicines spoke of "spermatorrhoea," which meant impotence. Usually a "professor" in a Vandyke beard would claim that here was available a pill which could remedy the debility. There were also "youth" pills, various rays, pads, belts, packs, jars, mechanical developers, salts, and glandular extracts. The typical health belt was a contraption of copper and zinc disks, clamped to a belt of red flannel or to strips of yellow cotton flannel and connected by wires—an arrangement of metals and absorbents suggesting a wet battery.

Every patent medicine flaunted the name of some doctor on its label to make the product look more impressive.

Most tonics depended upon their alcoholic content, which was often large. Paine's Celery Compound had 21%, Hood's Sarsaparilla 18%, Burdock's Blood Bitters 25% and Hostetter's Bitters 44%. At the end of the 1800's, Pe-ru-Na tonic had 28% and was considered a good substitute for the firewater used by the Indians. In fact, the U.S. Office of Indian Affairs finally stopped the sale of it to Indians.

One drug that actually was *patented* was Castoria. In 1868, Dr. Samuel Pitcher was granted a patent on the method of preparing senna extract and incorporating it into a liquid medicine which he called Castoria. Although the patent ran out and several companies began to manufacture a product called Castoria, now only one remains.

At one time the number of "patent" medicines ran into the thousands, although probably no more than half a dozen were actually patented. This situation resulted because the United States Patent Office does not issue a patent on a product unless it can be shown that the article or product in question is in fact a new and useful invention. Few "patent" medicines qualified. Medicine manufacturers protected their interests instead by giving their mixtures fanciful names and then registering the name as a trademark. Trademarks are good for twenty years, are renewable after that period, and best of all, are not subject to any sort of questioning by the government.

The *name* thus became a perpetual monopoly and a thing of value, which accounts for the vast amount of advertising done in the 1880's.

The medicine business was clearly a lucrative one. Poor sanitation, the shortage of doctors, and the general rigors of colonial life resulted in a high mortality rate. No wonder the less scientific side of medicine flourished! Quack doctors abounded; apothecaries provided questionable pills and powders; druggists advertised whenever they expected a new shipment—often of goods from England. Among the imports were Bateman's and Stoughton's Drops, Daffy's and Squire's Elixirs, Anderson's and Lockyer's Pills, Anodyne necklaces, British Rock-Oil, Turlington's Balsam, Durham Flour of Mustard, Greenough's Tincture for the Gums and Teeth, Eaton's Styptick, James's Fever Powders, and Dr. John Hopper's Female Pills. Some of these medicines claimed to cure no less than fifty-one different ailments, all of which were listed on the wrapper. Eventually only the bottles were imported to be filled with American concoctions, and in time even the bottles were native-made.

After the Civil War, the patent medicine industry really boomed. Much illness developed as a result of that war. There were wounds, malaria, and the results of typhoid, pneumonia, and dysentery to contend with in later years—the accummulated effects of all the miseries suffered during the war. In addition, the "Westering" movement added illness and hardship. People were few and far between on the frontier, and there was demand for mail-order cures, particularly versatile ones. Liniments were big items of sale. One, Minard's Liniment, was advertised as the great internal and external remedy "for Man or Beast," and probably did equal service in house, barn, and stable.

There being no legislation to control advertising in the 19th century, the medicine men made claims that were anything but modest. One medicine was said to cure as many as twenty-five different ailments, ranging from headache to painful feet. The buyer was always told that the medicine would work if it was used according to directions. In addition, there was usually a brochure containing "testimonials," many of which came from people

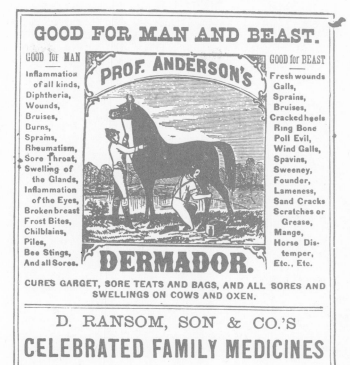

who had subsequently died of the disease the medicine was said to have cured. Certain sure-fire phrases recur in this advertising, the most popular being "secret Indian remedy."

One surprising aspect of 19th-century patent medicines is the number of cures there were for bad habits such as drinking, smoking, or taking drugs. Sears Roebuck advertised a Cure for the Opium and Morphine Habit and a White Star Liquor Cure, sent in a plain, sealed package to be administered secretly to the victim in his coffee or other beverage. However, as so many of these patent medicines were heavily loaded with drugs, such as morphine, or with alcohol, their effectiveness as cures seems at best dubious.

Almanacs
of
Patent Medicines

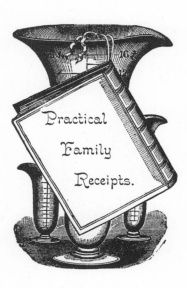

*Manufacturers of patent medicines
tried to reach as many potential customers as possible.
One means of attracting these people was to give them
something free they could use, such as almanacs and booklets.
Some were true almanacs to be used by the farmer
in his planting. Others were cook books for
the housewife or else booklets on home medicine.
Firms also distributed "dream books," song books,
game books, and children's reading books.
Sometimes the books were free;
at other times customers sent in a label to get the book desired.
They also were to be found on the counters of the local druggists.
In any case, the books and almanacs were well used
and the manufacturer accomplished his aim. Naturally, every one
of these almanacs contained pages and pages of advertisements
and testimonials for the manufacturer.
In this section will be seen a sampling
of the many booklets published and issued.
They are fairly representative of the material printed at the time.*

THE MEANING OF DREAMS

ACCORDION—To hear the music of an accordion in your dream, denotes that you will engage in amusement which will win you from sadness. Thus you will be able to take up your burden more cheerfully.

BASEBALL—To see this game in your dream, denotes you will be easily contented and you will be a popular companion.

CANDLE—A long taper with a steady beam is happiness in your love; a short one with a flickering flame, disappointment in your children.

DANDELIONS—A meadow yellow with dandelions means laughter and a party.

EAGLE—To see an eagle soaring overhead means honor and fame. To see one on a nest means plans carried to a successful conclusion.

FLAGS—Waving flags mean honor and triumph.

GIRAFFE—You will shortly see a friend who comes from a long distance.

HAY—Hay being cut means riches after poverty.

IDIOT—An idiot seen in your dreams means sorrow and misfortune.

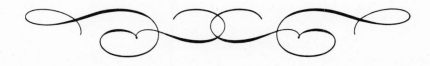

The Meaning of Dreams

Abdomen:—To see your abdomen in a dream, foretells that you will have great expectations, but must redouble your energies on your labor, as pleasure is approaching to your hurt. 20, 16, 80

Abscess:—To dream that you have an abscess, means that you will be overwhelmed with misfortune. 4, 96, 12

Absent:—Should you see absent persons in your dreams, they will shortly return. 16, 3, 84

Abstinence:—If you dream of abstaining from all pleasures you will soon have an opportunity of going on a long journey. Such a journey will bring knowledge and amusement, but should you decide to remain at home, a new love will come to your door. 23, 4, 10

Abyss:—To dream of looking into one means that you will be confronted by threats of seizure of property; to fall into one means your disappointment will be complete. 36, 8, 22

Accident:—An accident is a warning to avoid any mode of travel for a short period, as you are threatened with loss of life. 62, 9, 81

Accordion:—To hear the music of an accordion, denotes that you will engage in amusement which will win you from sadness. Thus you will be able to take up your burden more cheerfully. 4, 8, 17

Accusation:—To dream of accusing someone means unhappiness; to be accused means loss of money. 10, 32, 3

Acid:—To drink any acid is an adverse dream, bringing you much anxiety. 21, 16, 8

Acorn:—Seeing acorns in dreams, is portent of pleasant things ahead, and much gain is to be expected. 94, 18, 6

Acrobat:—To dream of seeing acrobats, denotes you will be prevented from carrying out hazardous schemes by the foolish fears of others. 2, 7, 15

Acting:—If you dream you are an actor on the stage, you will want to hide from unpleasant gossip in a few days. If you dream you are at the theatre watching a play it shows you will shortly enter into a period of good business. 18, 97, 61

Adornment:—If you dream of beautiful

clothes and jewels worn by yourself it means extreme good fortune within a year. If worn by someone else, you may expect disappointment. 44, 15, 6

Adultery:—Should you dream you are committing it, be ready for a letter containing bad news. 66, 1, 77

Advertisement:—To read advertisements, denotes that enemies will overtake you, and defeat you in rivalry. 6, 14, 2

Airplane:—An airplane signifies an unexpected guest. 73, 15, 7

Album:—To dream of an album denotes you will have success and true friends. 19, 2, 48

Alley:—To dream you are in a narrow alley signifies coming illness. 5, 11, 45

Alligator:—To dream of an alligator, unless you kill it, is unfavorable to all persons connected with the dream. 6, 12, 47

Almanac:—To dream of an almanac, means variable fortunes and illusive pleasures. To be studying the signs, foretells that you will be harassed by small matters. 2, 9, 18

Almonds:—This is a good omen. It has wealth in store. However, sorrow will go with it for a short time. 26, 40, 8

Altar:—To dream of this always denotes marriage within a short time. 33, 10, 9

Amazement:—Should you dream of being greatly amazed, you are likely to have an accident. Be careful when motoring especially for a period of five weeks. 52, 5, 71

Amethyst:—To see this purple stone clearly and distinctly means avariciousness. If it is set in a gold ring it means fidelity of a loved one. 13, 7, 10

Ammonia:—Ammonia seen in a dream, means displeasure will be felt by the dreamer at the conduct of a friend. Quarrels with friends will follow this dream. 17, 43, 5

Amputation:—Ordinary amputation of limbs, denotes small offices lost; the loss of entire legs or arms, unusual depression in trade. To seamen, storm and loss of property. 2, 16, 12

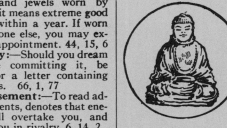

HUNGER:—Your dearest wish will be granted. 35, 12, 9

Hurl:—Should you be hurling some object with great force, your present anxieties will be lifted. 29, 4, 81

Hurt:—If you are suffering some physical hurt, your lover will be unfaithful. 17, 26, 44

Hurry:—To dream that you are hurrying and out of breath means that you will have to combat unkind gossip. 29, 62, 71

Husks:—Husks or parings mean vice and wantonness. 45, 6, 19

Hysteria:—Denotes worry over the health of another. 29, 46, 10

Ice Cream:—Eating ice cream signifies success in your love affairs. 33, 6, 79

Idiot:—An idiot seen in your dreams means sorrow and misfortune. 4, 17, 88

Idle:—To dream of living in idleness denotes failure of your business plans. 39, 41, 5

Idol:—Worshipping an idol means a humble spirit and modesty. 77, 6, 41

Ill:—To dream you are ill means laughter mingled with tears. 52, 7, 18

Impatience:—Signifies rebellion against the life you are living at present. 6, 17, 29

Improper:—To dream your conduct is improper, you will be called upon to shield a friend. 18, 34, 79

Indians:—If you are being pursued by them, unexpected guests will arrive; if they are going in the opposite direction, the small trouble you have been experiencing will fade away. 10, 46, 5

Infant:—A sign of happiness and freedom from petty worries. 14, 33, 76

Influence:—To dream of someone influencing you to do evil means the treachery of someone you know well; should they persuade you to do good, you will experience pleasure. 54, 35, 16

Innocent:—Dreaming of being innocent in thought, word and deed, shows that you are suffering for some wrong you have committed. 24, 65, 3

Insanity:—Should you dream you were insane, it is a bad sign. Look out for sudden illness or an accident. 41, 55, 3

Jacket:—Wearing a short jacket indicates a small expedition; probably a picnic or informal party. 25, 61, 16

Jars:—If they are large, wide-mouthed jars, wealth and plenty will come to you; if they are small and narrow, you will be disappointed. 53, 27, 3

Jaw:—Dreaming of moving jaws denotes shame for a lie you have spoken. 29, 36, 69

Jealousy:—Denotes amusement and an invitation from an unexpected source. 51, 65, 5

Jewels:—Dangers and worries beset your path. 95, 2, 17

Jockey:—To see a jockey on a horse winning a race, the move you shortly will make will be a fortunate one; if he be losing, be prepared for disappointment. 43, 91. 8

Juggler:—Watching a juggler means a round of parties and gaiety. If his hand slips and spoils a trick, you will be sorry for a friend. 66, 47, 3

Kettle:—Scrubbing a kettle denotes an apology you will have to make for unkind words; if you are cooking something in one, an acquaintance will come to your door to make trouble. 57, 21, 3

Dentist:—You will have reason to doubt the sincerity of some person with whom you have dealings. 8, 24, 60

Derrick:—These indicate strife and obstruction in your way to success. 2, 9, 18

Desert:—To dream you are in a desert means you have told a lie which has caused sorrow. 5, 26, 52

Deserted:—If you are alone and deserted, you are suffering because you have been unfaithful to some trust. 32, 66, 4

Detective:—To dream one is following you and you are innocent denotes that fortune and honor are drawing nearer each day. 6, 87, 3

Devil:—To dream of this evil person means that you will make a journey or move to a new home. After this change you will be more successful. If a maiden has this dream she will shortly marry; if a man, his business will take a turn for the better. 36, 76, 44

Dice:—This is indicative of unfortunate speculations. Also foretells contagious sickness. 11, 55, 9

Dictionary:—If you are referring to one it signifies that you depend too much upon the opinions of others in the management of your affairs. 20, 31, 8

Dinner:—To dream that you eat dinner, denotes that you will often have cause to think seriously of the necessities of life. 22, 4, 6

Discovery:—If you dream of making a startling discovery, you will shortly have cause to be frightened. 77, 14, 21

Disguise:—If you are in disguise, you are afraid of being discovered in something you have done. If someone else is in disguise, a long absent friend will return. 69, 76, 10

Dishonor:—Should you dream of being dishonored, you are worrying about your love affairs. 32, 62, 4

Diving:—This denotes a favorable termination of some embarrassment. 31, 6, 43

Divorce:—To dream of divorce, denotes you are not satisfied with your companion and should

KITTENS—Dreaming of kittens playing means joy in the near future.

LACE—A lace gown or lace trimmed garment indicates vanity and moral excesses.

MAGNET—This means popularity and many invitations.

NEST—This is always a good sign. It means tranquility in the home, and good-tempered children.

OAR—An oar is a symbol of success.

PONY—A white pony means a death of which you hear. A black pony means a birth.

RED—This vivid color denotes passion. You are inclined to be faithless.

FORTUNE TELLING
CARD CHART

ACE OF CLUBS—Foretells serenity, wealth, an interesting existence.

KING OF DIAMONDS—Spiteful nature, quick tongue, hold a grudge long.

QUEEN OF HEARTS—Great beauty. May not make the best kind of wife.

JACK OF SPADES—A good friend, glad to be of service to you. Inclined to be lazy.

TEN OF CLUBS—Unexpected wealth, probably through death of friend. Grief will be deep.

NINE OF DIAMONDS—Indicates a nomadic person discontented with his sphere or activity.

EIGHT OF HEARTS—Weak and vacillating though lovable. Inclined to extremes.

SEVEN OF SPADES—Death may claim one you know.

SIX OF CLUBS—Business will prosper. Fortunate in your associates.

FIVE OF DIAMONDS—Marriage partner will be tender and kindly. Will have clever children.

HOROSCOPES

MAY 21 to JUNE 21: Gemini—The Twins

Happy and contented marriage comes to women born in this month as well as wealth. They are always punctilious and reliable, making desirable friends and associates.

OCTOBER 24 TO NOVEMBER 22: Scorpio—The Scorpion

A woman born under this sign is often extravagant and lazy. She may benefit through the generosity of others, rather than through her own perseverance or industry. She is, however, amiable and pleasant of speech, never dishonest or immoral. The man of October makes an excellent marital mate for he is loyal and affectionate, just in his dealings, successful in business and blessed with a fine mind.

SIGNS OF RAIN

You may expect rain—
when birds fly close to the ground
when crows caw long and loud
when chairs creak louder than usual.
when curly hairs becomes unruly
when chickens huddle together outside the coop
when ducks and geese quack louder than usual

FORTUNE TELLING
BY DOMINOES

Shuffle the dominoes well by laying them face downward and moving them about with the hands. When they are thoroughly intermixed, draw one and find its meaning as listed below:

DOUBLE-FIVE—A fortunate move.

FOUR-ONE—Debts are piling up.

SIX-THREE—A brief but happy motor trip.

SIX-BLANK—Unhappy hours caused by gossip.

FORTUNE TELLING
BY DICE

Shake 3 dice well in a small box and then cast once with the left hand.

18—Luck does not come to you, but you will acquire wealth and prominence through hard labor. 3—A quarrel followed by unhappiness and apologies. 7—Gossip will bring tears to your door. 17—A trip on a boat brings much happiness.

ALMANACS

The almanac, an important family friend, covered a wide range of subjects. To offset its lack of timeliness, it generally engaged in forecasting such

imponderables as the weather, and thereby spawned a host of such prognosticators as books that explained dreams or told fortunes. Most almanacs were produced by suppliers of pills and other cures who filled them with ads and promotional material and presented them to prospective customers. As a look at the dates shows, such "commercial" almanacs were produced until quite recently.

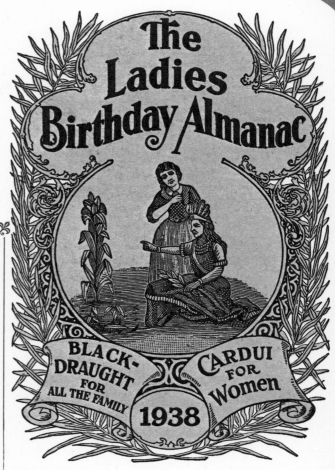

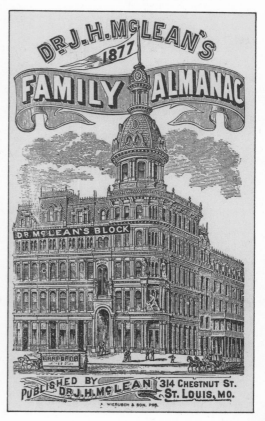

Fortune by Tea Leaves

In using this method, much depends on the imagination and natural aptitude of the reader. You must have the "seeing eye" which will interpret the formation of the leaves correctly, but this readily comes with practice.

Method: Drain cup of the tea being careful not to lose any of the leaves in so doing. Then reverse the cup on the saucer and twist it around three times to the left. After doing this, turn the cup right-side up and read the emblems.

Anchor: This is the sign of trade and travel, both carried on successfully. If standing alone at the top of the cup it indicates true love.

Birds: You have doubtless had worries, but the "tea leaf" birds carry them away. If surrounded by other leaves it means a pleasant journey.

Child: Standing alone it signifies innocent merriment and friendship. Surrounded closely it means fickleness and many love affairs.

Clouds: Small, light clouds mean the granting of your dearest wish. If they are heavy and lowering, disappointment.

Coffin: This may mean, as it does in dream, and in other methods of fortune telling, death or a serious illness either of the hearer, or a friend. Closely surrounded, it means an inheritance.

Cross: Standing alone, your troubles will soon clear. In the thick, more troubles will come.

Dog: Clearly seen and alone, it denotes popularity and friends. If thickly surrounded you may expect deception from one you have trusted. If seen at the extreme bottom of the cup, someone is envious of you.

Fish: This denotes successful enterprises, especially on, or beyond the seas. If well-surrounded, worries encircle you.

Garden: Clearly indicated, you will have good and loyal friends. Encompassed by other leaves, beware of false acquaintances.

Lily: As you would suppose, the lily is a sign of virtue and innocence. Seen clearly and alone, it indicates a mate with a spotless reputation, long life and happiness, but seen in the bottom, thickly surrounded, it is an omen of trouble and discouragement.

Lion: (Or any wild animal) Good fortune to eminent persons, if clear and distinct. Envy and jealousy if in the thick.

Moon: Social and political prominence will come to you if the moon shines alone. If clouds surround it, regret, for a short period.

Mountain: A chain of mountains is a sign of treacherous associates.

The Famous Oraculum

(The Oracle of Hermes)

as used by

The Great Napoleon

Culled from Ancient Egyptian Manuscript

Long ago when Napoleon Bonaparte lived and reigned, he regarded this Oraculum as one of his greatest treasures. The original manuscript was discovered and brought to him while he was in Egypt. It is said that whenever he thought of engaging on a new venture of any kind, he consulted it and followed the advice obtained to the best of his ability. It is thought that had not he been so much engrossed in his success toward the last, he might have retained his hold on popularity and greatness through continued consulting of this astonishingly accurate oracle. Since it was made available to the public after the defeat of the French army, many people have made use of its warnings and advice to their advantage. The original complete book is now in the British Museum. A short but clear version is included in this book for the benefit of all those who are interested in the occult and in the future. A clear explanation preceding the Oraculum Table will simplify its use.

How to use the Table:

Make dots as illustrated below, using four lines. When you have done this, count the dots appearing in each line proceeding from left to right. Should they be odd in number, jot down one

mark; if they be even, use two. Should the number of dots be more than nine, use only the surplus.

Refer to the Oraculum Table when you have decided what question you wish to have answered. You will perceive that dots appear there,

arranged like those made by you. By casting your glance along the identical column, you will find the letter which coincides with the figure of the question you have in mind. Then take the column at the top of which appears the same letter. You will thus obtain the correct answer.

EXAMPLE:

In the above, the number of dots in the first is odd;
In the second, even;
In the third, odd;
In the fourth, even.

Therefore the key to your answer would be:

    (odd)
    (even)
    (odd)
    (even)

There are certain days upon which you are warned not to consult the oraculum, nor should you seek to engage in new concerns at these times. Try each question only once in one day.

January: 1, 2, 4, 6, 10, 20, 22.
February: 6, 17, 28.
March: 24, 26.
April: 10, 27, 28.
May: 7, 8.
June: 27.
July: 17, 21.
August: 20, 22.
September: 5, 30.
October: 6.
November: 3, 29.
December: 6, 10, 15.

Mouse: Standing alone it is an omen of recovery of a lost object. Almost indistinguishable among other leaves, you must prepare for disappointment in this respect.

Man: Seen clearly and unsurrounded it will mean an early marriage. It also denotes good business and happiness.

Ring: Always means marriage. If clear, it brings marital happiness. Surrounded, it warns you to be careful as to friends whom you trust. Seen in the bottom of the cup it means a separation that brings grief.

Oraculum Table of Questions

Number	QUESTIONS																	Number
1	Will my wish be granted?	A	B	C	D	E	F	G	H	I	K	L	M	N	O	P	Q	1
2	Will my undertakings prove successful?	B	C	D	E	F	G	H	I	K	L	M	N	O	P	Q	A	2
3	Does good or ill luck mark my cause?	C	D	E	F	G	H	I	K	L	M	N	O	P	Q	A	B	3
4	Shall I live far from the place of my birth?	D	E	F	G	H	I	K	L	M	N	O	P	Q	A	B	C	4
5	Will my new acquaintance return?	E	F	G	H	I	K	L	M	N	O	P	Q	A	B	C	D	5
6	Will what is lost be returned to me?	F	G	H	I	K	L	M	N	O	P	Q	A	B	C	D	E	6
7	Is my friend one in whom I can place confidence?	G	H	I	K	L	M	N	O	P	Q	A	B	C	D	E	F	7
8	Must I make a journey or shall I remain at home?	H	I	K	L	M	N	O	P	Q	A	B	C	D	E	F	G	8
9	Is my love reciprocated?	I	K	L	M	N	O	P	Q	A	B	C	D	E	F	G	H	9
10	Will my marriage bring joy?	K	L	M	N	O	P	Q	A	B	C	D	E	F	G	H	I	10
11	What manner of mate will I have?	L	M	N	O	P	Q	A	B	C	D	E	F	G	H	I	K	11
12	What sex will be my child?	M	N	O	P	Q	A	B	C	D	E	F	G	H	I	K	L	12
13	Will the sufferer regain health?	N	O	P	Q	A	B	C	D	E	F	G	H	I	K	L	M	13
14	Will the sinner gain forgiveness and mercy?	O	P	Q	A	B	C	D	E	F	G	H	I	K	L	M	N	14
15	Is this day one of good or ill fortune?	P	Q	A	B	C	D	E	F	G	H	I	K	L	M	N	O	15
16	What is the meaning of my dream?	Q	A	B	C	D	E	F	G	H	I	K	L	M	N	O	P	16

Answers to Oraculum

A

Your wish will shortly be granted you.

Misfortune and tears.

On this day let circumspection guide you. Otherwise bad luck will assail you.

Death visits the one about whom your fears are centered, causing grief to many.

Death will not come at once but will arrive some time later.

Beauty is an ornament to your favorite child, but she will cause you sorrow and worry.

Piety and honor will mark the one whom you choose for a mate.

Even though you are happily married to this person, envy and tears will follow you.

Deceit is a characteristic of the one who offers this love. The affection is neither lasting nor honest.

Success will not come this time, so defer your journey.

The affection of true and loyal friends exists between you.

Much to your joy, that which has been taken from you will be returned.

The one in whom you are interested will come back and happiness will descend upon you.

Be content where you are for no change will take place for some time to come.

You will be blessed in your undertaking.

Try to possess your soul in patience for luck is not with you.

B

When good fortune smiles upon you, be prepared for envy and jealousy.

Do not seek to obtain your desires at this time. It is not propitious.

Someone will unexpectedly show you a kindness.

Be warned; there are people who bear ill-will and would do you harm if they could.

After vicissitudes and great trouble, this one will be forgiven.

Unfortunately, the one who is ill will not recover.

The babe will be a boy who will bring honor and credit.

Your marital mate will be well endowed with this world's goods.

Marriage with this individual will be happy and prosperous.

Be joyful for the love that is offered you is sincere and deep.

The journey will be crowned with success.

You will be disillusioned regarding a friend.

You may lift your heart for that which has been taken from you will be returned.

He is prevented from returning at once, but you may expect him later.

You will make a change in your residence.

Let prudence and caution lead you, for good fortune hides her face.

C

God will be with you and bring you success.

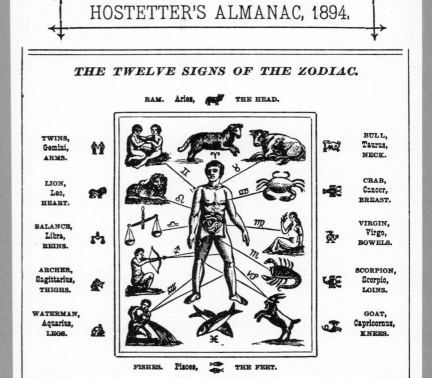

DREAMS AND FORTUNE-TELLERS

Some almanacs stressed practical information, such as the rising and setting times for sun and moon. Others engaged primarily in explaining dreams or expounding ways to forecast the future. The almanac at right purported to do both.

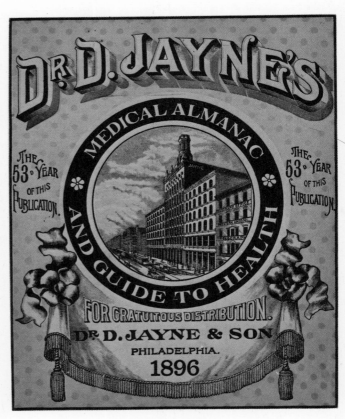

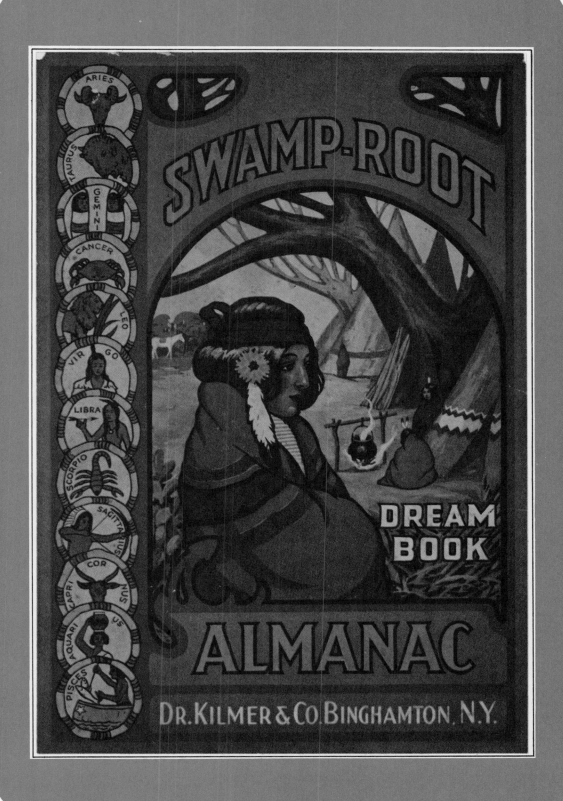

For forty years it stood the test
And ranks for general use the best.
Let each one to his home repair,
And give it trial full and fair,
And when we prove reports are true
We'll gladly give the praises due.
So all agreed, throughout the year
To keep POND'S EXTRACT always near.

II

The baby Bears that thought to steal
From watchful bees a toothsome meal,
Received a dose that closed their eyes
And swelled their head to twice the size;
But through the kind and tender care
Of cunning-minded mother bear,
POND'S EXTRACT promptly was applied
Till pain and swelling did subside.

WISDOM IN FABLE

I

Some beasts that sore afflictions stood
Assembled in a darksome wood,
With plastered heads and blistered paws,
Rheumatic joints and poulticed jaws.
"There is," said one, "a certain kind
of remedy that aids mankind.
POND'S EXTRACT has the power to heal
the aches and pains and wounds we feel;

III

The Rabbit, Fox, and Badger gray
To honor Independence Day,

NOTE—*In 1885, the Pond's Extract Co. issued this phamphlet extolling the virtues of "POND'S EXTRACT: A General Family Remedy and Vegetable Pain-Destroyer, Healing and Soothing. Recommended and prescribed by Physicians and Surgeons. For two Generations a Household Favorite." The pamphlet is entitled WISDOM IN FABLE and is illustrated. There are many testimonials.*

Sat down at twilight in a row
To let their bombs and crackers go;
But some without much warning whizzed
And more in wrong direction fizzed,
Till burned and bruised at every point,
And sprained at wrist and ankle-joint—
By falling from the log in fright,
They reached the door as best they might;
and then POND'S EXTRACT came in turn
To take the smart from sprain and burn.

IV

Some Pigs, as round the door they played,
Were scalded by the kitchen maid,
Till from their backs the bristles fell
And patches of the skin as well;
When every muscle had been strained
Until their humble sty was gained,
POND'S EXTRACT healed each painful sore,
And soon they rooted as before.

V

While wolves were bearing home their loads
Along the drifted mountain-roads,
A sharp and sweeping blizzard froze
Their ears and tails, and half their toes;
But when POND'S EXTRACT was applied
Next morning to each stiffened hide,
The rheumatism brought about
By such exposure, faded out;
Then trace of frost departed soon
And all were well again by noon.

VI

But now, lest some should be misled,
This explanation here is spread:
These are no quadrupeds at all,
But human beings, great and small.
The children, husband, and the wife,
Are thus portrayed in daily life;
The boils, and burns, and cuts they show
Are all comprised in human woe.
The inflammations, bleedings, sprains,
The gnawing ache of bones or brains
Disturb the peace of youth and age,
In every station, clime, or stage.
POND'S EXTRACT comes with healing grace
To bring the smile on every face.

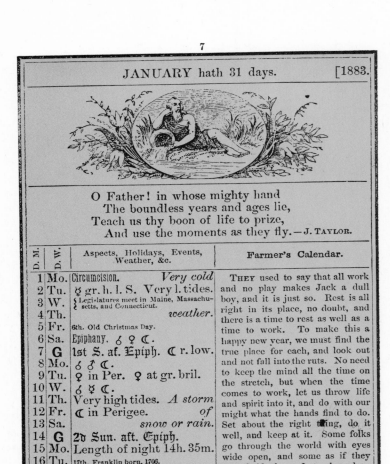

7

JANUARY hath 31 days.   [1883.

O Father! in whose mighty hand
The boundless years and ages lie,
Teach us thy boon of life to prize,
And use the moments as they fly. — J. TAYLOR.

D. M.	D. W.	Aspects. Holidays, Events, Weather, &c.	Farmer's Calendar.
1	Mo.	Circumcision. *Very cold*	THEY used to say that all work and no play makes Jack a dull boy, and it is just so. Rest is all right in its place, no doubt, and there is a time to rest as well as a time to work. To make this a happy new year, we must find the true place for each, and look out and not fall into the ruts. No need to keep the mind all the time on the stretch, but when the time comes to work, let us throw life and spirit into it, and do with our might what the hands find to do. Set about the right thing, do it well, and keep at it. Some folks go through the world with eyes wide open, and some as if they were half asleep. Let us learn how to live, how to think, how to act, learn to use the eye and the ear, and to keep every sense awake. By the way, why don't you give the cows a bit of salt now and then, or what is better, keep a big lump of rock salt where they can get at it all the time? Don't you think they need it now as much as they do in the spring and fall? Don't you know that more'n half the blood is made up of salt in some of its forms, and that it is all the time going off through the skin and the kidneys? Where are they to get it?
2	Tu.	☿ gr. h. l. S. Very l. tides.	
3	W.	Legislatures meet in Maine, Massachusetts, and Connecticut.	
4	Th.	*weather.*	
5	Fr.	6th. Old Christmas Day.	
6	Sa.	Epiphany. ☌ ♀ ☾.	
7	**G**	1st S. af. Epiph. ☾ r. low.	
8	Mo.	☌ ♂ ☾.	
9	Tu.	♀ in Per. ♀ at gr. bril.	
10	W.	☌ ♀ ☾.	
11	Th.	Very high tides. *A storm*	
12	Fr.	☾ in Perigee. *of*	
13	Sa.	*snow or rain.*	
14	**G**	2d Sun. aft. Epiph.	
15	Mo.	Length of night 14h. 35m.	
16	Tu.	17th, Franklin born, 1706.	
17	W.	☌ ♀ ☾, ☌ ♄ ☾. 18th and 19th. Great snow storm and gale in Gt. Britain, 1881.	
18	Th.	Low tides.	
19	Fr.	☾ runs high. ☌ ♃ ☾.	
20	Sa.	♄ stat. Cess. of hostilities btw Great Britain and U.S. ag'd to, 1783.	
21	**G**	Septua. Sunday. ♀ in ☊.	
22	Mo.	☿ gr. elong. E. *Thawing*	
23	Tu.	High tides. Callao and Lima surr. to the Chilians, 1881.	
24	W.	25th. Guiteau found guilty of the murder of President Garfield, 1882.	
25	Th.	Conversion of St. Paul.	
26	Fr.	☿ in Perih. *weather.*	
27	Sa.	☌ ♅ ☾. ☿ stat.	
28	**G**	Sexa. Sunday. ☾ in Apo. *Cold winds.*	
29	Mo.		
30	Tu.	Dr. H. W. Bellows, well-known clergyman, died, aged 67, 1882.	
31	W.	♀ gr. hel. lat. N.	

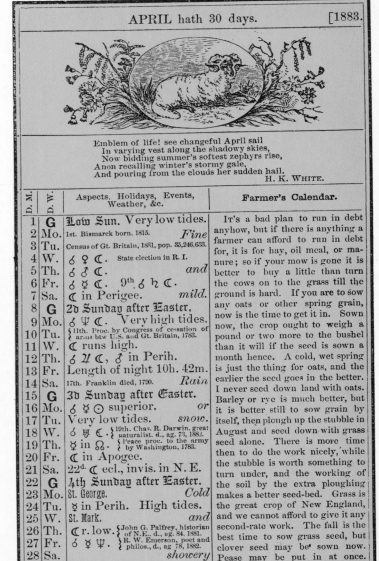

13

APRIL hath 30 days.   [1883.

Emblem of life! see changeful April sail
In varying vest along the shadowy skies,
Now bidding summer's softest zephyrs rise,
Anon recalling winter's stormy gale,
And pouring from the clouds her sudden hail.
H. K. WHITE.

D. M.	D. W.	Aspects. Holidays, Events, Weather, &c.	Farmer's Calendar.
1	**G**	Low Sun. Very low tides.	IT's a bad plan to run in debt anyhow, but if there is anything a farmer can afford to run in debt for, it is for hay, oil meal, or manure; so if your mow is gone it is better to buy a little than turn the cows on to the grass till the ground is hard. If you are to sow any oats or other spring grain, now is the time to get it in. Sown now, the crop ought to weigh a pound or two more to the bushel than it will if the seed is sown a month hence. A cold, wet spring is just the thing for oats, and the earlier the seed goes in the better. I never seed down land with oats. Barley or rye is much better, but it is better still to sow grain by itself, then plough up the stubble in August and seed down with grass seed alone. There is more time then to do the work nicely, while the stubble is worth something to turn under, and the working of the soil by the extra ploughing makes a better seed-bed. Grass is the great crop of New England, and we cannot afford to give it any second-rate work. The fall is the best time to sow grass seed, but clover seed may be sown now. Pease may be put in at once. There is no time to lose. The rule is, to be up early and down late, as the work begins to press.
2	Mo.	1st. Bismarck born. 1815. *Fine*	
3	Tu.	Census of Gt. Britain, 1881, pop. 35,246,633.	
4	W.	☌ ♀ ☾. State election in R. I.	
5	Th.	☌ � ☾. *and*	
6	Fr.	☌ ♀ ☾. 9th ☌ ♄ ☾.	
7	Sa.	☾ in Perigee. *mild.*	
8	**G**	2d Sunday after Easter.	
9	Mo.	☌ ♆ ☾. Very high tides.	
10	Tu.	11th. Proc. by Congress of cessation of arms btw U.S. and Gt. Britain, 1783.	
11	W.	☾ runs high.	
12	Th.	☌ ♃ ☾, ♂ in Perih.	
13	Fr.	Length of night 10h. 42m.	
14	Sa.	17th. Franklin died, 1790. *Rain*	
15	**G**	3d Sunday after Easter.	
16	Mo.	☌ ☿ ☉ superior. *or*	
17	Tu.	Very low tides. *snow.*	
18	W.	☌ ♅ ☾. 19th. Chas. R. Darwin, great naturalist. d., ag. 73, 1882.	
19	Th.	☿ in ☊. Peace proc. to the army by Washington, 1783.	
20	Fr.	☾ in Apogee.	
21	Sa.	22d ☾ ecl., invis. in N. E.	
22	**G**	4th Sunday after Easter.	
23	Mo.	St. George. *Cold*	
24	Tu.	☿ in Perih. High tides.	
25	W.	St. Mark. *and*	
26	Th.	☾ r. low. John G. Palfrey, historian of N.E., d., ag. 84, 1881.	
27	Fr.	☌ ☿ ♆. R. W. Emerson, poet and philos., d., ag 78, 1882.	
28	Sa.	*showery*	
29	**G**	Rogation Sunday.	
30	Mo.	*weather.*	

A B C JINGLES

A stands for All external Ails,
And Hanford's Balsam's many sales
Attest its use for Man or Beast
In the North or South, West or East.

B may mean Bruise or painful Burn,
and then to Hanford's Balsam turn;
For quick relief from pain to bring
To cool a burn, it is the thing.

C stands for Cut of any kind,
And for such hurts please bear in mind
Use Hanford's Balsam right away,
To cleanse and heal without delay.

D for Don't has always stood;
Don't take the bad, don't miss the good;
When Hanford's Balsam always suits,
Don't let them sell you substitutes.

E for Earache,—children know
Just how it causes keenest woe;
Keep Hanford's Balsam near at hand,
At night, it may be in demand.

F for Frostbite surely stands,
On nose or toes, on ears or hands;
Rub Hanford's Balsam on the place,
The pain away to quickly chase.

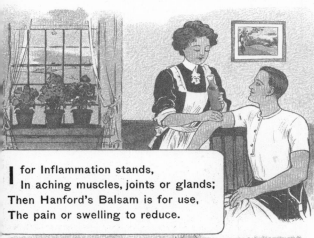

I for Inflammation stands,
In aching muscles, joints or glands;
Then Hanford's Balsam is for use,
The pain or swelling to reduce.

J is for Joy that patients know
Who find their aches and lameness
go,
And Hanford's Balsam every day
Brings joy in just this goodly way.

L means any place that's Lame.
Joints or muscles, all the same,—
Rub Hanford's Balsam on the spot;
This is the treatment to be sought.

N is for Neck that's stiff and sore.—
To turn it hurts you more and more;
Use Hanford's Balsam well applied,
It is a help that's true and tried.

O stands for Old; those things are best
That age has given every test,
And Hanford's Balsam it appears,
Has been on sale for many years.

Q stands for Question; when you're
sent
To buy a salve or liniment,
Be sure to ask in accents plain
For Hanford's Balsam, foe of pain.

R is for Rhyme, and when you read,
Be sure this lesson well you heed:
For Cut or Burn or Sore or Bruise,
Then Hanford's Balsam always use.

Q stands for Question; when you're sent
To buy a salve or liniment,
Be sure to ask in accents plain
For Hanford's Balsam, foe of pain.

S is for any Strain or Sprain;
Use Hanford's Balsam to stop pain
And makes the swelling disappear,
So always keep a bottle near.

T is for the Throat that's sore;
Buy Hanford's Balsam at the store,
Apply it as directions tell,
To make the throat strong and well.

U for Useful ought to stand;
A useful thing to keep at hand
Is Hanford's Balsam, for you see
It's made for all the family.

W is for Wound or open Sore,
That you've tried to heal before;
Seek Hanford's Balsam where for sale,
Then use it after others fail.

X for Ten in number stands,—
The fingers on your little hands;
When they have a cut or burn,
To Hanford's Balsam you should turn.

Y is for Yearling on the farm;
Or any stock that comes to harm,
From kicks or sores or bleeding wound,
Use Hanford's Balsam to make sound.

Z is where the alphabet ends;
We say good-bye to you dear
friends,
Recall the sayings you have passed,—
Use Hanford's Balsam first and last.

STRICTLY BUSINESS

WHAT is the Swift Specific Company? Who compose the organization? Is it a clap-trap patent medicine humbug, gotten up to deceive and make money out of the people? These questions we think are answered by the officials and citizens of our city, state and country.

———

Atlanta, Ga., Nov. 10, 1888.
We own all the stock of The Swift Specific Company, and the affairs of said Company are managed by us entirely, and everything which we say of Swift's Specific is true, and all the testimonials are reliable.
LAMAR, RANKIN & LAMAR.
C. T. SWIFT.

———

We know the gentlemen composing the firm of Lamar, Rankin & Lamar, and of The Swift Specific Company. They are prominent citizens of our state, men of means and of high character and standing.

W. A. HEMPHILL, Pres. Capital City Bank.
J. H. PORTER, Pres. Merchants' Bank.
PAUL ROMARE, Vice-Pres. Atlanta Nat. Bank.
L. J. HILL, Pres. Gate City Nat. Bank.
JNO. B. GORDON, Governor of Georgia.
ALFRED H. COLQUITT, U. S. Senator.
J. T. COOPER, Mayor of Atlanta.
H. W. GRADY, Editor Atlanta Constitution.

PLAIN HISTORY

Swift's Specific is a simple vegetable compound, prepared from roots gathered freshly from the forest, and contains nothing of the mineral kingdom, or any poisonous substance, or any article at all which comes from the chemist's laboratory.

The formula of the remedy was obtained from the Creek Indians in Middle Georgia, by reliable white men, who had witnessed the wonderful cures made by that tribe of Indians of blood diseases. Mr. Hugh L. Dennard of Houston, Co., Ga., began using Swift's Specific in 1829 and continued its use all of his life, and asserted that he had never known it to fail to cure any case of scrofula, blood taint or contagious blood poison. This testimony has been corroborated every day for years. The present Company was formed in 1879 and have since made known to the world the virtues of Swift's Specific, and to-day it is sold in every city, town and country store all over America, in Great Britain, and many other portions of the world. We have two valuable books on Blood Diseases, which we mail free.

UANITA'S SECRET

In the land of Amicola,
Where the Chattahoochie mirrors
Stars of Heaven in its water,
Dwelt the chieftain Unawanga.
Sick was he, of cruel poison
Burning in his veins like fire,
And before his lodge he waited
For the coming of the summons.
From the distance came his daughter—
Uanita—knowing nothing
Of her father's grievous ailing.
As she walked she gathered blossoms,
Roots and grasses of the wildwood—
Halted at the Cimmeraga—
"Pool of Darkness"—idly dreaming,
One by one her gleanings dropping.
Scarcely had they touched the water,
Ere the dingy surface lightened,
Purged it seemed of all pollution
Till the depths became as crystal,
Snowy pebbles gleaming thro' them.

Open were his arms to greet her,
Blanched her lips as when she kissed him
Learned she that his life was ebbing.
Like a sunbeam thro' the darkness
Came the thought of Uanita—
"Sweet the lesson of Manitou,
That which purifies the water,
Cleanseth blood of Unawanga!"
Like a deer to woodland sped she,
Soon returned with roots and blossoms
Steeped them, and their blended juices
Gave she to her father. Wonder!
Purged was he of the poison,
And he rose and blessed his daughter.

Uanita saw and wondered,
Raised her eyes unto Manitou
Thankful for the secret taught her.
Soon she came unto her father—
Unawanga—sick with poison.

Later unto Amicola,
Came a pale faced preacher, teaching
Peace and progress to the natives,
Wooed and won he Uanita;
She to nobler make his calling,
Whispered to him nature's secret—
Told him of the herbs so potent
For the healing and the saving.
Thus it was the "Swift's Specific"
Brought unto the world its blessing;

NOTE—*The booklet was issued by The Swift Specific Company of Atlanta, Ga. manufacturers of Swift Specific.*

BLOOD·HUMORS

*B*OILS, pimples, blotches on the skin, eruptions, etc., evidence the fact that the blood is not in a good condition. These symptoms result from the effort of nature to throw off the impurities, in which she should be assisted by Swift's Specific. This will remedy the disturbance, and bring speedy and permanent relief by forcing out the poison, and will build up the system from the first dose.

Over land and over water
Went the priest and Uanita;
Bringing to the people tidings
Of relief from blood contagion—
Of a salutary agent
That would purge them of all poison
And the decades since are teeming
With the glowing testimonies
Of the powers antidotal
Blended in the "Swift's Specific."
Scrof'lous patients and rheumatics,
Sufferers from all blood poisons,
These are purged of taint and weakness
By the wondrous "Swift's Specific."

MERCURIAL RHEUMATISM

is said to be the most torturing form of this disease. It is most frequently the result of mercurial treatment persisted in for the cure of diseases of the blood. The system becomes saturated and poisoned with this mineral, and develops itself in this form of Rheumatism. The only way to remove this mineral poison is to take Swift's Specific. It seems to cure the Rheumatism by removing the mercury. We have hundreds of testimonials of cures of this horribly painful disease in our books on blood and skin diseases, which we will mail free to any address.

CANCER

is a form of blood poison which is not understood by the medical profession as to its real nature and character, but it is evidently hereditary in its nature. It may accidently develop itself without any predisposition or evidence of such existing poison. The knife or caustic salves have heretofore been the so-called remedies for it, but all honest practitioners will tell you that this treatment fails to cure, and only hastens fatal results. Thousands of cases of Epithelioma (skin) Cancers, and a great many cases of Scirrhus Cancers have been entirely cured by the use of Swift's Specific. It forces the poison out through the Cancer itself, and the pores of the skin.

Send for our books on Blood and Skin Diseases—mailed free.

Copyright, 1881, by Seth W. Fowle & Sons.

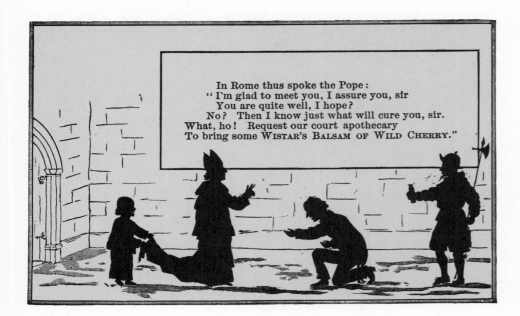

In Rome thus spoke the Pope:
" I'm glad to meet you, I assure you, sir
You are quite well, I hope?
No? Then I know just what will cure you, sir.
What, ho! Request our court apothecary
To bring some WISTAR'S BALSAM OF WILD CHERRY."

THE LAY OF THE LONESOME LUNG

A saddened man was Bung,
Although a prosperous and wealthy one;
He only had one lung,
And that, alas, was not a healthy one:
But this condition was, remember, ere he
Had taken WISTAR'S BALSAM OF
WILD CHERRY.

He hated all M.D.'s,
And positively wouldn't hear of 'em:
I think he grudged their fees;
He swore 'twas 'cause he stood in fear of 'em:
And if he hated doctors, think how very
Opposed he was to BALSAM OF WILD
CHERRY.

"To foreign parts I'll fly,"
Said Bung, "no sort of use resisting me;
If I die I must, why I
Can do so without your assisting me.
So find some other chap to drug and
blister,
"I'm off," said he. "You are," said Dr.
WISTAR.

The captain of the ship
Observed, "Dear me, you look quite poorly, sir;
I hope this little trip
Will do you lots of good; but surely, sir,
Beside sea air you need some tonic whole-
some:
Try this," producing WISTAR'S
CHERRY BALSAM.

In London streets he met
A portly man, before he's been an hour there,
Who said to him, "I'll bet
I know why you so at the Tower stare;
Just read that bill," said he, "You need it,
Mister."
It read, "Try BALSAM OF WILD
CHERRY,—WISTAR."

To Paris next he ran,
And found, not least among its mysteries,
That nearly every man
Knew very well who Dr. Wistar is;
For everybody said to him, "Mon chéri,
Try DR. WISTAR'S BALSAM OF
WILD CHERRY."

To Berlin next he went,
But found no one in all the city who,
 In blank astonishment,
Did not exclaim, "Meinherr, I pity you!"
 Such ignorance as Bung's, in fact, appals
  'em;
"What! Never heard of WISTAR'S
CHERRY BALSAM?" . . .

Poor Bung ran off and hid
In Egypt, to escape admonishing;
 He saw a pyramid,
And cried aloud, "This is astonishing!
 For on its sides, in letter mighty, very,
 He read, "Try WISTAR'S BALSAM OF
WILD CHERRY."

"Enough!" cried Bung, "I'll buy
This stuff, to find out what its powers are."
 He bought a lot to try—
His lungs are now as sound as ours are!
 He went, quite cured, directly back to
  Aden
Was married to the handsome Indian maiden,
 Has children now, I hear, is fat and merry,
 And all through WISTAR'S BALSAM
OF WILD CHERRY.

NOTE—*This pamphlet was copyrighted in 1881 by Seth W. Fowle & Sons of Boston, Mass. to advertise Peruvian Syrup and Wistar's Balsam of Wild Cherry.*

HOOD'S
Practical Cook's Book.
Soups.

SOUP stock may be made from meat procured for the purpose, or from the trimmings and "left overs." Mrs. Lincoln says: "Every pantry should have a 'catch-all.' It is vastly more important there than in the sewing-room or on the toilet-table. The coal-hod, refuse-pail and sink catch all in many households. One or two large bowls — not tin, but deep earthen dishes, provided they are sweet and do not leak — will better answer the purpose. After breakfast or dinner, do not put away the remnants of steaks or roasts on the platters, but look them over, and put by themselves any pieces that can be used again, or in made dishes. Then put all the bones, trimmings, fat, gristle, and everything, especially the platter gravy, which usually flavors the dishwater, into the 'catch-all.' If you have just one bone from a steak or chop, if it be not burned, it is worth sav-

Gravel.

Daniel W. Reynolds, Watson, Ill., writes Dr. Fenner:

"For nearly two years my little son Grover, aged 4, suffered from kidney and bladder disease. Finally a gravel was forced into the urethra and remained there producing blood poisoning and dropsical effusion. He was treated by a council of eminent physicians.

They made incisions to let out the water and did all that could be done to help the little sufferer except by a surgical operation, which they very properly advised, but at the same time had to express the opinion that he wasn't likely to survive it.

I refused consent and commenced giving Dr. Fenner's Kidney and Backache Cure. The child managed to survive until about one bottle had been taken, when the stone or gravel had become so far dissolved by it that it passed out of itself, after which he rapidly recovered, and is well and strong to-day. This is regarded as a wonderful cure and shows the power of the medicine in dissolving stone."

Fish and Oysters.
Boiled Fish.

Salmon should be put on to boil in salt water when boiling; also bass and rock fish. To a gallon of water put four tablespoonfuls of salt, and a wineglass of vinegar to give it firmness. To boil other fish; if a common kettle is used, lay the fish on a plate, run a skewer through to hold the head and tail together; wrap all in a napkin and cover with cold water. When done take out by lifting the cloth; serve on a hot platter garnished with lemon parsley, or anything desired.

Codfish Balls.

1 pint of potatoes, peeled; 1 scant pint of fish: picked fine. Boil together. When done, drain off water and beat together well; add butter size of an egg;a little pepper and 1 egg, well beaten. Drop in hot lard and fry.

Creamed Oysters.

1 quart of oysters; 1 cup of cream.

Put the liquor and cream in a sauce pan, bringing to the boiling point. Thicken with 1 tablespoonful of flour and 1 of butter. Put in the oysters and cook until they begin to curl. Add pepper and salt, and turn over toast or into patty cases.

MEATS.
Baked Hamburg Steak.

Take 1 egg, well beaten; mix well with 1 pound fresh Hamburg steak. Add ½ cup of bread crumbs; butter size of a walnut; salt and pepper. Form into a roll 2 inches thick, and bake ½ hour. A tablespoonful of water in the baking dish; baste occasionally. This is enough for four persons, and is fine, either hot or sliced cold for luncheon or tea.

Kidney Disease.

Galesburg, Ia.

Dr. M. M. Fenner, Fredonia, N. Y.

Dear Sir:—A little over two bottles of Dr. Fenner's Kidney and Backache Cure gave me permanent relief from kidney complaint that bothered me for a year or more. It is an excellent remedy and has my indorsement, I can safely recommend it to any one suffering with kidney trouble.   G. F. HECHLER.

It Did Him Good.

Talmage, Ia.

Dr. M. M. Fenner, Fredonia, N. Y.

Dear Sir:—I can say your Kidney and Backache Cure and Cough Honey are two of the leading sellers I have. Mr. J. S. Lucas of this place, after using two bottles of your Kidney and Backache Cure, claims it did him more good than anything he ever used.

A. W. HARDY.

Bladder Trouble.

Kansas City.

Dr. M. M. Fenner, Fredonia, N. Y.

Dear Sir:—Four years ago I found myself practically confined to my bed from a bladder and kidney trouble. My back ached constantly and I could neither stand up nor lie down for any length of time. The doctors told me that the seat of the trouble was my kidneys, but that is the extent of the good they did me, I took medicine until the very word was loathsome to me. I was discouraged, and was about convinced that nothing could cure. It seemed that I had tried everything in existence, but it all had the same result. I got worse, and every day seemed harder to get through than the last. Finally a business friend who dropped in to see me, told me of his case. I also tried Dr. Fenner's Kidney and Backache Cure. Three bottles effected a cure. I was able to attend to my business as usual when I had finished the first bottle. I have not been troubled with either kidney nor bladder complaints since.   S. C. TAYLOR.

1414 Grand Ave.

Severe Backache.

Des Moines, Ia.

Dear Sir:—It is a pleasure for me to state to you that your Kidney and Backache Cure has given me wonderful relief from severe backache trouble, caused by diseased kidneys. My speedy relief and cure has given me confidence in your Remedy. I shall recommend it to my friends, and feel confident that it will do for others what it has done for me.

RICHARD E. DORAN.

More economical then any other. Dr. Fenner's Vanilla Extract.

For delicacy of flavor nothing equals Dr. Fenner's Lemon Extract.

HOROSCOPES

Aquarius

Aries

Despite the fact that ascertaining your destiny through the planets involves a little more difficulty and trouble than by any other means, it is proportionately more accurate and helpful. You must first find out the time of your birth definitely; then by consulting an Almanac for your particular year you will learn what particular planet influences you, what others were in the ascendancy at that time, and the positions of the sun and moon. If the former is just entering your sign, its meaning will bear fully upon you, though its properties are not so strong if it is in the middle or on the wane.

Remember to also take into consideration the day of the week on which you were born as listed elsewhere in this book. If the day be a fortunate one it will strengthen the good portents, but if poor will minimize them.

Then study carefully and thoughtfully the explanation given herewith regarding your planet so that you may have a better understanding of your character, its weakness and strength, and the vicissitudes and pleasures you may expect through life.

JANUARY 21 to FEBRUARY 19
Aquarius—The Water Bearer

This person constantly desires change both in friends and love. He is, therefore, inclined to fickleness and the unhappiness this propensity brings. He loves travel and new sights. A full moon is better for any of his ventures, for a new one only adds to his trepidation. Despite his tendency to "make mountains out of molehills" he will find many real troubles along his path.

Pisces

FEB. 20 to MAR. 20
Pisces—The Fishes

The woman born in this month makes a faithful and affectionate wife and loving, conscientious mother, wise and just in all she does. Her courage and foresight make her successful in the business world, though she never loses her delightful femininity. She never fears peril and her outlook on life is one of courage and optimism. If she is born directly under this sign she is destined not to travel far from home, though if the planet only has an influence, she will find success across the water.

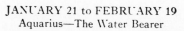

Gemini

MARCH 21 to APRIL 19
Aries—The Ram

Fortunate the person who arrives in this world in the blustering month of March. Whatever sex it matter not—he or she will be successful in all undertakings and will acquire wealth. March gives an amiable temperament, the ability to make many friends, though a tendency to a quick temper should be guarded against. The influences of Jupiter and Venus are beneficial, but if Mars or Saturn have a direct bearing there will be a general alteration in the trend of life.

APRIL 20 to MAY 20
Taurus—The Bull

Patience and perseverance in the face of disappointment and misfortune are needed for April's child. Should Venus, Jupiter or the new moon be in the ascendant, it mitigates their lot. Men born in this month may be hardy and willful, demanding attention and consideration, yet never

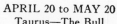

Taurus

AUGUST 23 to SEPTEMBER 23
Virgo— The Virgin

August gives some of the most delightful comrades possible, in both men and women.

Scorpio

NOVEMBER 23 to DECEMBER 21
Sagittarius —The Archer

Love predominates in the lives of those born in this month.

Sagittarius

28

JUNE 22 to JULY 22
Cancer—The Crab

To the blonde people born in June life holds many thrills and adventures and they will reach a position of prominence in the world. While successful, people of dark complexion are not so likely to be contented for they are more subject to vagaries and bad temper, prone to make a fuss over petty bothers.

Leo

JULY 23 to AUGUST 22
Leo—The Lion

The lion is a capricious creature and delights in bringing about sudden and startling changes. A child born in poverty is bound to one day acquire wealth, while the child "born with a silver spoon in his mouth" often ends his days in want. A frail infant finds health in later years, and a robust one is subject to illness in manhood.

SEPTEMBER 24 to OCTOBER 23
Libra—The Scales

September produces the moderate person, temperate in his affections and desires, actuated by no undue passion, living along serenely and happily. You will find him honest and wise, faithful and true, and ever fond of peace.

OCTOBER 24 to NOVEMBER 22
Scorpio—The Scorpion

A woman born under this sign is often extravagant and lazy. She may benefit through the generosity of others, rather than through her own perseverance or industry. She is, however, amiable and pleasant of speech, never dishonest or immoral. The man of October makes an excellent marital mate for he is loyal and affectionate, just in his dealings, successful in business and blessed with a fine mind.

MINE MODER-IN-LAW

BY CHARLES FOLLEN ADAMS

Dhere was many qveer dings, in dis land off
    der free,
    I neffer could qvite undershtand;
Der beoples dhey all seem so deefrent to me
    As dhose in mine own faderland.
Dhey gets blenty droubles, und indo mishaps,
    Mitoudt der least bit off a cause;
Und, vould you pelief id? Dhose mean Yangee
    chaps,
    Dhey fights mid dheir moder-in laws!

Shust dink off a vhite man so vicked as dot!
    Why not gife der oldt lady a show?
Who was id gets oup, vhen der nighdt id vas
    hot,
    Mit mine baby, I shust like to know?
Und dhen in der vinter vhen Katrine vas sick,
    Und der mornings vas shnowy und raw,
Who made righdt away oup dot fire so qvick?
    Vhy, dot vas mine moder-in-law. . . .

Veek oudt und veek in, id vas alvays der same,
    Dot vomans vas boss off der house;
Budt, dhen, neffer mindt! I vas glad dot she
    came,
    She vas kind to mine young Yawcob Strauss.
Und vhen dhere vas vater to get vrom der
    shpring,
    Und fire-vood to shplit oup und saw,
She vas velcome to do it. Dhere's not anyding
    Dot's too goot for mine moder-in-law.

SEQUEL TO "DOT MODER-IN-LAW."

Ve hear off dot Strauss, und hees moder-in-
    law,
    Und how "she" vas boss off der house;
Und dot der oldt shentleman don'd care a
    straw,
    Pecause she vas kindt to young Strauss.
Der reason vas blain, as you'll see potty qvick,
    Vhy she was n't like soom oldt gorilla:
She keeps strong und helty, und neffer vas
    sick,
    For she uses Hood's Sarsaparilla.

A moder-in-law vas a potty goot ding,
    Vhen sickness vas coom in der house,
To vatch mit der sick vones, und qviet to
    pring,
    Vhen der shiltren vas making a touse;

Und vhen mit der baby she gets oup at nighdt,
  Der coldt, frosdy air don'd could chill her;
Und dis vas der reason; her plood vas all
    rightdt
  Py using Hood's Sarsaparilla

Dhere vas many a feller dot radder pe hung
  As to ask soom young girl for hees vife,
Hees girl's fader's boot, und her moder's sharp
    tongue
  Makes him almosd affrait off hees life.

That Tired Feeling

Is occasionally experienced by nearly every one. You feel all tired out, without strength to do anything; ambition seems to be all gone, and you have little or no appetite. This condition may be due to change of season, climate, or life, to overwork, or nervous ailments. Whatever the cause, Hood's Sarsaparilla overcomes it quickly, creates an appetite, rouses the liver, cures headache, and gives renewed strength and vigor to the whole body.

"My wife's health seemed all broken up, and she was under the doctor's care six months, but did not get help. She then began to take Hood's Sarsaparilla and at once began to improve. She is now taking only the second bottle and is able to do her work for six in family. We have recommended it to many others, believing that if they will try it, it will speak for itself." A. J. BROWN, North Manlius, N. Y.

"My wife and myself were both generally run down. Hood's Sarsaparilla brought us out of that tired feeling, and made us feel like young people again. It has done more for us than all other medicines together." RICHARD HAWKHURST, Amityville, Long Island, N. Y.

(14)

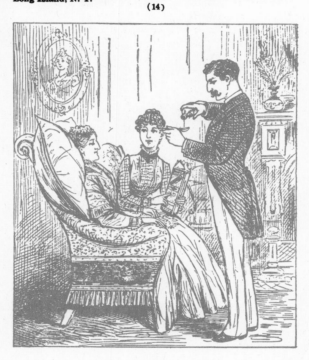

Dhose parents' digestion vas peen outdt off
    tune!
  Und eff he vas anxious to fell a
Varm blace in dheir hearts, he should call
    potty soon
  Mit blendy Hood's Sarsaparilla

TESTIMONIALS IN FAVOR OF WISTAR'S BALSAM OF WILD CHERRY.

From SEYMOUR THACHER, M. D., of Hermon, New York.

"WISTAR'S BALSAM OF WILD CHERRY gives universal satisfaction. It seems to cure a cough by loosening and cleansing the lungs and allaying irritation, *thus removing the cause instead of drying up the Cough and leaving the cause behind.* I consider the Balsam the best Cough medicine with which I am acquainted."

From R FELLOWS, M. D., of Hill, N. H.

"I have made use of this preparation for several years, and it has proved to be very reliable and efficacious in the treatment of severe and long standing Coughs. I know of one patient, now in comfortable health, who has taken this remedy, and who but for its use, I consider would not now be living."

J. F. Lawrence Printing Co., Chicago, Ill.

No. 22042.
1000 $1.25.   500 90c.   250 60c.

No. 22043.   1000 $1.00.
500 75c.   250 50c.

No. 22044.   1000 $1.00.
500 75c.   250 50c.

No. 22045.   1000 $1.00.
500 75c.   250 50c.

No. 22046.
1000 $1.25.   500 90c.   250 60c.

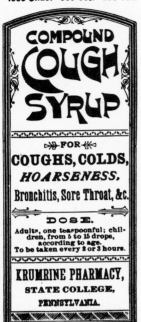

COMPOUND COUGH SYRUP

FOR COUGHS, COLDS, *HOARSENESS,* Bronchitis, Sore Throat, &c.

DOSE.

Adults, one teaspoonful; children, from 5 to 15 drops, according to age. To be taken every 2 or 3 hours.

KRUMRINE PHARMACY,
STATE COLLEGE, PENNSYLVANIA.

Pure GLYCERINE

NEIL CURRIE,
Druggist.
TRACY, MINNESOTA.

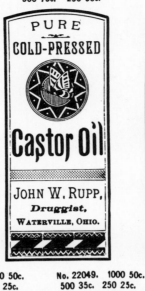

PURE COLD-PRESSED Castor Oil

JOHN W. RUPP,
Druggist,
WATERVILLE, OHIO.

SPIRITS TURPENTINE

H. McCOY & SON,
PHARMACISTS,
SEYMOUR, IOWA.

SUN CHOLERA MIXTURE

(National Formulary.)

A combination of equal parts of the Tinctures of Opium, Capsicum and Rhubarb and Spirits of Camphor and Peppermint.

An exceedingly popular remedy of many years standing for Cholera Morbus, Diarrhœa, Dysentery and *Summer Complaints.*

DOSE.—From 25 to 30 drops in a little sweetened water, repeated every half-hour. It should not be given to children.

GROVER DRUG CO.,
Cor. Illinois and South Sts.,
INDIANAPOLIS,   INDIANA.

No. 22048.   1000 50c.
500 35c.   250 25c.

No. 22049.   1000 50c.
500 35c.   250 25c.

No. 22050.   1000 50c.
500 35c.   250 25c.

TOOTHACHE DROPS.

DIRECTIONS.—Saturate a little cotton. Apply in hollow of tooth.

J. M. McCANN,
Prescription Druggist,
TOLEDO, OHIO.

OIL OF CLOVES

SCRIBNER & ALDWORTH,
PHARMACISTS,
Cor. Monroe and Ottawa Streets,
GRAND RAPIDS, MICH.

CORN CURE

DIRECTIONS.—Apply 4 nights in succession then soak feet in warm water and corn can be removed with finger nail.

DR. HULEATT,
Drugs and Chemicals,
ARKANSAW, WISCONSIN.

No. 22053.   1000 70c.
500 50c.   250 35c.

No. 22047   1000 $2.50.   500 $1.75.   250 $1.25.

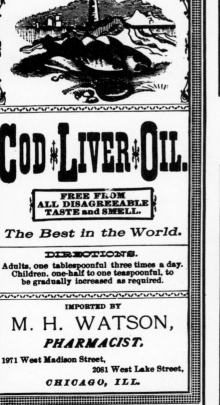

GENUINE EMULSION

COD LIVER OIL.

FREE FROM ALL DISAGREEABLE TASTE and SMELL.

The Best in the World.

DIRECTIONS.

Adults, one tablespoonful three times a day. Children, one-half to one teaspoonful, to be gradually increased as required.

IMPORTED BY

M. H. WATSON,
PHARMACIST,

1971 West Madison Street,
2081 West Lake Street,
CHICAGO, ILL.

No. 22051.   1000 50c.
500 35c.   250 25c.

TRIPLE EXTRACT
White Rose.

GEO. W. DIXON,
Druggist,
AUBURN,   ALABAMA.

No. 22052.   1000 $1.25.   500 90c.   250 60c.

A valuable remedy for Scalds, Burns, Chapped or Rough Skin, and in all cases where a Salve, Ointment or Embrocation is needed.

PETROLEUM JELLY.

(PETROLATUM, U. S. P.)

DRS. THOMAS & CHILDS,
Physicians and Surgeons,
ARGENTA,   -   -   ILLINOIS.

SWEET SPIRITS —OF— NITRE

DOSE.

A teaspoonful every two or three hours taken in a little cold water. For children in proportion to age.

E. DIKEMAN,
Pharmacist,
GOSHEN, NEW YORK.

No. 22054.   1000 $1.00.
500 75c.   250 50c.

No. 22055.   1000 $2.00.   500 $1.50.   250 $1.00.

PURE CONCENTRATED EXTRACT OF VANILLA

For Flavoring ICE CREAM, CUSTARDS, JELLIES, PASTRY, Etc.

SAYLE & ASHBY,
Druggists,
501 Main Street, cor. 5th,
LITTLE ROCK, ARK.

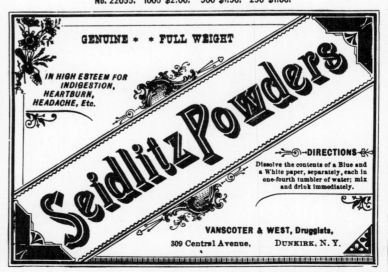

GENUINE ** FULL WEIGHT

IN HIGH ESTEEM FOR INDIGESTION, HEARTBURN, HEADACHE, Etc.

Seidlitz Powders

DIRECTIONS

Dissolve the contents of a Blue and a White paper, separately, each in one-fourth tumbler of water; mix and drink immediately.

VANSCOTER & WEST, Druggists,
309 Central Avenue,   DUNKIRK, N. Y.

Labels
of
Old Patent
Medicines

*Since there were hundreds of
different manufacturers of patent medicines down through the generations,
and since each concocted dozens of different formulas,
both liquid and solid, the resultant labels have
become collector's items of considerable value.
The texts and illustrations in many cases stir nostalgic memories of childhood.
In addition to the labels, the companies producing the patent medicines
usually manufactured small boxes of varying
sizes for pills, powders and other non-liquids.
These, too, are part of the lore.*

1178

OUR SEAL BRAND HOUSEHOLD
AMMONIA
FOR FAMILY USE.

AMMONIA GIVES A SNOWY WHITENESS TO PLAIN GOODS, BUT DOES NOT INJURE
FASTEST DYED FABRICS. IT SAVES HALF THE SOAP...
TIME...

AMMONIA WILL PRODUCE A MOST LUXURIANT AND HEALTHY GROWTH
IN PLANTS AND FLOWERS, WHEN USED BY PUTTING A FEW DROPS TWICE
A WEEK IN THE WATER PUT ON THEM.

Directions

FOR THE LAUNDRY, pour one tablespoonful into a pail or three
gallons of water...
FOR GLASS...
BRUSHES AND COMBS...
FOR THE TOILET...

GUARANTEED AND PREPARED BY

THE VANGUARD PHARMACY

ROCK CREEK ROAD   NIGHT SERVICE
& GEORGIA AVE., N.W.   "RING THE BELL"
WASHINGTON, D.C.

CAREFULLY SELECTED
Superior Bay Rum
BOTTLED BY
Arthur D. Jones,
Pharmacist,
McDonough,   Georgia.

LABELS
FOR SPECIAL
PURPOSES
WILL BE SENT
UPON
REQUEST.

1176

EXTRACT
WITCH HAZEL
THE GREAT REMEDY
FOR
RHEUMATISM, BURNS, SCALDS, SORES, PILES,
CHILBLAINS, NEURALGIA, BITES OF INSECTS &c.

*Bathe the afflicted parts freely with the Extract,
to be diluted in cases of Ulcers and Sores Taken
internally the dose ranges from 10 to 30 drops.*

Standard Drug Co.
W. R. CHRISTOPHE DRUGGIST
Front Street.   NEWPORT, ARK.

SPANISH OIL Liniment

....FOR....

*Cuts, Bruises, Burns,
Bites, Stings,*
RHEUMATISM, NEURALGIA,
Headache, Backache,
Sore Throat, Sprains, etc.

DIRECTIONS.
Apply freely and rub well.

MADE BY
ROBBINS
N. LITTLE ROCK, ARK.

1202

Beef
WINE AND IRON

This combination is considered one of the most
energetic blood makers and vital restoratives and
the most certain means of invigoration in exhaustive
diseases, loss of blood or debility.

A tablespoonful for adults and one tea to a dessert-
spoonful for young persons three or four times a day.

PREPARED BY

Georgetown Drug Co.,
DRUGGISTS
GEORGETOWN, S.C.

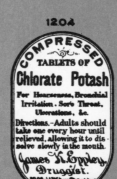

COMPRESSED TABLETS
OF
SODA MINT
FOR DYSPEPSIA, INDIGESTION, FLATULENCE,
SOUR STOMACH AND NAUSEA
Allow one or two to dissolve slowly
in mouth, repeat if necessary

WM. McCORKLE,
PHARMACIST.
S.W. cor 12th & Somerset Sts.
PHILA.

1204

COMPRESSED
TABLETS OF
Chlorate Potash
For Hoarseness, Bronchial
Irritation, Sore Throat,
Ulcerations, &c.
Directions.—Adults should
take one every hour until
relieved, allowing it to dis-
solve slowly in the mouth.
James K. Eppley,
Druggist,

1206

COMPRESSED
TABLETS
OF
PEPSIN
AND
SODA MINT
FOR
DYSPEPSIA, INDIGESTION
FLATULENCE, SOUR STOMACH
AND NAUSEA
Let one or two dissolve slowly
in the mouth, repeat if necessary
THE SUN
LOS ANGELES,
CAL.

.Jasteless.
Castor Oil.

Pleasant to Take.
Children Like It.

DIRECTIONS
DOSE. For children from one to two teaspoonfuls. Adults, one to two tablespoonfuls.

PREPARED BY
ANDREW HECK,
Apothecary,
Patterson Park Ave.
BALTIMORE.

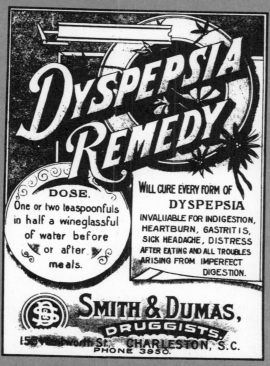

Dyspepsia Remedy

DOSE.
One or two teaspoonfuls in half a wineglassful of water before or after meals.

Will cure every form of
DYSPEPSIA
INVALUABLE FOR INDIGESTION, HEARTBURN, GASTRITIS, SICK HEADACHE, DISTRESS AFTER EATING AND ALL TROUBLES ARISING FROM IMPERFECT DIGESTION.

SMITH & DUMAS,
DRUGGISTS.
15 Wadworth St. CHARLESTON, S.C.
PHONE 3850.

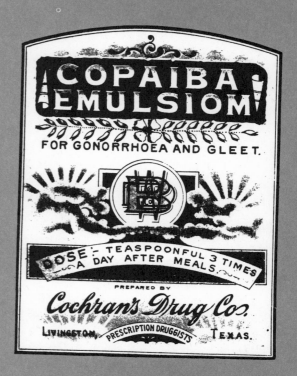

COPAIBA EMULSION

FOR GONORRHOEA AND GLEET.

DOSE :- TEASPOONFUL 3 TIMES A DAY AFTER MEALS.

PREPARED BY
Cochran's Drug Co.
LIVINGSTON, PRESCRIPTION DRUGGISTS, TEXAS.

1242   1000 $3.50.   2000 $2.50.   3000 $2.00
4000 $1.80. – 5000 $1.60.   10,000 $1.10 per M

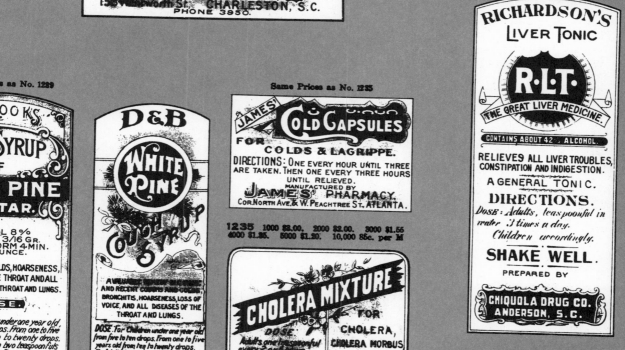

Same Prices as No. 1239

BROOKS
COMP. SYRUP OF
WHITE PINE AND TAR.

ALCOHOL 8%
MORPHIA 3/16 GR.
CHLOROFORM 4 MIN.
PER OUNCE.

FOR COUGHS, COLDS, HOARSENESS, BRONCHITIS, SORE THROAT AND ALL DISEASES OF THE THROAT AND LUNGS.

DOSE.

For children under one year old from five to ten drops. From one to five years old, from ten to twenty drops. For adults, from one to two teaspoonfuls every 2 or 3 hours, or as often as necessary.

PREPARED AT
COLLEY
PHARMACIES,
3 STORES,
WILKES-BARRE, PA.

D & B
WHITE PINE
Cough Syrup

A valuable remedy for recent coughs and colds, bronchitis, hoarseness, loss of voice, and all diseases of the throat and lungs.

DOSE. For children under one year old from five to ten drops. From one to five years old and from ten to twenty drops. For Adults from one to two teaspoonfuls every two or three hours or as often as necessary.

Douglas & Breeden
DRUGGISTS
BENNETTSVILLE, S.C.

Same Prices as No. 1235

JAMES' COLD CAPSULES
FOR
COLDS & LAGRIPPE.
DIRECTIONS: ONE EVERY HOUR UNTIL THREE ARE TAKEN. THEN ONE EVERY THREE HOURS UNTIL RELIEVED.
MANUFACTURED BY
JAMES' PHARMACY.
COR. NORTH AVE. & W. PEACHTREE ST. ATLANTA.

1235   1000 $3.00.   2000 $2.00.   3000 $1.55
4000 $1.35.   5000 $1.20.   10,000 85c. per M

CHOLERA MIXTURE
DOSE.
Adults one teaspoonful every 2 or 3 hours. Children 5 to 20 drops according to age. To be taken in a little sweetened water.

FOR
CHOLERA,
CHOLERA MORBUS
DIARRHŒA,
DYSENTERY,
ETC.

HOOKS' PHARMACY
PHONE 75.
S.W. COR. JACKSON & LAMAR STS. AMERICUS, GA.

RICHARDSON'S LIVER TONIC
R·L·T·
THE GREAT LIVER MEDICINE.

CONTAINS ABOUT 42% ALCOHOL.

RELIEVES ALL LIVER TROUBLES, CONSTIPATION AND INDIGESTION.
A GENERAL TONIC.

DIRECTIONS.
DOSE: Adults, teaspoonful in water 3 times a day. Children accordingly.

SHAKE WELL.

PREPARED BY
CHIQUOLA DRUG CO.
ANDERSON, S.C.

No. 24011.   1000 50c.   500 35c.   250 25c.

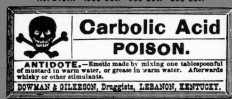

Carbolic Acid
POISON.

ANTIDOTE.—Emetic made by mixing one tablespoonful of mustard in warm water, or grease in warm water. Afterwards whisky or other stimulants.

BOWMAN & GILKESON, Druggists, LEBANON, KENTUCKY.

4000 $2.10.   5000 $1.90.   10,000 $1.30 per M

ECKELS'
BLOOD TONIC

FOR

ALL IMPURITIES OF THE BLOOD

DIRECTIONS

TEASPOONFUL IN WATER THREE TIMES A DAY, AFTER MEALS, GRADUALLY INCREASE TO TABLESPOONFUL

Eckels' Pharmacy
"THE REXALL STORE"
CROWLEY, LA.
THANKS FOR YOUR CONFIDENCE.

GUARANTEED BY ECKELS' PHARMACY UNDER THE FOOD AND DRUGS ACT, JUNE 30 1906. SERIAL NO. 45193.

4000 $2.50.   5000 $2.25.   10,000 $1.50 per M   4000 $1.50.   5000 $1.30.   10,000 90c. per M

YERKES
WHITE LINIMENT
WITH
CHLOROFORM.

MAXIMUM ALCOHOL 5%
CHLOROFORM 5%.

FOR MAN OR BEAST.

AS AN EXTERNAL REMEDY FOR RHEUMATISM, SPRAINS, BRUISES, STIFF JOINTS, SWELLINGS, SORENESS, ACHES AND PAINS OF ALL KINDS.

DIRECTIONS:

RUB PARTS AFFECTED WITH THE LINIMENT FREQUENTLY FOR SEVERAL MINUTES.

GUARANTEED UNDER THE FOOD AND DRUGS ACT. JUNE 30TH 1906. SERIAL No. 2558.

PREPARED BY

VAUGHN-CRUTCHFIELD Co.
WHOLESALE & MANUFACTURING DRUGGISTS.
WINSTON-SALEM, N.C.

NERVE
AND
BONE
LINIMENT

FOR
ACHES, PAINS, BRUISES, CUTS, WOUNDS, SORES & FOR OPEN WOUNDS APPLY FREELY.
WHEN THERE IS PAIN AND NO WOUND RUB WELL AND LONG.

SHAKE BEFORE USING.

KIRK'S
PHONE 96.
NAVASOTA, TEX.

1213   1000 $3.25.   2000 $2.30.   8000 $1.7
4000 $1.50.   5000 $1.30.   10,000 90c. per M

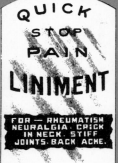

QUICK
STOP
PAIN
LINIMENT

FOR — RHEUMATISM NEURALGIA, CRICK IN NECK, STIFF JOINTS, BACK ACHE.

APPLY FREELY AND RUB WELL IN.
IT IS TOO STRONG FOR OPEN CUTS.
FOR TOOTH-ACHE AND EARACHE APPLY ON SMALL PIECE OF WARM COTTON.
FOR COLIC ADULT DOSE ½ TEA-SPOONFUL IN WATER.
FOR COLIC IN HORSES GIVE TWO TABLESPOONFULS IN WATER.
AFTER APPLYING FOR RHEUMA-TISM, WORK JOINTS AND MUS-CLES TILL TIRED NIGHT AND MORNING.

PREPARED BY

EHRLICH & COOPER,
DRUGGISTS.
BAINBRIDGE.   GA.

1211   1000 $4.00.   2000 $2.80.   8000 $2.50
4000 $2.10.   5000 $1.90.   10,000 $1.80 per M

F. X. WOLF
DRUGGIST
343 S. SIXTH ST. READING, PA.

PRICE 50¢

WOLF'S
ANTI
RHEUMATISM

ALCOHOL ABOUT 36%.

A MOST WONDERFUL REMEDY FOR RHEUMATISM.
SURE, QUICK AND SAFE.

DOSE-FOR AN ADULT ONE TEASPOONFUL 3 TIMES A DAY BEFORE MEALS.
NO SUGAR AND WATER.

GUARANTEED UNDER THE FOOD AND DRUGS ACT JUNE 30, 1906. SERIAL No 13331.

CONCENTRATED EXTRACT

WITCH HAZEL

OR HAMAMELIS

FOR THE RELIEF OF SPRAINS, BRUISES BITES OF INSECTS, BURNS, SCALDS WOUNDS, PAINFUL SWELLINGS, LAME BACK, PILES, SORE THROAT, NEURALGIA, RHEUMATISM, CHILBLAINS, ETC.

DIRECTIONS: For all external inflammation, bathe freely with the Extract and if convenient apply a cloth wet with the Extract and keep it moist till Relieved.
For open Wounds, Ulcers, old Sores, sore Nipples, sore Eyes &c. dilute one half with pure water and use in the same way.
TAKEN INTERNALLY DOSE 10 TO 30 DROPS 4 TIMES PER DAY.

PREPARED BY

City Drug Store
125 Chadbourne St.
SAN ANGELO, TEXAS.

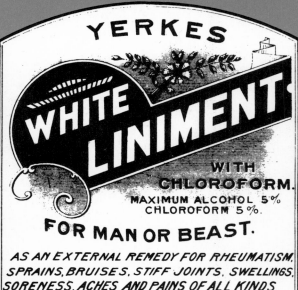

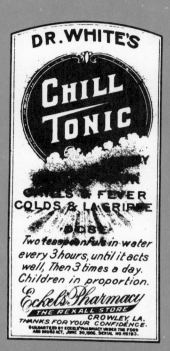

DR. WHITE'S
CHILL TONIC

CURES FEVER
COLDS & LA GRIPPE

DOSE

Two teaspoonfuls in water every 3 hours, until it acts well, Then 3 times a day. Children in proportion.

Eckels' Pharmacy
THE REXALL STORE
CROWLEY, LA.
THANKS FOR YOUR CONFIDENCE.
GUARANTEED BY ECKELS' PHARMACY UNDER THE FOOD AND DRUGS ACT, JUNE 30, 1906. SERIAL NO. 95193.

1247 1000 $2.50. 2000 $2.50 3000 $3.00

EFFERVESCING Solution

Citrate of Magnesia

IT A SUBSTITUTE FOR SALTS
IT A SUBSTITUTE OF BITTERNESS AND BY ITS PLEASANT ACIDITY OF TASTE AND ITS EFFERVESCING CHARACTER, IS RENDERED A VERY AGREEABLE AND REFRESHING DRINK.

DIRECTIONS:
AS A COOLING AND LAXATIVE MEDICINE FROM A TABLESPOONFUL TO A WINEGLASSFUL EVERY HOUR OR TWO UNTIL THE DESIRED EFFECT IS PRODUCED. AS A CATHARTIC AN ADULT MAY TAKE THE CONTENTS OF ONE BOTTLE HALF OF IT AT FIRST AND THE REMAINDER IN ONE OR TWO HOURS. THE BOTTLE SHOULD BE KEPT CORKED IN THE INTERVALS OF TAKING THE MEDICINE A GLASS OF COLD WATER INCREASES ITS ACTIVITY AS A PURGE.

✚ BRADFORD & MEADOWS.
DRUGGISTS
1240 BROAD ST. COLUMBUS, GA.

4000 $2.50. 5000 $2.80. 10,000 $1.90 per M

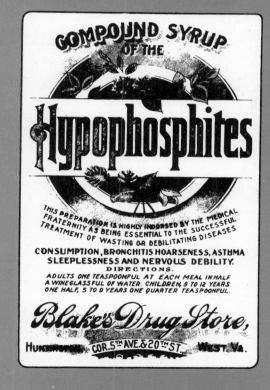

GOMPOUND SYRUP
OF THE

Hypophosphites

THIS PREPARATION IS HIGHLY INDORSED BY THE MEDICAL FRATERNITY AS BEING ESSENTIAL TO THE SUCCESSFUL TREATMENT OF WASTING OR DEBILITATING DISEASES

CONSUMPTION, BRONCHITIS HOARSENESS, ASTHMA SLEEPLESSNESS AND NERVOUS DEBILITY.

DIRECTIONS.
ADULTS ONE TEASPOONFUL AT EACH MEAL IN HALF A WINEGLASSFUL OF WATER. CHILDREN, 9 TO 12 YEARS ONE HALF, 5 TO 9 YEARS ONE QUARTER TEASPOONFUL.

Blake's Drug Store,
HUNTINGTON, COR. 5TH AVE. & 20TH ST. WEST. VA.

CONCENTRATED
ESSENCE
JAMAICA GINGER
—FOR—

Dyspepsia, Cholera Morbus, Flatulent Colic, Enfeebled State of Alimentary Canal, Nausea, &c.

◆—DOSE—◆

For an adult, from one-half to one teaspoonful; for a child of one year, one to three drops; of three years, five to eight drops; of ten years, fifteen to twenty-five drops. This essence must always be taken in a little water.

PREPARED BY

I. J. RIGELHAUPT & CO.,
THE STAR DRUG STORE,
1164 Clark Ave., Cor. Iona Street,
CLEVELAND, OHIO.

1203

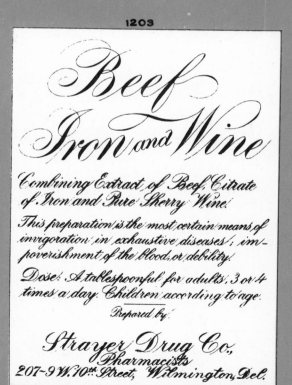

Beef
Iron and Wine

Combining Extract of Beef, Citrate of Iron and Pure Sherry Wine.

This preparation is the most certain means of invigoration in exhaustive diseases; impoverishment of the blood, or debility.

Dose: A tablespoonful for adults, 3 or 4 times a day. Children according to age.

Prepared by:

Strayer Drug Co.,
Pharmacists
207–9 W. 10th Street, Wilmington, Del.

No. 24010. 1000 30c. 500 35c. 250 25c.

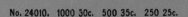

PAREGORIC.

ORDINARY DOSE.

2 days old, -	2 drops.	2 years old, -	12 drops.
1 week old, -	6 drops.	10 years old, ½ teaspoonful.	
1 year old, -	10 drops.	Adults, -	1 teaspoonful.

C. H. DUSTIN, Prescription Druggist,
Cor. Central Avenue and Kennard St., CLEVELAND, OHIO.

A—550

DR. SHAWL'S
>>⊃≡⊂<<
GREAT REMEDY
Cures Dyspepsia, Sick Headache, Constipation, etc.

DIRECTIONS FOR TAKING
PEPTONIC
Shake the Bottle before using

ADULT DOSE.—One teaspoonful in half a glass of water after each meal.

CHILDREN—Same in proportion. Should the bowels not keep regular, take a teaspoonful of Epsom Salts or Phosphate of Soda in half glass of water before breakfast.

Stick to the remedy and note the result.

THE DR. SHAW REMEDY COMPANY.
DETROIT, MICH.

Sears Roebuck Drug Catalog

Occasionally, Sears Roebuck would take one section of its large catalog
and reprint it and send it along to its customers.
Whenever a special reprint of this kind was distributed, it was certain that the particular
department concerned was a successful one.
Such was the case with this Special Catalog of Drugs, issued in June, 1906 and
containing not only medication for man but also for beast.
If you look through the items listed,
you might be surprised at how many are still being sold today.

On page 836, for example, there are
advertisements for both Dr. Fletcher's Castoria and for Murine,
although the prices are slightly higher today than they were in 1906.
This is a very rare catalog
since seldom were such sections preserved by the persons
who received them. They kept the
large catalog to use as reading matter, if need be,
but hardly ever the small, unimportant parts.

DR. FLETCHER'S CASTORIA

**THE GENUINE WELL KNOWN CASTORIA.
THE KIND YOU HAVE ALWAYS BOUGHT.**

Each Bottle Contains Nine Hundred Drops of Castoria. Each Bottle Bears the Facsimile Signature of Dr. Charles H. Fletcher. The Best known Remedy for all Stomach and Bowel Complaints of Infants and Children.

PROMOTES DIGESTION, CHEERFULNESS AND REST. ABSOLUTELY FREE FROM ANY POISONOUS MINERAL OR NARCOTIC. EVERY PACKAGE CONTAINS THE RECIPE OF THE OLD DR. SAMUEL PITCHER.

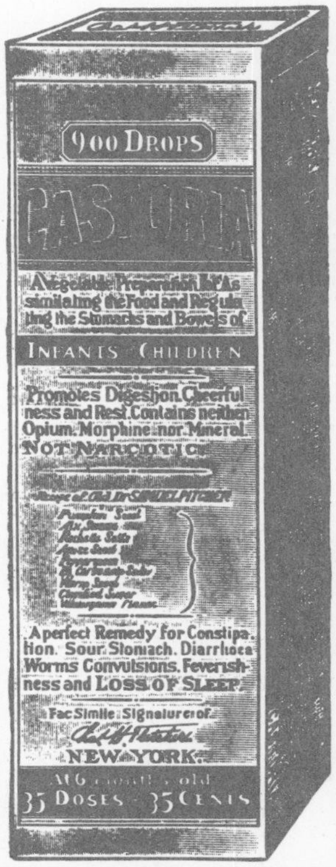

CASTORIA is truly a wonderful medicine for children. Doctors prescribe it, medical journals recommend it, and more than a million mothers are using it in place of paregoric, Bateman's Drops, so called soothing syrups and other narcotic and stupefying remedies. Castoria is the quickest thing to regulate the stomach and bowels the world has ever seen. It is guaranteed to be perfectly harmless.

MORTALITY. Nearly every married couple have children, and every infant and child is sick more or less during the first and second years. Infant mortality is something frightful, and we can hardly realize that 22 per cent, or nearly one-fourth, of all born die from stomach and bowel troubles before the age of one year. This being true, it is very essential that their young bodies be closely watched and irregularities quickly corrected. If now one remedy was to be selected which would cure all these ills, but one name would be on every tongue—Castoria, Castoria; nothing but Castoria. The best physicians of today prescribe it, recommend it, and even go so far as to state that if a child's stomach and bowels were kept in perfect condition with some harmless remedy like Castoria, that infants and children would be free from nearly all their more serious ills. Castoria is the one remedy that meets all the requirements of children; it is the one medicine that is known the world over as The Mother's Blessing and the Baby's Friend.

OUR PRICE, ONLY
26c
Regular Price, 35c.

CHILDREN CRY FOR IT. Children cry for Castoria because they like it. No trouble to give; is beneficial and makes the child healthy and cheerful. We do not hesitate in saying that Castoria has done more for suffering children than all other remedies combined. The least irregularity in the food of the nursing mother upsets the stomach and bowels of the child, then comes indigestion, sour stomach, wind colic, constipation, loss of sleep, etc. The child becomes cross and feverish, and sickness follows. Every mother then thinks of but one remedy—Castoria; only Castoria. The popularity of this wonderful remedy has so increased until it now stands alone among druggists and physicians as the only reliable and harmless regulator of children's complaints. It is being used more and more every week, until the sales of this beneficial remedy double every three years. This proves but one thing—Castoria is very beneficial, is harmless and does the work. It is truly a Mother's Blessing, a Baby's Friend and a Father's Comfort. Every mother has the satisfaction when giving Castoria to know that she is giving her children a purely vegetable remedy, the formula of which is placed upon every package. Castoria is pleasant to take, children cry for it, and is very effective in results.

THIS GENUINE CASTORIA has been upon the market for over thirty years, is known in every household, and when once used would never be without it. It takes the place of castor oil and all other forms of narcotic remedies; is a thousand times more pleasant to take and just as effective in results. Castoria may be given to anyone and at any time. It is superior in its effects to any other castoria or quieter. It is free from danger of narcotic properties. Castoria is without doubt the best remedy for children and infants the world has ever known. In it mothers have something absolutely safe, pleasant to give, effective in results and perfectly satisfactory in every respect. Castoria assimilates the food, regulates the stomach and bowels and produces perfect and natural sleep. With this valuable medicine on hand much sickness may be avoided, the child kept cheerful and robust and the parents obtain their needful sleep.

DR. FLETCHER'S CASTORIA being the world's medicine for children, it is grossly imitated and adulterated. The patents on this article having expired, many castorias have naturally been offered upon the market. If you want the genuine article, the highly advertised, world recommended, long tried Castoria, Fletcher's is what you desire. All castorias offered under the name of Pitcher's Castoria are imitations of this product and, naturally, are sold at cheaper prices. If you want the genuine, don't allow anyone to sell you anything else on the plea that it is just as good. If you wish the genuine, you want Dr. Charles H. Fletcher's Castoria. Dr. Fletcher's Castoria is sold for 35 cents per bottle, but now consider our exceptionally low price of 26 cents upon this genuine article. Order now and obtain a supply. It should be in every home.

No. 8F347 Regular price, per bottle, 35 cents; our price, 3 bottles for **75c**; each. **26c**
Unmailable on account of weight.

PITCHER'S CASTORIA

(The Old Reliable Brand)

AN IDEAL REMEDY FOR INFANTS AND CHILDREN

PROMOTES DIGESTION, CHEERFULNESS AND REST.

FREE FROM HARMFUL SUBSTANCES.

THIS CASTORIA is made from the same formula as the genuine Fletcher's Castoria. It has been upon the market for many years and enjoys a tremendous sale. We do not claim this to be the genuine Fletcher's Castoria (see No. 8F347), but we do know that it has been used by thousands of persons who, appreciating the difference in price and accepting the guarantee of the manufacturers, ordered this article and getting excellent results from it, continue its use.

PITCHER'S CASTORIA is sold and guaranteed by the manufacturers to be equally pleasant in taste, effective in results and as satisfactory to the customer as any castoria ever manufactured. Fletcher's Castoria is a patented medicine, and the patent upon this product having expired, many manufacturers have put out castorias made after the general formula of Dr. Pitcher. Some of the products are made cheap and others very good, but all of them sold under the general name of Pitcher's. We handle under the name of Pitcher's only the old reliable brand, which has been upon the market now many years and given very good satisfaction.

OUR PRICE, ONLY
18c
Regular Price, 25c.

WHAT IT IS.

DR. PITCHER'S CASTORIA is composed of the medicinal properties of Pumpkin Seed, Alex. Senna, Rochelle Salts, Anise Seed, Peppermint, Bicarbonate of Soda, Worm Seed, Clarified Sugar and Wintergreen. A pure vegetable preparation for assimilating the food and regulating the stomach and bowels of infants. Promotes digestion, cheerfulness and rest. Has neither opium, morphine or any form of narcotic. A perfect remedy for constipation, sour stomach, diarrhea, worms, convulsions, feverishness and loss of sleep.

A FEW FACTS FOR MOTHERS.

No medicine should be given to children without knowing what you are giving. Castoria is purely vegetable, and the ingredients are given upon every package.

CASTORIA IS HARMLESS, is the standard prescription of Dr. Pitcher, and has been in constant use by thousands of mothers for many years.

CASTORIA KEEPS INDEFINITELY, and knows no danger of spoiling by age. The last drop is just as effective as the first one taken from the bottle.

DR. PITCHER'S CASTORIA is usually sold for 25 cents per bottle, but note our exceptionally low price of 18 cents.

MANY CHEAP IMITATIONS of this product are sold as low as 9 cents to 15 cents, but in no case will you find the old reliable brand of Dr. Pitcher's Castoria ever sold for as low as 18 cents. We have only been able to obtain this price by buying and selling this product in tremendous quantities, and we are therefore pleased to offer our customers this exceptionally low and never before heard of price of 18 cents. Order now and obtain a supply.

No. 8F345 Regular price, per bottle, 25 cents; our price, 3 bottles for **50c**; each, **18c**
Unmailable on account of weight.

OUR DRUG DEPARTMENT is conducted differently from all other drug stores. We handle only remedies that are standard and we sell them at a reasonable price.

Murine Eye Remedy.

A Safe and Positive Cure for Eye Troubles; Reliable, Efficient and Absolutely Harmless.

Murine positively and thoroughly cures Pink Eye, Redness, Itching, Smarting, Burning, Watering, Dryness, Mattering, Irritation, Inflammation, Granulation, Blurring and Cloudiness of the Eyes; sties, cysts, ulcers, pimples, and scales on the eyelids, restores eyelashes, makes weak eyes strong, dull eyes bright, does not smart, soothes eye pain. A favorite toilet accessory. Quickly removes redness and swelling of the eyes caused by weeping, or the excessive use of tobacco and stimulants. Endorsed by the medical and optical men everywhere; 48-page booklet on eye troubles free with each package. Regular price, 50 cents.

No. 8F350 Our price........**40c**
If by mail, postage extra, 10 cents.

Murine Eye Salve.

Promotes growth and prevents loss of eyelashes. A remedy for diseased eyelids. Promptly allays inflammation (redness) and irritation of the eyes and eyelids. Removes scales from eyelids, cures and prevents sties, cysts and ulcers. It is a soothing application to eyes that smart and feel dry. Regular price, $1.00.

No. 8F351 Our price........**83c**
If by mail, postage extra, 10 cents.

Granuline.

For old and chronic cases of sore eyes, granulated lids, spots, scums, and opacities on the eyes; old and stubborn cases which have resisted the ordinary methods of treatment and where most positive action is desired. Granuline is a tonic, antiseptic and astringent. It is a valuable collateral remedy to Murine. "Two drops" in the above conditions. Regular price, $1.50.

No. 8F353 Our price.....**$1.30**
If by mail, postage extra, 10 cents.

Banene.

Stimulates the circulation of the blood supply which nourishes the eye. An internal treatment for cloudiness or dimness of vision, floating or stationary spots or webs before the eye, poor circulation in the eyes, retinal and optic nerve diseases, affections of the choroid, sluggish action of the pupil, hemorrhage in the eyes and weakness of the ocular muscles. For lessening of the acuteness of vision from age or disease, inability to wear glasses with comfort, Banene and Murine have no equals. Murine and Banene should be in the hands of every individual who wears glasses, and Banene should be used at the first indication of discomfort. Regular price, $1.25.

No. 8F352 Our price....**$1.10**
If by mail, postage extra, 10 cents.

IF YOU BUY FROM US, WE WILL SEND YOU A FREE PROFIT SHARING CERTIFICATE.
SEE PAGES 1 AND 2

ORANGEINE.

A harmless combination of Podophyllin, Blue Flag, Sodium Bicarbonate, Acetanilid, Nux Vomica and Caffeine, carefully balanced by years of human test and guaranteed by manufacturers not to leave any injurious effect.

Highly advertised and recommended by manufacturers for curing headache, neuralgia, colds, biliousness, rose cold and hay fever. Relieves from fatigue, nourishes and regulates the brain, nerves and stomach.

Full directions with each package.

No. 8F354 Regular 25-cent size; our price..........**19c**
No. 8F355 Regular 50-cent size; our price..........**38c**

ORANGE WINE STOMACH BITTERS.

Retail price, $1.00; our price, each.................................60c

GUARANTEED ABSOLUTELY PURE, AND THE HIGHEST GRADE ON THE MARKET.

DO NOT COMPARE our Orange Wine Stomach Bitters with the bitters that are being sold generally at $1.00 to $1.50 a bottle, bitters that are made from the very cheapest ingredients. Our Orange Wine Stomach Bitters are made from the following ingredients, well known for their tonic and healing effect upon the stomach.

ORANGE WINE STOMACH BITTERS contains the following ingredients in correct proportions: Orange peel (bitter), gentian, ginger, cardamom, cinnamon, caraway, aromatic spirits ammonia, wine q. s.

THIS IS A PLEASANT BITTERS.

OUR PRICE, ONLY
60c
Regular Retail Price, $1.00

Is unsurpassed as an appetizer and it is a recognized cure for dyspepsia when its use is continued for some time. As a general bracer up of the whole system there is none superior, and the taste is so pleasant that the most fastidious enjoy taking it. Owing to the intrinsic and widely established therapeutic value of its chief constituents, which are helpful to good digestion, this preparation furnishes admirable means for treating gastric ailments, indigestion, want of appetite, malarial diseases, low spirits, and nervousness; it removes that tired feeling. It exerts a most wonderful power in sustaining the system during arduous labors and journeys. It is an agreeable and wholesome stimulant, and imparts a pleasant taste with an agreeable sense of warmth which permeates the entire system.

No. 8F105   Price, per bottle.........$0.60
    3 bottles for.................................. 1.70
Unmailable on account of weight.

THE GENUINE GERMAN HERB LAXATIVE TEA.

Retail price, 25 cents; our price, per box.........................12c

A HARMLESS VEGETABLE REMEDY and a successful treatment for constipation, with no bad after effects. It is composed of herbs and roots familiar to the peasants of Germany, especially those who nurse the sick. Through irregular living, poorly cooked food, improper habits of eating, nearly all persons are suffering more or less from **constipation** and the resultant sick headaches; although there may be a daily movement of the bowels, there is still much fecal matter adhering to the intestines and poisoning the blood. Our Herb Tea, made of the simple, harmless herbs, will, when taken regularly for a short time, **thoroughly cleanse the stomach and bowels of all unclean matter.** The blood becomes purified and the person greatly improved in health.

HERB LAXATIVE TEA contains in correct proportions: **American saffron, elder flowers, senna leaves, fennel seed, licorice root, anise seed, dog grass.**

No. 8F107   Price, 3 boxes for 33c; per box........12c
If by mail, postage extra, per box, 7 cents.

BLACKBERRY BALSAM.

Retail price, 50 cents; our price, each.........................20c

A RELIABLE, necessary and highly beneficial family remedy. Very agreeable to the taste, and may be given to both adults and children.

BLACKBERRY BALSAM contains in correct proportions the following: Rhubarb, pancreatin, golden seal, Jamaica ginger, cassia, potassium bicarbonate, catechu, balmony, oil peppermint, blackberry root.

OUR PRICE, ONLY
20c
Regular Retail Price, 25 cents.

IT WILL PREVENT SERIOUS ILLNESS if used promptly and often be the means of saving life. It is a pleasant, safe, speedy and effectual remedy for dysentery, diarrhea, looseness, cholera morbus, cholera infantum, summer complaint, colic, cramps, griping pains, sour stomach, sick and nervous headache, pain or sickness of the stomach, vomiting, restlessness and inability to sleep, wind in the stomach and bowels, and for all bowel affections. We have received thousands of statements from families bearing the strongest testimony in its favor.

Our Blackberry Balsam is indeed a household remedy and should be in every home. Taken at the very beginning it will save a great amount of pain and check what might become a serious ailment.

No. 8F108   Price, 3 bottles for 50c; per bottle.........20c
If by mail, postage and tube extra, 16 cents.

PURE BLACKBERRY BRANDY.

AN EXCEPTIONALLY fine and absolutely Pure Blackberry Brandy, made from the ripe blackberry, fine dark red color, heavy body, and guaranteed to be nothing but the juice of the pure large blackberry. Held by every pure food law as absolutely pure. Many grades of Blackberry Brandy are not pure, but our product is guaranteed. Used and prescribed by the best physicians as one of the simplest and most effective remedies for all derangements of the stomach and bowels. Does not constipate. Fine in taste, agreeable and tones up and invigorates the system.

No. 8F117   Price, per pint bottle.........................$0.28
No. 8F118   Price, per case of 1 dozen pints...............2.85
No. 8F119   Price, per quart bottle.......................... .48
No. 8F120   Price, per dozen quarts 5.00
Unmailable on account of weight.

DR. ROSS' KIDNEY AND BLADDER CURE.

Retail price.....................................$1.00
Our price, each........................$0.58
Our price, 3 bottles for............. 1.60

IF YOUR KIDNEYS ARE WEAK AND INACTIVE, if there is any bladder trouble noticeable in your case, we can recommend Dr. Ross' Kidney and Bladder remedy as a very effective preparation; one that will give prompt relief in most disorders of the kidneys and bladder.

OUR PRICE, ONLY
58c
Regular Retail Price, $1.00

DR. ROSS' KIDNEY AND BLADDER CURE contains in correct proportions: Sodium phosphate, sodium benzoate, couch grass, corn silk, potassium acetate, shepherd's purse, queen meadow, senna, hexamethylene tetramine, hydro-alcoholic menstruum, syrup.

The great value of Dr. Ross' Kidney and Bladder Cure is derived from the fact that this combination of remedies acts directly upon the organs affected, stimulating the filtering activity of the kidneys and restoring vigor and tone to the whole system. The kidneys are one of the most important parts of the digestive system and if they are in a weakened condition, if they do not perform their duties properly, every other organ of the body will feel its effect and a general break down of your health may quickly result.

WE WANT YOU TO GIVE Dr. Ross' Bladder and Kidney Cure a trial because we believe that after you have given it a test, you will find that it is the best kidney and bladder remedy on the market today. You can make this trial without any risk to yourself. There is absolutely nothing harmful in this remedy, so you can feel perfectly safe in using it as directed and experience its beneficial effects within a short time. The remedy is guaranteed to give satisfaction and if you do not receive any benefit from its use and will write us to that effect, we will promptly refund to you the full amount that you have paid for the first bottle.

No. 8F121   Price, 3 bottles for $1.60; per bottle.......................58c
Unmailable on account of weight.

OUR LAXATIVE FIG SYRUP.

Retail price.................25c and 50c
Our price, 25c size, per bottle.....$0.17
Our price, 25c size, 3 bottles for.. .48
Our price, 50c size, per bottle.... .30
Our price, 50c size, 3 bottles for.. .85

FOR CONSTIPATION. The great remedy of the age for this trouble. Laxative Fig Syrup was never retailed for less than 25 cents. Our special price is 17 cents. If you suffer from constipation, order a large bottle of **Laxative Fig Syrup** and you will find immediate relief and in time a permanent cure. It contains in correct proportions: Figs, senna, cascara sagrada, mandrake, rhubarb, tamarinds, aromatics, syrups.

OUR PRICE, ONLY
17c
Regular Retail Price, 25 Cents.

Laxative Fig Syrup is Nature's own remedy for restoring the bowels to a healthy and normal condition. Unlike pills and purgatives, it strengthens instead of weakening and enfeebling their action. For chronic constipation, to secure the best results a remedy is required that will not only act quickly on the bowels, but will produce a tone and stimulating effect upon the inner coating of the intestines, strengthen the muscular action and restore the paralyzed functions. Laxative Fig Syrup, if taken regularly, will cure constipation with its attending ills. Laxative Fig Syrup is perfectly harmless. It is a liquid made from fruits, plants and herbs, is mild in form and easy to take, and when used in cases of bowel, stomach, kidney and liver complaints its effect upon the system is marked.

No. 8F124   Price, regular size bottle, 3 for 48c; per bottle 17c
No. 8F125   Price, large size bottle, 3 for 85c; per bottle.............30c
Unmailable on account of weight.

SPEEDY CURE PILE REMEDY.

Retail price. 50c
Our price, per box.........................$0.20
3 boxes for.. .50

WHY SUFFER from Piles when 20 cents spent for our Speedy Cure Pile Remedy will give relief and may perform a cure. This preparation affords immediate relief and a prompt cure in many cases. It allays at once the extreme soreness and tenderness of all parts, reduces the inflammation and heals all ulcerative conditions. It is equally serviceable for itching piles. We have sold thousands of boxes and have received splendid reports. If you have tried other remedies without getting relief, try our Speedy Cure; you will find results satisfactory.

No. 8F126   Price, per box...........20c
    3 boxes for.................................50c
If by mail, postage extra, per box, 4c.

BRANDY CORDIAL.

FOR MEDICINAL AND DOMESTIC USE. MADE FROM THE JUICE OF SELECTED BLACKBERRIES. ABSOLUTELY PURE.

This is not an ordinary blackberry wine, but a sweet, wholesome cordial of the finest quality, equally useful as a medicine for bowel complaints. Also used for flavoring pastry and fruit sauces.

A VALUABLE ARTICLE FOR EVERY HOME. EXTRA FINE QUALITY AND FULL STRENGTH.

No. 8F128   Price, per pint bottle.........................$0.28
No. 8F130   Per quart bottle.............................. .48
No. 8F131   Original cases of 12 pints....................2.85
No. 8F132   Original cases of 12 quarts...................4.75
Not mailable on account of weight.

CUROLENE.

VAPORIZED CURO-LENE cures while you sleep. A remedy for whooping cough, asthma, catarrh, diphtheria, croup, colds, coughs, etc.

89c

VAPORIZED MEDICINES have for years been recognized as the best means for curing all diseases of the nose, throat and lungs. By this means every particle of air becomes charged and loaded with medicine and as we breathe or inhale every part of the channel becomes coated. The vaporizing has heretofore been usually performed by means of a spray atomizer, but in doing this some liquid must be used with the remedy, and this being heavier than the air, soon settles and does not have the beneficial results as though no liquid was used. With this point in view we have devised the new aluminum Curolene Vaporizer. The Curolene liquid is placed in the small pan above the little alcohol lamp, lighted, and before long the Curolene will be converted into a vapor, the air around becomes loaded and, being heated, it rises and gives place to more air. In this way all the air becomes charged and, before long, every crevice, every nook and corner becomes filled with these beneficial and curing vapors. By this means the air is not loaded with moisture, but with nothing except the medicine itself. This will not settle, but, on the other hand, will purify every spot.

THE GERM THEORY. It is now acknowledged by all physicians that the causes of scarlet fever, diphtheria, whooping cough, croup, asthma, etc., are from minute germs, which, once present, grow and increase the severity of the disease until killed. To successfully accomplish this some strong and effective remedy must be used and this remedy can now be successfully accomplished by Curolene Vapors.

CUROLENE is a strong antiseptic and germicide with marked germ destroying properties. Curolene vapors permeate every crevice and afford the only means of quickly and surely curing all forms of germ diseases. The vapors of Curolene are pleasant, of the nature of carbolic acid, yet will not injure the youngest child. The vapors are carried to every passage and cell of the respiratory organs and this is the reason it has such a beneficial effect upon all diseases of the nose, throat and lungs.

SHOULD BE IN EVERY HOME. A complete Curolene outfit should be in every home. Croup, whooping cough, diphtheria and many other germ diseases arise very quickly and you should have a vaporizing outfit always ready for any emergency. It may save the life of your child. It will not deteriorate with age and the vaporizer will last a lifetime. No home with children can afford to be without it.

No. 8F140 Regular price, complete, comprising the new aluminum stand, aluminum vaporizing pan, alcohol lamp and 2-oz. bottle Curolene, $1.50. Our price ....(Not mailable).....................89c

DR. WALKER'S CELEBRATED SKIN OINTMENT.

Retail price........................50c
Our price, each....................26c
Our price, 3 bottles for 75c

Considered one of the best remedies for all skin diseases and blemishes and superior to any other skin ointment in the market, furnished by us at less than one-half its selling value. This skin ointment is highly recommended for eruptive and skin diseases, pimples, blotches, eczema, salt rheum, erysipelas, ringworms or any scaly or scabby eruptions, often healing cracked or rough skin on the hands, face or any part of the body by a few applications. We are in a position to furnish this excellent remedy for skin diseases and blemishes for only 26 cents a box. You could obtain no remedy that is better or can equal it in healing qualities if you were to pay $1.00 per package.

No. 8F157 Dr. Walker's Skin Ointment. Price, per box.................26c
3 boxes for...........(If by mail, postage extra, 3 cents)................75c

RELIABLE WORM SYRUP AND WORM CAKES.

YOU CAN SAVE YOUR CHILDREN from much suffering and in many cases save their lives. No other disease is so fatal to children as worms. Unfortunately they are seldom free from them, and as the symptoms resemble those of almost every other complaint, they often produce alarming effects without being suspected. Worms are not only a cause of disease in themselves, but by their irritation aggravate all other diseases, wandering from one part of the body to another, winding themselves up into large balls, obstructing the bowels and frequently the throat, causing convulsions and too often death.

OUR RELIABLE WORM SYRUP effectually destroys the worms and removes the nest in which their young are deposited. It moves the bowels very gently, the worms being to a greater or less extent dissolved by the action of the medicine, can scarcely be recognized in the stools, but the improvement in the health of the child will be sufficient evidence of the beneficial effects of the medicine.

EVERY MOTHER ought to have a bottle of the syrup or a box of the cakes always in the house. The syrup and the cakes are two medicines used for the same purpose. The syrup is more pleasant to the taste and more suitable for very young children. The cakes can be given to older people; even adults can be benefited by using them, as grown up folks, as well as children, often suffer from worms. These reliable worm medicines are not only worm destroyers, but act as a general tonic, destroying sourness of the stomach and producing a healthy appetite. Mothers, keep your children healthy.

No. 8F111 Worm Syrup. Price, 3 bottles for 50c; per bottle. ..18c
If by mail, postage and tube extra, per bottle, 16 cents.

No. 8F112 Worm Cakes. Price, 3 boxes for 50c; per box...........18c
If by mail, postage extra, per box, 2 cents.

CORN AND BUNION REMOVER.

Retail price, 25c; our price....................... 9o

THE GREAT CHINESE CORN and Bunion Remover, never fails to give immediate relief, and a complete cure is certain when directions are faithfully followed. No one suffering from corns, or bunions should fail to give our great Chinese Corn and Bunion Remover a trial. We have tried it ourselves and found relief, therefore can testify knowingly as to its great merits.

No. 8F139 Price........................... 9c
If by mail, postage extra, 3 cents.

ANGEL'S OIL.
The Remedy for Curing Pain.

Retail price........................50c
Our price, each.................... 28o
Our price, 3 bottles for.......... 75o

COMPOSED OF VEGETABLE OILS. Offers great relief in cases of rheumatism, neuralgia, gout, sciatica, pleurisy, backache, quinsy sore throat, stiffness of the neck and joints, sprains, lumbago and swellings, inflammations, chilblains, bites and stings of poisonous insects, weak ankles and joints, sore feet, pain in the back and limbs, or any other bodily pain or ailment. This liniment is one of those standard household remedies which comes in handy upon many occasions where a remedy is needed quickly to afford relief and to give protection against more serious complications. After giving it a trial you will never be without a bottle in the house. We make the price very low so that every one of our customers may afford to have a bottle constantly at hand.

No. 8F142 Price, per bottle 28c
If by mail, postage and tube extra, per bottle, 14 cents.

ELECTRIC LINIMENT.

Retail price.............. 50c
Our price, each.......... 23c

THIS LINIMENT is an excellent remedy in cases of rheumatism, sprains, old sores, bruises, growing pains, contracted muscles, lame back, stiff joints, frosted feet, chilblains, etc. Persons suffering from lameness or cold in the arms and legs will be rendered great benefit by its use; also as an application for the throat and chest; in cases of inflammation, for stiff neck, bruised or contracted muscles and in all cases requiring external treatment great relief will be experienced with this, one of the most penetrating and best liniments ever made. We call this remedy Electric Liniment because its application produces a feeling similar to the feeling produced by a mild charge of electricity. This is a liniment that should find a place in every family. It will offer relief in hundreds of different cases. Electric Liniment once used will make for itself a place in every home.

No. 8F115 Price, 3 bottles for 60c; each...........23c
Not mailable.

INJECTION No. 7.

Retail price,.......$1.00
Our price, each.....59c

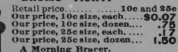

CURES IN ONE TO FIVE DAYS. No other medicine required. No fear of stricture. No bad results. A French specific, having a great reputation abroad as a reliable cure for all troubles of the urinary organs in either male or female; has a very quick effect and leaves no bad results. Either gonorrhoea or gleet quickly and easily cured. Full instructions and valuable information with each package.

No. 8F133 Price, each............ ....$0.59
3 bottles for................................. 1.50

If by mail, postage and mailing case extra, each, 18 cents.

No. 8F822 Hard Rubber Syringe, to be used with this remedy. Price. (Postage, 2c extra) .16c

BROMO VICHY.

Retail price........... ...10c and 25c
Our price, 10c size, each.....$0.07
Our price, 10c size, dozen.... .75
Our price, 25c size, each..... .17
Our price, 25c size, dozen... 1.50

A Morning Bracer.
A Headache Reliever.
A Brain Clearer.
A Nerve Steadier.

THIS IS BY FAR THE BEST "BROMO" preparation at present offered to the public. One or two teaspoonfuls taken in half a tumbler of cold water will instantly dispel any sickness of the stomach, relieve a severe headache, clear up the brain and steady the nerves. It is a thirst quencher, and causes a pleasant feeling to revall all through the body. It is a quick remedy for nervous headaches, neuralgia, sleeplessness, over brain work, depression following alcoholic excesses, and all nervous troubles. A little should always be on one's bureau table for use in the morning or at night.

No. 8F136 Price, 10c size,................ 7c
No. 8F137 Price, 25c size,................ 17c
No. 8F138 Price, 50c size,................ 38c
If by mail, postage extra, small size, 4 cents; large size, 8 cents.

YOU SHARE IN OUR PROFIT We send you a valuable PROFIT SHARING CERTIFICATE and you can soon get something valuable entirely FREE, as shown on pages 1 and 2

WHITE STAR SECRET LIQUOR CURE.

Regular retail price...$2.50
Our price, complete, box of thirty treatments...............................94

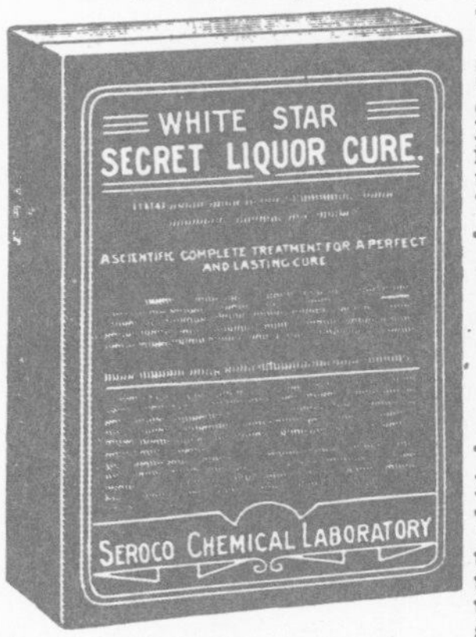

THIS EXCEEDINGLY SUCCESSFUL LIQUOR CURE is designated as a Secret Liquor Cure because it can be administered secretly without the knowledge of the drinker and can be given in tea, coffee or food, without the consent of the unfortunate victim of the drink habit.

OUR PRICE, ONLY **94c** Regular Retail Price, $2.50

THE WHITE STAR SECRET LIQUOR CURE contains the following ingredients in correct proportion: Gold Chloride, Ammonium Muriate, Scutellaria, Erythroxylon Coca, Ext. Cayenne, Ext. American Valerian, Cephalis Ipecac, Ext. Bleeding Heart, Saccharaum Lactis.

THIS REPRESENTS an odorless and tasteless preparation in powdered form, which, given to the drinker in tea, coffee or food will not upset the patient, but by its action on the system and the tonic stimulating effect upon the nerves, it often removes that desire, that craving for intoxicating liquor, in a comparatively short time.

IT IS NOT CLAIMED that there is a liquor cure, secret or otherwise, that is absolutely infallible in all cases, but so many have been entirely cured and stayed cured, so many have been reclaimed for months or years before they suffered a relapse that it would really seem a neglect of duty not to make the attempt to help them, even save them against their will, especially when you can undertake this treatment without the slightest risk, so far as expense is concerned, without any risk whatever of harming the patient.

THE WHITE STAR SECRET LIQUOR CURE will do no harm in any case. It will always improve the general condition of the drinker to a marked degree. It is considered one of the best prescriptions to be employed secretly in the treatment of the liquor habit. Neither you nor we ourselves can tell, however, beforehand, what it can and will accomplish for the patient whose treatment you contemplate, nor do we wish you to be disappointed in the results and we therefore make you the following liberal offer.

SEND FOR A BOX of the White Star Secret Liquor Cure, which contains thirty treatments, give it according to directions, a small powder in tea or coffee. After you have made a fair trial according to instructions, if there is no benefit derived, write us. State that this is the first box that you have tried and we will promptly refund your money.

REMEMBER, the price is only 94 cents per box of thirty complete treatments.

Full directions sent with each box. Medicine sent in a plain sealed package.
No. 8F151 Price, 3 boxes for, $2.50; per box.......................................94c
If by mail, postage extra, per box, 12 cents.

WINE OF COD LIVER OIL WITH LIME, IRON AND CHERRY BARK.

THIS IS A PLEASANT, ELEGANT PREPARATION, recommended and prescribed by physicians for the treatment of pulmonary affections and as a general system tonic.

WINE OF COD LIVER OIL contains the active medicinal principles of cod liver oil in a palatable form, avoiding the nauseating effect of the oil. It is preferred by many to plain cod liver oil, and at the same time admits of combining with it the very best tonics, tissue and blood builders, making the Wine of Cod Liver Oil with Lime, Iron and Cherry Bark one of the most satisfactory cod liver oil preparations obtainable.

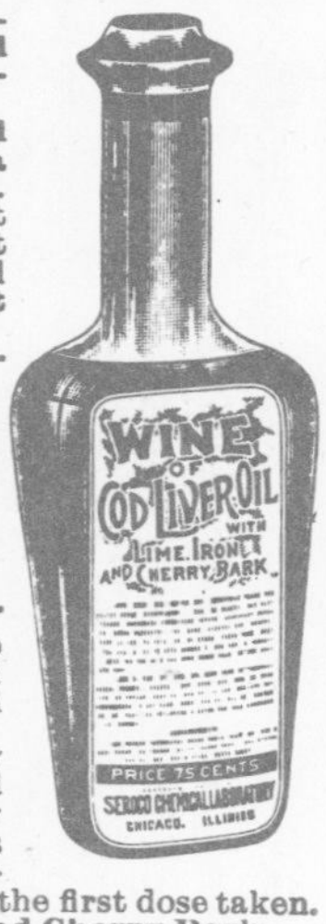

WINE OF COD LIVER OIL with Lime, Iron and Cherry Bark is a remedy that should always be used by patients who are constantly weakening and who are debilitated and wasting away. It is undoubtedly very valuable in the treatment of all lung troubles, colds and chronic coughs, scrofula, blood disorders and skin affections, as well as diseases of the joints and spine. It will build up the strength of the entire system, giving renewed health and vigor to the weak and debilitated, increasing the functional activity of every organ of the body.

OUR PRICE, ONLY **38c** Regular Retail Price, 75 cents.

WINE OF COD LIVER OIL with Lime, Iron and Cherry Bark is a valuable general tonic; its pleasant taste makes it very palatable. It is easily taken by the patient, who will like it and relish it. It is quickly assimilated and taken up by the system. Consequently it will improve the patient's condition almost from the first dose taken.

No. 8F160 Wine of Cod Liver Oil with Lime, Iron and Cherry Bark.
Our price, 3 bottles for $1.00; per bottle.......................................38c
Unmailable on account of weight.

GENUINE ENGLISH PILE REMEDY.

Retail price...50c
Our price, each...30c
Three boxes for..80c

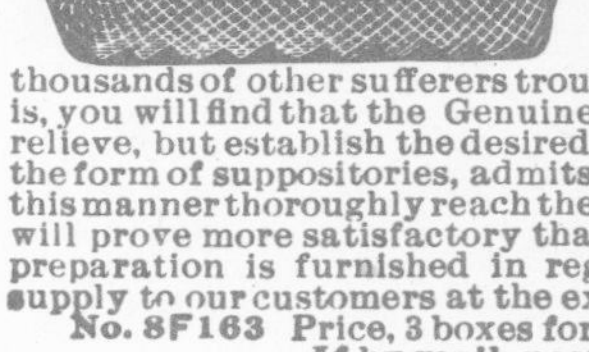

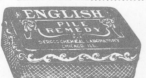

A scientifically prepared pile remedy in suppository form, soothing, healing and for the most effective curing of blind, itching or bleeding piles. Speedy in relief, safe in its action, permanent in its effect. No matter what you may have employed for the treatment of this trouble, if all else has failed to afford you relief and cure, you should send for the Genuine English Pile Remedy at once. You may have the same experience as have thousands of other sufferers troubled with different forms of this ailment, that is, you will find that the Genuine English Pile Remedy will not only promptly relieve, but establish the desired result. The remedy having been prepared in the form of suppositories, admits of easy and convenient application, and will in this manner thoroughly reach the affected parts, and by its prompt healing action will prove more satisfactory than almost any mode of treatment of piles. The preparation is furnished in regular 50-cent size boxes, which we, however, supply to our customers at the exceedingly small price of only 30 cents per box.

No. 8F163 Price, 3 boxes for 80c; per box.......................................30c
If by mail, postage extra, per box, 3 cents.

CASCARA CATHARTIC TABLETS.

A VERY PLEASANT LAXATIVE.

FOR CONSTIPATION AND ALL GENERAL STOMACH, LIVER AND BOWEL COMPLAINTS.

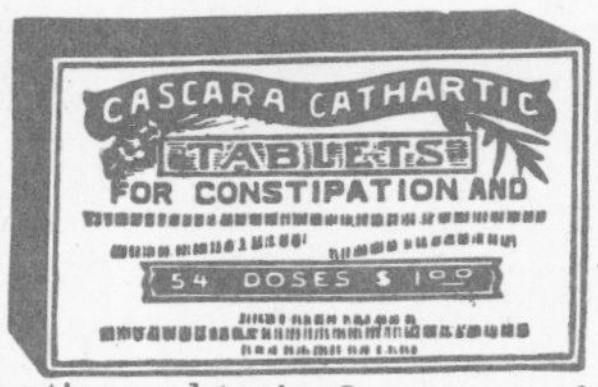

A pleasant, efficient laxative and stimulative tonic, the most effective remedy for the quick relief and cure of constipation, jaundice, nausea, dyspepsia, biliousness and all complications resulting from a disordered condition of the stomach and bowels. **Our Cascara Cathartic Tablets are a combination of the most successful,** yet perfectly harmless remedies, recommended and used by the most eminent physicians, as a positive laxative and tonic. On account of their mild action on the bowels they are not only a valuable cathartic, but at the same time the most pleasing treatment for the cure of symptoms for which they are intended. **You will never know how easy it will be to keep yourself in a perfect and regular condition,** how quickly you can dispel those apparently unimportant yet exceedingly distressing little troubles resulting from a disturbed digestion or an irregularity of the bowels. Using two or three Cascara Cathartic Tablets for a few days will tone up the entire system, strengthen the digestive organs and bowels connected with the function of digestion and the elimination of waste matter. You will feel lighter, brighter, more restful and cheerful and free from the nervous and painful state which always follows indigestion and bowel trouble. Less valued remedies of this kind are usually sold at 50 cents in boxes containing 30 to 35 doses. Our price for 54 doses is 27 cents. We guarantee our Cascara Cathartic Tablets to give satisfaction.

No. 8F165 Price, large size, containing 54 doses, 3 boxes for 70c; per box.......................................27c
If by mail, postage extra, per box, 4 cents.

DR. ALLEN'S ASTHMA CURE.

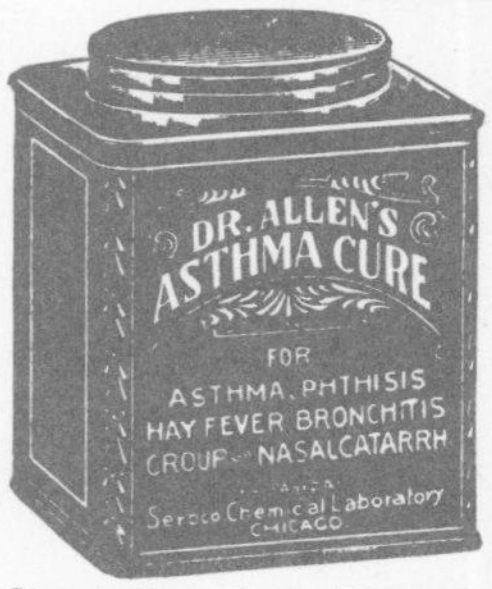

DR. ALLEN'S ASTHMA CURE is for the relief of all forms of Asthma, Hay Fever, Bronchitis, Croup and Nasal Catarrh. It is a scientific combination of oxygenating chemicals with such herbs and barks as have proven themselves effective for the relief of asthma and other affections of the respiratory organs, attended with short, difficult or spasmodic breathing. It is the result of many years' study and experiment in the treatment of diseases of the lungs and air passages, and all stages of asthma. **It has never failed to give some relief or effect a cure when a fair trial was given and used according to directions.** This remedy is used by inhalation and as its virtues reach the air passages direct, the relief obtained is instantaneous. **Plain directions and valuable information enclosed in each box, and if the sufferer will follow these directions carefully, mild forms of asthma, hay fever, etc., are often cured in a week or two; but if the disease is old and deep seated and has obtained a firm hold on the system, the treatment ought to be continued for several months, even though the patient may believe himself entirely cured.**

OUR PRICE, ONLY **62c** Regular Retail Price, $1.00

No. 8F169 Full size box. Price, 3 boxes for $1.75; per box.........62c
If by mail, postage extra, per box, 5 cents.

DR. WALTERS' CHILL CURE.

DR. WALTERS' WELL KNOWN CHILL CURE is a specific for the cure of all diseases due to malarial poisoning. It will promptly relieve intermittent fever or fever and ague, remittent fever, dumb ague, periodic headache or malaria. It completely destroys the germs of malaria in the blood, thus removing the cause of the disease from the entire system. Dr. Walters' Chill Cure should be used by persons living in a malarial district. It will protect them and act as a preventive and protector from malarial diseases. There is no reason why you should suffer from malarial poisoning when you can secure Dr. Walters' Chill Cure, a very efficient remedy for all malarial diseases. This remedy will quickly restore the blood to a normal and healthy condition. It will quickly relieve you of malaria, backache, headache, general debility, aching bones or any ailment due to malaria. **It will act as a powerful tonic, appetizer and general invigorant for the entire nervous system.** Those living in a malarial country can protect themselves from malaria germs by taking a few doses daily for a short time.

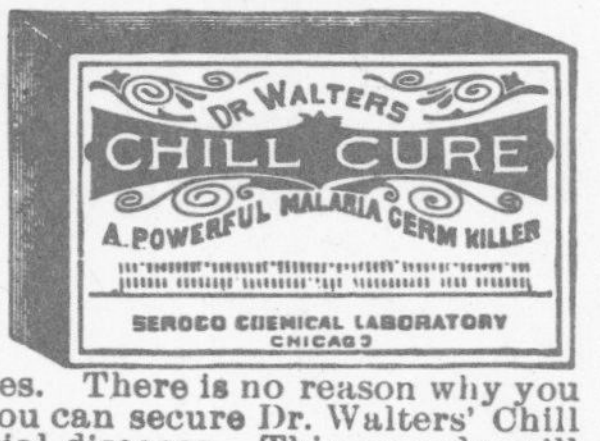

No. 8F171 Dr. Walters' Chill Cure.
Price, 3 boxes for 95c; per box.......................................36c
If by mail, postage extra, per box, 4 cents.

CATARRH-OL SOLUTION.

A VERY HIGHLY RECOMMENDED AND BENEFICIAL TREATMENT FOR CHRONIC CATARRH.

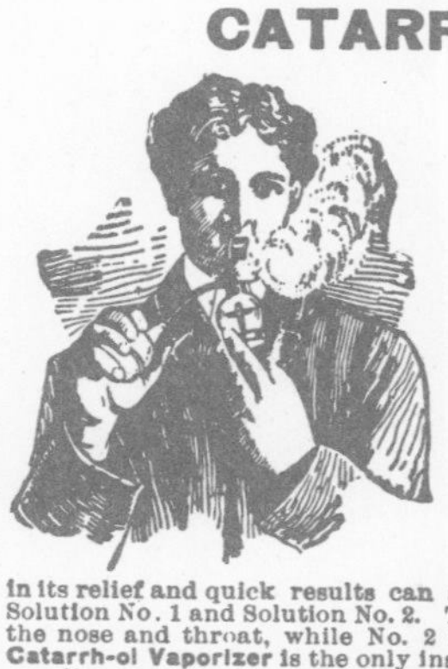

This new local treatment for catarrh in the head or nose and throat, as well as all affections of the bronchial tubes and lungs, consists of a combination of the most powerful antiseptic and germ destroying ingredients, prepared for the purpose of preventing infectious diseases of the breathing organs and for the cure of catarrhal diseases of the head and lungs, and when applied with the Catarrh-ol Nebulizer or Vaporizer will prove of greatest benefit in the treatment of catarrh in all its different forms. **Catarrh-ol is cleanly, inexpensive and guaranteed to reach most cases in an effective manner.** Its antiseptic and curing influences when it is properly used are simply remarkable. It does not cause even the slightest irritation. It is prompt in its relief and quick results can always be assured. Catarrh-ol Solutions are furnished as Solution No. 1 and Solution No. 2. The first is of especial value in the treatment of catarrh of the nose and throat, while No. 2 is intended for bronchial trouble and lung diseases. The Catarrh-ol Vaporizer is the only instrument of its kind on the market, and, on account of its peculiar construction and patented features, will nebulize the solutions and carry the same over the entire surface of the mucous membrane, the seat of all catarrhal trouble, reaching every portion of the nasal passages and the air passages, the bronchial tubes and, through them, the lungs, soothing, healing and curing.

No. 8F172 Catarrh-ol No. 1. For catarrh of nose and throat. Price, 47c
No. 8F173 Catarrh-ol No. 2. For bronchial and lung trouble. Price, 47c
No. 8F174 Catarrh-ol Vaporizor. Price.......................................89c
No. 8F175 Catarrh-ol Solution Treatment, including one bottle Catarrh-ol No. 1, one bottle Catarrh-ol No. 2, sufficient for three months' treatment, and one patent Vaporizer, all complete. Price...............$1.58
Unmailable on account of weight.

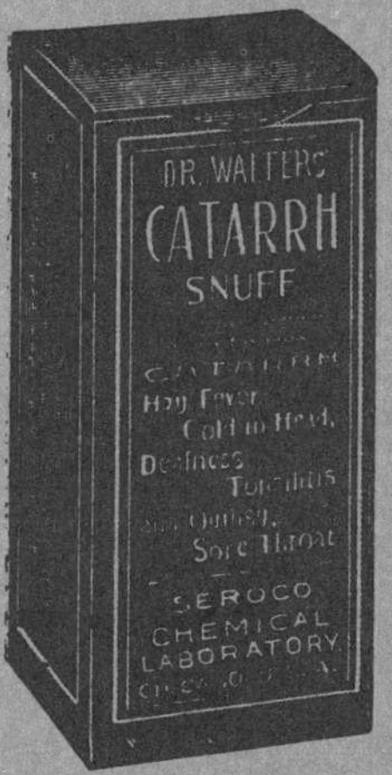

DR. WALTER'S CATARRH SNUFF.

The best known local catarrh remedy. Affords relief and great benefit in nine cases out of ten.

For all catarrhal affections—**Headache, catarrh of the mucous membrane of the nose, cold in head, etc., nothing acts so quickly as WALTER'S CATARRH SNUFF. PERFECTLY HARMLESS.** It contains no injurious drugs or chemicals. Every bottle comes supplied with blower, by means of which the healing powder can be applied directly to the inflamed parts, stopping and healing any discharges, pain or irritation. **OUR PRICE FOR THE CATARRH SNUFF IS 21 CENTS,** complete with blower. **If you have friends who have suffered with this dread disease—catarrh—tell them of this catarrh snuff, that the price has been reduced to only 21 cents. Never sold for less than 50 cents by others.**

OUR PRICE, ONLY **21c**
Regular Retail Price, 50 Cents.

No. 8F176 Price, per bottle.......................**21c**
3 bottles for..**55c**
If by mail, postage extra, 7 cents.

DR. WALTER'S DIGESTIVE ELIXIR.

For the prompt relief of dyspepsia, indigestion and stomach complications generally.

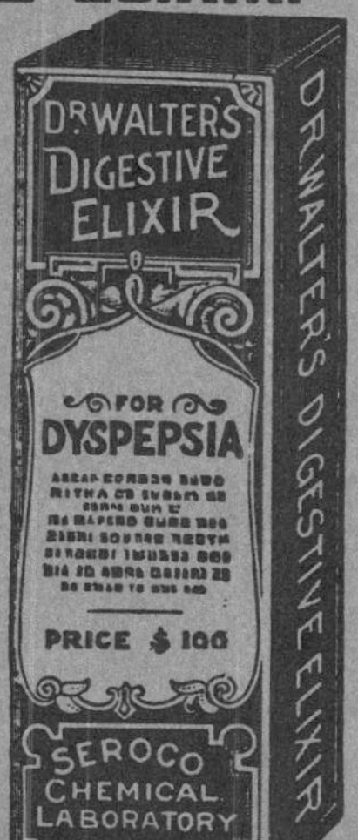

DR. WALTER'S DIGESTIVE ELIXIR contains, in correct proportions: Pepsin, diastase malt, rennin, menthol, thymol, baptisia, eucalyptol, rochelle salts, hydrochloric acid, lactic acid, elixir simplex.

DOES YOUR STOMACH DISTRESS YOU? Do you suffer with dyspepsia? Are you troubled with indigestion? Send for a bottle of Dr. Walter's Digestive Elixir. It will be furnished to you with the understanding that after you have used the first bottle and if you have not tried this remedy before, if you do not find results entirely satisfactory, all you have to do is to notify us of that fact, and the full amount that you have paid for the first bottle of this remedy will be refunded to you at once.

OUR PRICE, ONLY **52c**
Regular Retail Price $1.00

DR. WALTER'S DIGESTIVE ELIXIR increases the gastric juices, aids digestion, makes the food antiseptic, tones the system, removes all gas and makes the stomach strong, healthy and able to perform its work.

PLEASE BEAR IN MIND that Dr. Walter's Digestive Elixir is a digestive remedy; a preparation that will have a beneficial effect upon the entire digestive system by performing a portion of its work in a most natural way, thus resting the stomach when in a weakened condition and by this rest which it affords to the digestive system will strengthen these organs so that they soon can and will perform their work without any medical aid.

DYSPEPSIA is a very common and exceedingly distressing disease and as a rule manifests itself by the following symptoms: A feeling of fullness and weight in the stomach after eating, flatulency, decomposing of food from slow and imperfect digestion, which produces gases, swelling of the stomach, great discomfort or pain, constant belching, heartburn, frequent fainting, sick headache and constipation.

THE ABOVE SYMPTOMS are usually caused by a weak stomach, inability to digest the food, so that it sours in the stomach and the trouble starts.

BY USING DR. WALTER'S DIGESTIVE ELIXIR you will not only assist the digestion of the food but this remedy will gradually strengthen the stomach and the entire digestive system, resulting in the proper assimilation of the food, furnishing the right nourishment and building up your general health to a point where you can eat all kinds of food without being distressed: enjoy all your meals to the fullest measure.

DR. WALTER'S DIGESTIVE ELIXIR combines in an agreeable form some of the best medical substances used for the cure of dyspepsia and indigestion in all its forms.

ONE TEASPOONFUL of this remedy taken three or four times a day after meals will increase the gastric juices, free the stomach from all gas, aid digestion, and in a very short time you will know what it means to be free again from dyspepsia and indigestion. When using Dr. Walter's Digestive Elixir you can eat nearly everything that you like without experiencing any discomfort or ill effects in the least.

No. 8F180 Dr. Walter's Digestive Elixir, each bottle, 12-ounce capacity.
Price, 3 bottles for $1.40; per bottle.......................................**52c**
Unmailable on account of weight.

DR. CURTIS' SORE THROAT CURE.

The great remedy for sore throat and all acute throat affections.

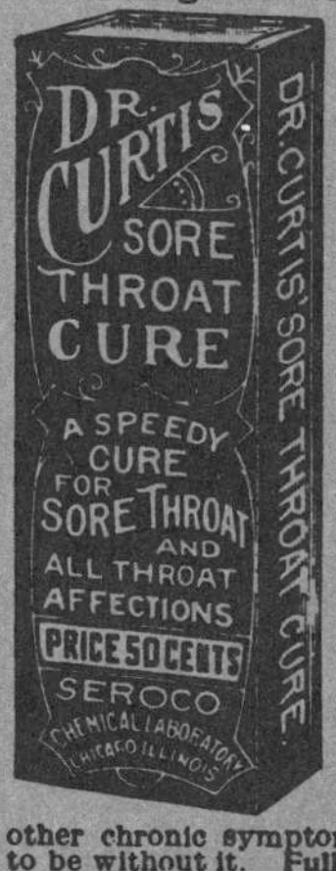

COMPOSITION. Dr. Curtis' Sore Throat Cure is the formula used by this eminent throat specialist for years in his private practice and contains in permanent solution, chlorine, ferric iron, chlorates, oxychlorides, etc., combined in such a manner as to continually liberate free chlorine, oxygen and oxychlorides. The efficiency of these gases in sore throat and early diphtheria is well known and combined with other beneficial substances forms one of the foremost treatments for these conditions.

OUR PRICE, ONLY **32c**
Regular Retail Price, 50 Cents.

ITS USES. Dr. Curtis' Sore Throat Cure may be used locally or internally as conditions may require. The preparation is best used undiluted and should reach as nearly as possible every part of the throat. This is best accomplished by means of an atomizer, if at hand, otherwise by gargling and swallowing the quantity remaining in the mouth after each treatment.

IF YOU SUFFER FROM SORE THROAT, tonsilitis, enlargement of the tonsils, or any one of similar throat affections, we would urge you by all means to order a bottle of Curtis' Sore Throat Cure, as a trial. Use it according to directions and a severe sore throat can be prevented. It is far better to use the product as soon as possible after the soreness is noticed and before the inflammation becomes deep seated as it is then much harder to cure.

A HOUSEHOLD NECESSITY. This excellent sore throat cure should be in every household. None of us are able to tell just when we will experience a severe sore throat and then is just the time we want a good remedy. A bad sore throat should be carefully treated, otherwise diphtheria or other chronic symptoms may arise. With our liberal offer on this product you cannot afford to be without it. Full directions with each bottle. Regular retail price, per bottle, 50 cents.

No. 8F182 Price, three 4-ounce bottles, 80c; per bottle.......................**32c**
If by mail, postage and tube extra, per bottle, 19 cents.

SYRUP HYPOPHOSPHITES COMPOUND.

(Dr. Hammond.)

The Great Tonic and Reconstructive for Nervous Exhaustion, General Debility.

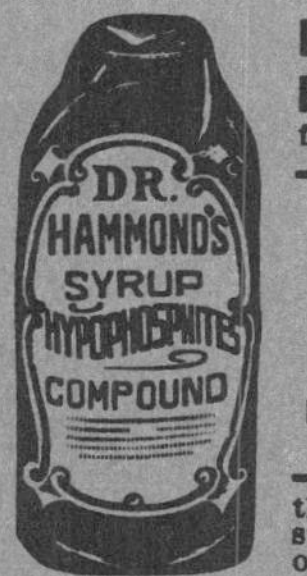

DR. HAMMOND'S SYRUP HYPOPHOSPHITES COMPOUND has for years been recognized as one of the very best reconstructive tonics, stimulating and toning the appetite, the functions of digestion and assimilation and the entire nervous system, while it also contains the necessary mineral constituents for supplying the required energy to aid in overcoming disease.

OUR PRICE, ONLY **64c**
Regular Retail Price, $1.00

COMPOSITION. The composition of this new but highly successful tonic comprises the hypophosphites of potassium, sodium, lime, manganese, iron and quinine. Potassium, sodium and lime serve as great constructive tonics to bone, muscle and nerve tissue. Manganese and iron supply the red color to the blood. Phosphorus, as it exists in the composition, forms a large per cent of the different parts of the body and especially the brain. Quinine, the main alkaloid of this preparation, acts as a tonic, keeping up the strength of the system, toning the appetite and improving all the functions of the body.

IN ALL AFFECTIONS OF THE BRONCHIAL TUBES, Dr. Hammond's Syrup Hypophosphites Compound should be given a trial. If used conscientiously, this syrup will diminish the tendency to consumption and may even prevent the further formation of tuberculous deposit after the disease has taken hold. In the first and second stages of tuberculosis this composition may, when rightly used, overcome the disease, and even in advanced stages great benefit will be derived from its use.

A UNIVERSAL TONIC. Dr. Hammond's Syrup Hypophosphites Compound may be considered the one universal tonic. It stimulates and increases the appetite and has a favorable influence upon the red corpuscles of the blood, tones up the functions of digestion and assimilation, strengthens the nervous system, supplies the necessary mineral constituents of the body and induces, by its tonic action on the digestive organs, regular and easy evacuation of the bowels. Patients taking this syrup, as a rule, gain flesh from the very first and it is considered to be one of the foremost tonics for use in a debilitated or weakened condition.

THIS REMEDY is sold under our liberal guarantee allowing our customer who has never used it, to order one bottle to ascertain whether this product reaches your condition and whether it will afford you benefit, otherwise the full amount paid will be refunded upon request.

No. 8F181 Price, three 16-ounce bottles for **$1.75**; per bottle.............**64c**
(Unmailable on account of weight)

DR. ROSE'S RED CLOVER COMPOUND.

This is a splendid remedy for worn out, tired, and exhausted conditions of the system.

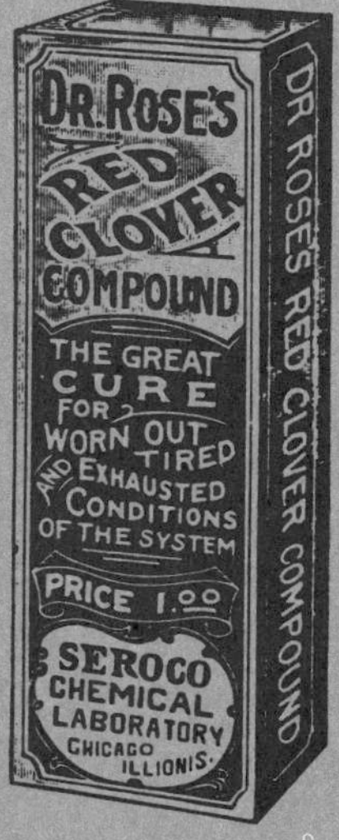

This well known and highly beneficial blood purifier is in all probability better known than any other combination ever offered. It is a system builder of the highest nature.

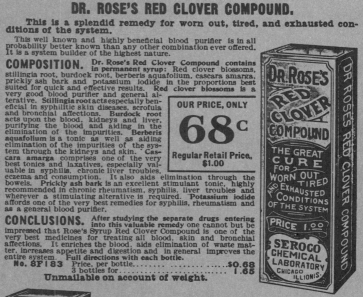

COMPOSITION. Dr. Rose's Red Clover Compound contains in permanent syrup: Red clover blossoms, stillingia root, burdock root, berberis aquafolium, cascara amarga, prickly ash bark and potassium iodide in the proportions best suited for quick and effective results. **Red clover blossoms** is a very good blood purifier and general alterative. **Stillingia root** acts especially beneficial in syphilitic skin diseases, scrofula and bronchial affections. **Burdock root** acts upon the blood, kidneys and liver, purifying the blood and aiding in the elimination of the impurities. **Berberis aquafolium** is a tonic as well as aiding elimination of the impurities of the system through the kidneys and skin. **Cascara amarga** comprises one of the very best tonics and laxatives, especially valuable in syphilis, chronic liver troubles, eczema and consumption. It also aids elimination through the bowels. **Prickly ash bark** is an excellent stimulant tonic, highly recommended in chronic rheumatism, syphilis, liver troubles and wherever a stimulating alterative is required. **Potassium iodide** affords one of the very best remedies for syphilis, rheumatism and as a general blood purifier.

OUR PRICE, ONLY **68c**
Regular Retail Price, $1.00

CONCLUSIONS. After studying the separate drugs entering into this valuable remedy one cannot but be impressed that Rose's Syrup Red Clover Compound is one of the very best medicines for treating all blood, skin and bronchial affections. It enriches the blood, aids elimination of waste matter, increases appetite and digestion and in general improves the entire system. **Full directions with each bottle.**

No. 8F183 Price, per bottle.......................**$0.68**
3 bottles for......................................**1.65**
Unmailable on account of weight.

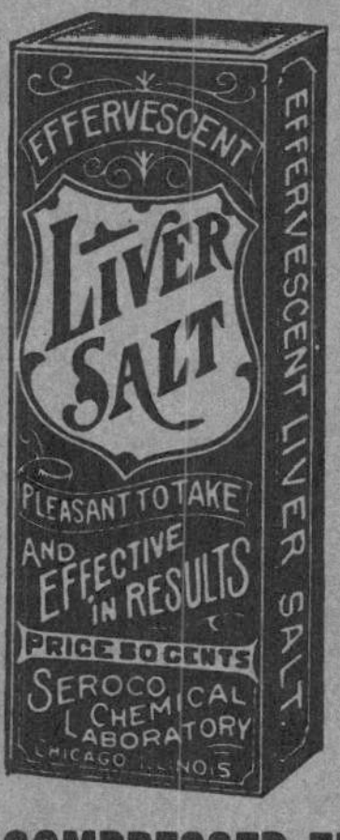

EFFERVESCENT LIVER SALT.

PLEASANT TO TAKE AND EFFECTIVE IN RESULTS.
Promotes Health and Prevents Disease.

An excellent combination, free from all harmful ingredients, for quickly relieving all forms of liver troubles.

OUR PRICE, ONLY **34c**
Regular Retail Price, 50 Cents.

CORRECTS THE LIVER. Effervescent Liver Salt is superior to most forms for correcting all the ills arising from lack of exercise, improper food, poor digestion and irregular meals.

LIVER SALT Affords ready relief in torpid liver, jaundice, constipation, sick headache, heartburn, bad breath, biliousness, distress after eating, gout, rheumatism, dizziness, prickly heat, hives, and all conditions arising from a clogging of the liver. Put up in large amber bottles. **Full directions with each bottle.**

No. 8F184 Price, per bottle.......**$0.34**
3 bottles for...........**.90**
Unmailable on account of weight.

COMPRESSED EFFERVESCENT LITHIA TABLETS.

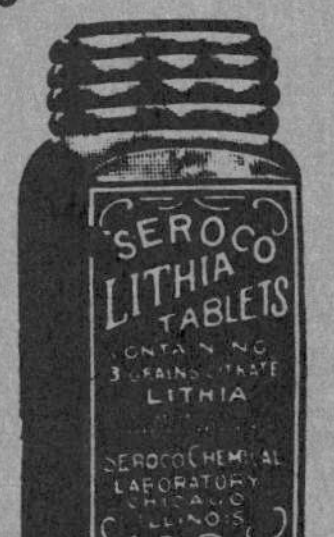

LITHIA SALTS have for years been recognized as one of the standard remedies for the treatment of subacute and chronic rheumatism, gout, uric acid, irritable bladder and all kidney affections depending upon an excess of uric acid in the system. Our Lithia tablets are absolutely pure, convenient, and accurate in dosage and possess many advantages not embraced by other forms of administration. One tablet dissolved in a glass of water makes a very agreeable, refreshing and beneficial effervescing draught.

No. 8F186 Price, per bottle, 3-grain tablets, 40 in bottle, **18c**
No. 8F187 Price, per bottle, 5-grain tablets, 40 in bottle, **23c**
If by mail postage extra, 15 cents.

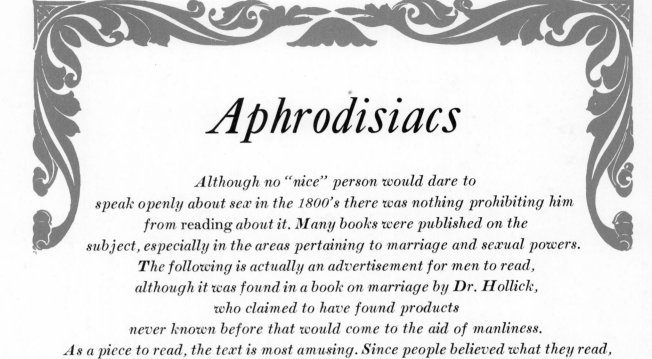

Aphrodisiacs

*Although no "nice" person would dare to
speak openly about sex in the 1800's there was nothing prohibiting him
from reading about it. Many books were published on the
subject, especially in the areas pertaining to marriage and sexual powers.
The following is actually an advertisement for men to read,
although it was found in a book on marriage by Dr. Hollick,
who claimed to have found products
never known before that would come to the aid of manliness.
As a piece to read, the text is most amusing. Since people believed what they read,
Dr. Hollick was very successful in his mail-order business.*

GENERAL DESCRIPTION OF APHRODISIACS AND HISTORY OF DR. HOLLICK'S APHRODISIAC REMEDIES

Medical Remedies are classified and named according to the mode in which they act. Some affect one part of the system, and others affect other parts. Those which act upon sexual organs, so as to preserve or restore their powers, are called APHRODISIACS. Remedies of this kind have always been eagerly sought, and paid for at any price: even gold itself has not been more eagerly prized, and

at this hour will be given in profusion for a good Aphrodisiac, though begrudged for anything else—for nothing does a man more crave than sexual power, and nothing does he more fear or regret to lose.

Numerous remedies called Aphrodisiacs have been in use in different parts of the world for ages past, with more or less repute; but their employment never resulted in much good, and often in much positive injury. It is the same at the present day—the greater part of such remedies now in use have no effect at all, and those which do act had better be left alone. . . .

When I first began to use the common remedies of this kind, I found that they were, for the most part, only traditional compounds, often dating back to the dark ages, and given merely because the physician did not know what else to give. . . .

I, therefore, set to work to investigate the whole subject of man's sexual nature, and all the action of all Aphrodisiac Remedies upon it for myself. For years I experimented with them, in thousands of cases, both simply and variously combined, carefully noting their effects, and thus by degrees finding out the true value of each, and how and when to use it. No one else, I really believe, ever went into this subject more thoroughly.

The result was, after endless trials, the formation of a compound possessing TRUE APHRODISIAC POWERS which, when judiciously employed, invariably increases and maintains sexual power, or restores it when lost. This remedy, from its great success in all cases not past aid, of impotence, sterility, and natural deficiency became very celebrated, and my practice—which comprised only such cases—rapidly extended. Every day the demand for my Aphrodisiac increased, and I soon found a difficulty in procuring enough for my professional use, on account of the limited supply and great cost of many of the ingredients.

Many of the most powerful and reliable Aphrodisiacs are among the rarest of Nature's products, and are obtained only from the least known and most inaccessible parts of the world; MUSK, for instance, which is a powerful Aphrodisiac, and of which I use a large quantity is always *worth its weight in gold,* and often much more. There are, however, other substances still more valuable, for which I have often given hundreds of dollars for a few grains. Some of these are natural and some artificial products, obtained by chemical means, and which can be produced only at immense cost. The great power of most of these articles fortunately makes a small portion go a long way in use, or they could scarcely be employed at all. In my remedy, there are altogether *thirty-three* different ingredients and of some of them not more than the *hundredth part of a grain* can be used as a dose. Each of these ingredients has some peculiar power of its own, or is necessary to the full development of the power of some other ingredient, so that the whole act together in producing that wonderful effect for which this Remedy is so celebrated.

DR. HOLLICK'S
APHRODISIAC REMEDY,

THE ONLY SURE AND RELIABLE AGENT

FOR THE

PERMANENT CURE OF

IMPOTENCE, STERILITY,

AND

NERVOUS AND SEXUAL DEBILITY,

IN EVERY FORM;

———

BEING THE CELEBRATED REMEDY USED FOR SO MANY YEARS IN

DR. HOLLICK'S EXTENSIVE PRACTICE,

DEVOTED EXCLUSIVELY TO SUCH CASES, AND NOW FOR THE FIRST TIME OFFERED

TO THE

PUBLIC.

At the same time, however, that it acts so energetically as an Aphrodisiac, it has no ill-effect in any other way, but is perfectly harmless to all parts of the system.

It will be readily seen that such a remedy must necessarily be costly, and can never come into common use; it must, in fact, ever remain a special luxury for those who have been favored with Fortune's golden gifts, or for those who are willing to make great sacrifices. . . .

In this way originated the Aphrodisiac Remedy, the most unique medicine perhaps ever compounded, and the most exceptional in its effects. No advertising or other means of disposing of it are necessary, for its value is so well known that the difficulty will rather be in supplying all who want it. Numbers of my patients always keep as much as I can spare to one person for fear of running short, and many of them would give thousands of dollars rather than run any risk of ever being without it.

As regards the obtaining of this Remedy, or any similar one, I may as well remark here that no one else but myself can possibly supply it! Not only because the proportions of the various articles comprising it, and the manner of combining them, is a secret only known to myself, but because the whole quantity produced of many of the most valuable articles, in my hands, or secured to me alone, by always paying large sums in advance, so that no one else can obtain a grain. . . .

It is, therefore, impossible for any one else to supply an Aphrodisiac Remedy like this, because no one else can obtain the components, nor knows how to combine them. All other so-called Aphrodisiacs can be formed only by the more common and inefficient remedies, such as are to be found in most apothecaries' shops but they in no respect resemble mine.

The subtle and apparently mysterious way in which this Remedy operates surprises most people, and it is therefore necessary to give an explanation of its physiological action. Medical agents act in different ways, some as stimulants to particular parts of the body, some as alternatives, and others again as special excitants of particular organs: thus some act on the bowels, some on the kidneys, some on the heart, and others on the skin. A few act on the nervous system through the brain, like alcohol and opium. Usually, they excite in the first place, and afterwards act as sedatives, or *stupefy*. The Indian Hemp or *Haschisch,* is of this class, and usually forms one of the main ingredients in all common *Exhilarants* and *Aphrodisiacs.* It is a dangerous drug when so used, and utterly valueless, when used alone, for any such purpose, but when properly combined with other articles, it becomes a valuable auxiliary.

Woe to those who use it and opium for the purpose of intoxication! Alcohol is harmless compared with them!

The true Aphrodisiac, as I compound it, acts upon the brain and nervous system, not as a stimulant, but as a *tonic* and *nutritive* agent, thus sustaining its power and the power of the *sexual* organs also, which is entirely dependent upon the *nervous power.*

A man's sexual vigor represents merely his excess of nervous vigor. All the function, both of body and mind, are carried on only by nervous power, which enables each organ to perform its peculiar function. The heart, stomach, lungs, and every other organ, act only from the stimulus which the nerves bring to them from the brain and spinal marrow. Cut these nerves through and stop the supply and they act no longer.

Now, every man only possesses a certain amount of nervous power, which varies in quantity according to the health and natural vigor of his system; if, therefore, too much of this power is employed in one of the functions, the others must run short, and, of course be imperfectly performed. Thus, if a man thinks too much, his brain uses up so much of his nervous power that he has not enough for other purposes, and some organs must act imperfectly. Most likely his *stomach* will be one of these, and then he becomes *dyspeptic,* or he may have heart disease or liver complaint, or any of those numerous diseases which we commonly see—all of which spring originally from impaired nervous action.

An imperfectly acting stomach again re-acts on the whole system, because it prevents proper *nutrition,* and thus causes general weakness or debility. No act, however, exhausts more of nervous power than the *sexual act!* and this is why its too frequent performance is so terribly injurious, and why the votaries of Venus so frequently become debilitated, weak-minded and impotent. . . .

It has long been known, as a general truth that there is an intimate connection between the nervous and sexual systems, but it has hitherto been generally thought to be merely *sympathetic.* It is now known, however, that the composition of the nervous substance and the seminal fluid are almost identical, that in fact they are essentially nearly the same thing. It has also been ascertained that in all cases of severe nervous or mental derangement, the actual substance of the brain and nerves either wastes away or undergoes a destructive change. And in the same way, in all cases of confirmed loss of sexual power, the seminal substance either wastes or becomes destructively changed in a similar manner. But what is still more important, the destruction or injury of either of these elements of our systems brings on inevitably a similar evil to the other.

Every man, therefore, who becomes *impotent,* is in imminent danger of becoming of weak intellect, and every one whose nervous substance is seriously impaired will almost certainly lose his sexual powers. The two are intimately dependent, the one on the other, and are affected for good or for evil, by the same external and internal causes.

At the present time a number of causes are in constant operation on most men, exceedingly destructive both to their nervous and their sexual powers, causing an actual waste of brain and seminal substance, and entailing bodily suffering and mental deficiency to an unknown extent. . . .

For convenience, I have it [my *Aphrodisiac*] so put up, in a dry form, air and water tight, that it can be kept uninjured, for any length of time, in any climate, and under any circumstances. It can also be taken without the inconvenience of measuring, using liquids, or any other troublesome requirement, thus ensuring secrecy and facility of use, let a man be situated however he may. A gentleman can keep it in his vest pocket without any fear of detection from smell, or appearance. It will go anywhere *by post,* with perfect safety, and in such a form that no one through whose hands it passes would ever suspect its *nature,* or that it is anything *peculiar!*

There are no agents for it anywhere at present, nor will there be except they are specially mentioned in my books, so that it can only be obtained from me personally by addressing through the post to "DOCTOR F. HOLLICK, New York, Box 3696." I do this to avoid trouble, and also to prevent counterfeiting which would be sure to be practiced if it were generally sold through agents. . . .

It is not a MERE STIMULANT, or INJURIOUS EXCITANT, acting only for the moment, but a true NERVINE AND SEXUAL TONIC AND RENOVATOR, producing new Nervous and Sexual material, when these have been wasted by excess, abuse, or disease.

Several of the articles which compose the *Aphrodisiac Remedy,* have been used from time immemorial, in a crude form, and separately, but no scientific combination of the whole was ever possible till now.

The celebrated DREAM DRUG of the

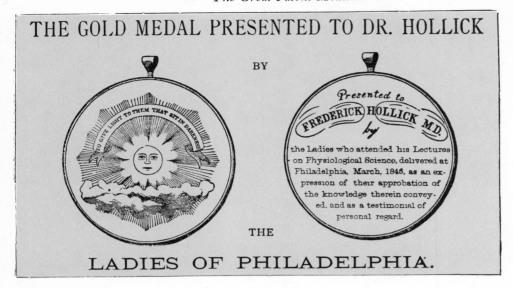

THE GOLD MEDAL PRESENTED TO DR. HOLLICK

BY

THE

LADIES OF PHILADELPHIA.

Presented to FREDERICK HOLLICK M.D. by the Ladies who attended his Lectures on Physiological Science, delivered at Philadelphia, March, 1846, as an expression of their approbation of the knowledge therein conveyed, and as a testimonial of personal regard.

East, the INDIAN HEMP, is often used as an Aphrodisiac, and will sometimes cause erotic dreams. This, however, is only occasional, and such an effect is always followed by unusual debility, terminating at last, if its use is continued, in complete sexual impotence.

In the Harems of Turkey, a compound is used called in Arabic, "LOVE'S ASSISTANT!" It is composed of various stimulating spices, with opium and MUSK, and has some power, when first used, but at last it eventually causes general weakness and decay both of body and mind. The late SULTAN OF TURKEY used this compound till he was nearly an idiot; and at last died from sheer exhaustion.

In China they have a Pill somewhat similar to this, and which causes almost identically the same results. Some time ago this *Chinese Remedy* was brought to France, and sold in Paris under the name of HONNEUR DE LA FAMILLE! (*Honor of the Family*) this being its Chinese name,—the evil results from its use, however, soon caused it to be but little called for.

In some parts of Arabia and Africa, an Aphrodisiac has also been long employed, as we can see from allusion in old Chronicles, and in various Poems. Even in the Hebrew Scriptures the *Mandrake* is spoken of as being so used. The *Hindoos* have always been great lovers of Aphrodisiacs, and they possess some powerful ones, which however, they used with-

out knowledge, and consequently derive but little good from them, and much harm.

All these articles, after much trouble, time, and expense, I have obtained and analyzed, so as to know exactly what they were.

The Aphrodisiac Remedy contains what is really good and effective in all of them.

The *Common Aphrodisiacs* are merely compounds of *Spanish flies, Opium, Strychnine, Arsenic, Phosphorus* and similar drugs; most of them are *rank poisons*.

Among other names used for Aphrodisiacs, by the Turks, Arabians, and Hindoos, we find the following: PARENT OF PLEASURE! —DELIGHT OF PARADISE!—FAMILY MULTIPLIER!—YOUTH PROLONGER! —HOPE OF THE AGED!—BRAIN STRENGTHENER!—FOUNTAIN OF POWER!—STRENGTH GIVER!—and numerous others, all indicating the same powers. All of these various articles therefore, imperfect though they are, have still gained a reputation, and are eagerly sought. How much more valuable, therefore, must be a compound which combines the execellences of all, *without any hurtful qualities whatever!*

Although never advertised, and only known through the reports of those who had been restored by its use, the Aphrodisiac of Dr. Hollick has become known, and sought for in all the principal cities of Europe! Many persons of eminence have regularly obtained it, privately, and in more than one instance the wishes and hopes of married people of high rank, have been fulfilled through its means.

Its fame has even reached Turkey and in *Constantinople,* itself, the *aphrodisiac is* rapidly supplanting the hurtful and inefficient drugs formerly in use. . . .

FEMALES who are *Childless, cold in temperament, Nervous, and sexually feeble,* are as much benefited by the *Remedy* as males, and many a solitary hearth has been blessed with children through its use.

For those who can not possibly visit Dr. Hollick, he will explain a simple mode of examination, by which the facts of the case can be fully ascertained, so that the patients at a distance can be treated by correspondence with perfect success. . . .

All letters are destroyed as soon as notes are taken of the case.

Electricity

221

ELECTRIC BELTS.

Try it and be Convinced.

DISCOUNT, ONE-THIRD.

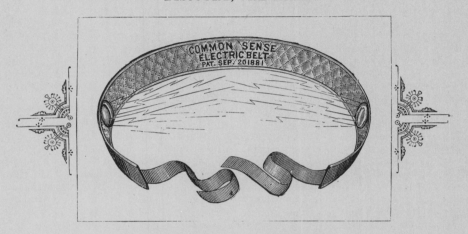

THIS BELT CURES

PARALYSIS,	LUMBAGO,	MALARIA,
NEURALGIA,	DYSPEPSIA,	LAME BACK,
RHEUMATISM,	FEVER AND AGUE,	LIVER COMPLAINT,
SPINAL IRRITATION,	SEMINAL WEAKNESS,	KIDNEY DISEASES,
NERVOUS EXHAUSTION,	FEMALE COMPLAINTS,	GENERAL DEBILITY.

FAC-SIMILE OF LABEL.

> # COMMON SENSE ELECTRIC BELT,
> ## THE BELT FOR THE MILLION.
> Warranted Equal to any of the High Priced Belts and Sold at a REASONABLE Price.
> ### Manufactured by the
> ## Common Sense Electric Belt Co.
> Pat. Sept. 20, 1881. **CHICAGO, ILL.**

Price, according to quality, $3.00, $4.00 and $5.00 each.

Sent by mail on receipt of price.   Address your orders to our agents,

CHAS. TRUAX & CO.

*At the same time that patent medicines were doing so well,
there were several other schools of thought about the treatment and
cure of the various ailments that afflicted man.
One of the most popular of these was the idea that electricity
could cure any ailment to be found. This was a lucrative business.
The appliances used for the electrical treatments were not cheap
and most homes had at least one type of appliance since it was found that every illness
could not be cured very easily with just medicine,
even if administered by a regular physician.
People, then as now, were gullible and ready to try anything.
Here is an advertising booklet issued by one of these
Electrical health appliance companies.
As you can see, it is supposed to be practically a cure-all.*

THE ELECTRIC ERA
Throw Physic to the Dogs.

SHAKESPEARE

The world, since its foundation, has gone through various eras, the Stone Era, the Iron Era, and we have now arrived at what may properly be termed the *Electric Era*. Everything is done by Electricity; our streets are lighted by it, our engines run by it, it carries our messages in the twinkling of an eye under the Broad Atlantic and conveys our voice from city to city by telephone.

And still the great inventors are every day putting the subtle current to new uses and preparing new surprises for us. While the Electric Light, the Electric Telegraph and Telephone were all great discoveries in their way, it remained for a famous German Electrician to invent a simple method to apply Electricity to the human body in the shape of a Belt, so that various diseases could be cured by its use, and we question if this discovery will not be of more real benefit to the human race than all the others mentioned put together.

The one great drawback to all Electric Belts heretofore has been that in many cases, they would produce sores on the body where worn.

The eminent Electrician and Physician, P. H. Van der Weyde, M.D., recognizing that these appliances had great curative merits, set about to find some way to overcome this difficulty. After several years of experimenting he invented a system which entirely overcame this great defect, and was granted Letters Patent on his invention by the U.S. Government on February 15, 1887.

He has granted to us the exclusive right to use his system in the manufacture of all our Belts and Appliances, and therefore we feel warranted in saying they are now perfect. And the very fact of our goods being made under Prof. Van der Weyde's patents is a guarantee of their great merit. . . .

POINTS OF SUPERIORITY

We claim that our Belt is far superior to any other Electric Appliance ever manufactured, for the following reasons:

First—No metals come in contact with the body, consequently it produces no sores, as is the case when poisonous metals are laid on the delicate surface of the skin.

Second—The battery being a complete circuit in itself there is no connection by wire used, and consequently no annoyance caused by the same constantly breaking.

Third—The cloth covering crosses up the current in such a manner that a positive and negative pole are formed from ANY TWO POINTS of contact.

Fourth—The cloth covering, being medicated, acts upon the skin and allows the current to be absorbed into the system and not carried simply to the surface, as is the case with other appliances.

ARE THEY ELECTRIC?

So many bogus appliances have been sold claiming to be Electric, that produced no action whatever, that many persons have come to the conclusion that no appliance can be made in this form that will generate a current. To settle the matter, we hereby guarantee;

THAT WE WILL FORFEIT FIVE HUNDRED DOLLARS ($500.00) IF A TEST BY MEANS OF A GALVANOMETER DOES NOT SHOW THAT THE GERMAN ELECTRIC BELT GENERATES A CURRENT.

THE GERMAN DUPLEX ELECTRIC BELT
PRICE—$5.00

Specially Adapted for the Cure of Dyspepsia Liver Complaint, Kidney Disease, Lame Back, Constipation, Rheumatism, Sciatica, etc.

This Belt consists of two double strength batteries, one of which goes over the small of the back and one over the region of the Liver and Stomach. The currents generated pass through the most important organs in the body, removing the cause of disease by strengthening and invigorating the nerves that control their action.

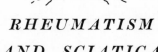

RHEUMATISM
AND SCIATICA

Rheumatism, Sciatica, Neuralgia, Etc., are caused by imperfect action of the kidneys, liver and skin, and their inability to throw off poisonous substances—uric acid, etc.,—from

THE ...

GERMAN ELECTRIC

BELTS AND APPLIANCES

Made Under U. S. Patent No. 357,647, Granted to

PROF. P. H. VAN DER WEYDE, M. D.

President of New York Electrical Society, and Late Professor of Chemistry of New York Medical College, Etc.

MANUFACTURED AND SOLD BY THE

GERMAN ELECTRIC AGENCY,

12 VESEY STREET, NEW YORK,

——— AND ———

28 Endsleigh Gardens, Euston Road, London, N. W.

the blood. The consequences are disorders, both local and constitutional, affecting the joints, muscles, and membranes, and characterized by pain and swelling more or less intense. It is well known by every sufferer that the various "medicines," "liniments," "reliefs," etc., do nothing to cure the disease—relief is only afforded at best. The German Electro-Galvanic Belt is infallible in such cases, often removing every trace of the disease in a short space of time, by equalizing the circulation and enabling the excretory and secretory ducts to perform their natural function. Thousands have been cured of Rheumatism, Sciatica, and other painful diseases by means of this appliance.

ARE THEY ELECTRIC?

So many bogus appliances have been sold claiming to be Electric, that produced no action whatever, that many persons have come to the conclusion that no appliance can be made in this form that will generate a current. To settle the matter, we hereby guarantee:

That we will forfeit Five Hundred Dollars ($500.00) if a test by means of a Galvanometer does not show that the German Electric Belt generates a current.

A Galvanometer is an instrument for showing the presence of an electric current, and one can be found in the possession of nearly every electrician or scientific man, so that it is easy to find out if we are speaking the truth or not.

Read the following from Roovers Brothers, the great Electricians, of Brooklyn, N. Y.:

OFFICE OF ROOVERS BROTHERS,
Manufacturing Electricians,
NO. 170 DEAN ST., BROOKLYN, N.Y.

GENTLEMEN—We have tested your German Electric Belt by means of a Galvanometer and an Electrometer and find it generates quite a strong current, much stronger in fact than any Belt or Appliance we have ever before seen. Respectfully yours,

ROOVERS BROS.

While all our Belts and Appliances are made on the same principle, they are necessarily of various forms, so as to be adapted for different diseases.

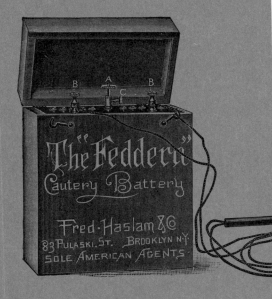

taste in the mouth, especially in the morning; fretfulness, lowness of spirits, imaginary fears, physical and mental suffering. The German Electro-Galvanic Belt acts speedily and effectually in these cases, and it may be amply verified, by the experience of the afflicted themselves, that no other treatment has a like effect.

The German Electric Lady's Belt.

Price, - - $5.00.

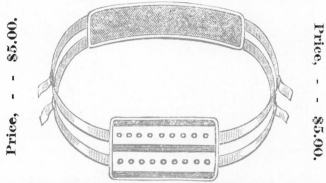

Price, - - $5.00.

Specially adapted to cure Female Complaints of all kinds.

This appliance consists of two powerful batteries, one of which goes over the small of the back and one over the abdominal region. The action is direct on the uterus (womb), and it has been used with marvelous results in some of the very worst cases of Prolapsus Uteri (falling of the womb), Leucorrhœa (Whites), Suppressed Menses, Painful Menstruation and Flooding. This appliance is light and pleasant to wear and can be worn under corsets without inconvenience.

Remember we give a written guarantee that this Belt will cure these diseases, and, if it does not, we will return the full amount paid.

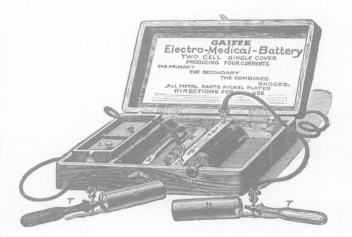

DAVIS & KIDDER'S ELECTRIC MACHINE.

Price to patients.................................$10 00.   See page 218.

DISEASES OF MEN.

Although Electricity, properly applied, is a wonderful remedy in nearly all classes of ailments, still it is in diseases of men that it is most employed by the medical profession. For this purpose we manufacture an article which we call

The German Electric Suspensory Belt.

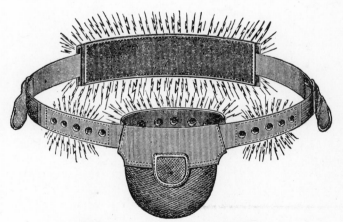

Price reduced to $5.00.

A positive and unfailing cure for **Nervous Debility, Weakness, Loss of Vigor, Varicocele, etc., etc.**

Remember we give a written guarantee that the Appliance will cure the diseases mentioned, and, if it does not, we will return the full amount paid.

Fig. 6.

Rubbing the Chest and Abdomen.

Adds Insult to Robbery.

A prominent New York Editor says: "The man who tries to make you take an inferior article instead of the thing you really want adds insult to robbery. He admits that he thinks you do not know what you want, and that you haven't very much brains anyhow. He imagines that you can be changed by the last words you hear, that because he offers to sell you for a few cents less an utterly worthless *substitute* you will take that in place of what you actually want and need."

DR. PIERCE'S FAVORITE PRESCRIPTION is the ONLY medicine for woman's peculiar ills which contains no alcohol and the only one the makers of which are not afraid to publish all the ingredients *in plain English*, on every bottle-wrapper. Is this not significant?

A full list of its ingredients, attested under oath, stands as a BADGE OF HONESTY on every bottle-wrapper. It is also guaranteed under the Food and Drugs Act of June 30th 1906—Serial No. 21.

All letters of consultation are treated as sacredly confidential and answers returned in plain envelopes. Address: World's Dispensary Medical Association, Dr. R. V. Pierce, Pres., 663 Main St., Buffalo, N. Y. Invalid women in need of experienced medical advice are invited to write; consultation costs you nothing.

A new and recently revised edition of **Dr. Pierce's Common Sense Medical Adviser** is now ready for mailing and is sent free on receipt of stamps to cover cost of mailing only—31 cents for cloth-bound and 21 cents for paper covered. Remit ONE OR TWO cent postage stamps. This book contains over 1000 pages and is profusely illustrated. The best family doctor book extant. Address, World's Dispensary Medical Association, 663 Main Street, Buffalo, N. Y.

I

THE PEOPLE'S
COMMON SENSE
MEDICAL ADVISER
IN PLAIN ENGLISH;
OR,
MEDICINE SIMPLIFIED.
BY
R. V. PIERCE, M. D.,
ONE OF THE STAFF OF CONSULTING PHYSICIANS AND SURGEONS, AT THE INVALIDS' HOTEL AND SURGICAL INSTITUTE, AND PRESIDENT OF THE WORLD'S DISPENSARY MEDICAL ASSOCIATION.

TWENTIETH EDITION.
420th THOUSAND.

Carefully Revised by the Author, assisted by his full Staff of Associate Specialists in Medicine and Surgery, the Faculty of the Invalids' Hotel and Surgical Institute.

BUFFALO, N. Y.:
PUBLISHED AT THE WORLD'S DISPENSARY PRINTING OFFICE AND BINDERY.
1889.

Fig. 14.

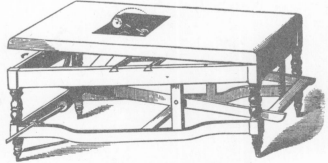

Apparatus for Kneading with Rollers.

Dr. Pierce

Invalids' Hotel and Surgical Institute, 663 Main Street, Buffalo, N. Y.

Dr. R. V. Pierce was a man of varied talents.
He wrote many books on health, ran
the Invalid's Hotel and Surgical Institute at Buffalo, New York
as well as the World's Dispensary Medical Association.
He treated people by means of all three.
He also sold medicines under the name
of Dr. Pierce and Dr. Sage.
His books such as
The People's Common Sense Medical Adviser were best sellers;
more than a million copies were sold throughout the world.

EDITOR'S NOTE

THE PEOPLE'S
COMMON SENSE
MEDICAL ADVISER
by R. V. Pierce, M.D.

sold over a million copies. This book is one complete advertisement for the patent medicines made by the author in his World's Dispensary. . . .

His most famous medicines were Dr. Sage's Catarrh Remedy, Dr. Pierce's Golden Discovery as well as a number of others sold under the Dr. Pierce label.

Although his volume seems to be an ordinary book on home medicine, it is far from one. He gives the symptoms and treatment for all ailments, as in other books but the treatment for every ailment includes the use of one of his medicines along with other treatment.

He also describes the Invalid's Hotel and Surgical Institute where patients could go from all parts of the country and world to be cured if the medicine by mail was not successful.

The book is full of testimonials from people who claimed to have been cured when they used the books, the medicines, or the Hotel. Not only the testimonials but the photographs are there. It would seem that anything and everything had been cured.

PREFACE TO THE
FIRST EDITION

Every family needs a **COMMON SENSE MEDICAL ADVISER**. The frequent inquiries from his numerous patients throughout the land, suggested to the Author the importance and popular demand for a reliable work of this kind. Consequently, he has been induced to prepare and publish an extensive dissertation on Physiology, Hygiene, Temperaments, Disease and Domestic Remedies. It is for the interest and welfare of every person, not only to understand the means for the preservation of health, but also to know what remedies should be employed for the alleviation of the common ailments of life.

The frequency of accidents of all kinds, injuries sustained by machinery, contusions, drowning, poisoning, fainting, etc., and also of sudden attacks of painful diseases, such as headache, affections of the heart and nerves, inflammation of the eye, ear and other organs, renders it necessary that non-professionals should possess sufficient knowledge to enable them to employ the proper means for speedy relief. To impart this important information is the aim of the author.

Moreover, this volume treats of Human Temperaments, not only of their influence upon mental characteristics and bodily susceptibilities, but also of their vital and non-vital combinations, which transmit to the off-spring either health, hardihood and longevity, or feebleness, disease, and death. It clearly points out those temperaments which are compatible with each other and harmoniously blend, and also those which, when united in marriage, result in barrenness, or produce in the offspring imbecility, deformity, and idiocy. These matters are freely discussed from original investigations and clinical observations, thus rendering the work a true and scientific guide to marriage.

While instruction is imparted for the care of the body, those diseases (alas how prevalent!) are investigated which are sure to follow as a consequence of certain abuses, usually committed through ignorance. That these ills do exist is evident from the fact that the Author is consulted by multitudes of unfortunate young men and women, who are desirous of procuring relief from the weaknesses and derangements incurred by having unwittingly violated physiological laws.

Although some of these subjects may seem out of place in a work designed for every member of the family, yet they are presented in a style which cannot offend the most fastidious, and with a studied avoidance of all language that can possibly displease the chaste, or disturb the delicate susceptibilities of persons of either sex.

This book should not be excluded from the young, for it is eminently adapted to their wants, and imparts information without which millions will suffer untold misery. It is a false modesty which bars the youth of our land from obtaining such information.

As its title indicates, the Author aims to make this book a useful and practical Medical Adviser. He proposes to express himself in plain and simple language, and, so far as possible, to avoid the employment of technical words, so that all his readers may readily com-

VOCABULARY

OF THE

COMMON SENSE MEDICAL ADVISER,

GIVING EACH TECHNICAL WORD EMPLOYED, REFERRING TO ITS ILLUSTRATION WHEN POSSIBLE, AND IN CASE THE WORD WILL NOT PERMIT OF A SHORT DEFINITION, REFERRING TO THE PAGE WHERE A FULL DESCRIPTION OF ITS MEANING MAY BE FOUND.

A

Abdomen. The part of the body between the diaphragm and pelvis, containing the stomach, intestines, etc. The belly.

Abdominal. Belonging to the Abdomen.

Abortion. Expulsion of the fœtus before the seventh month of pregnancy.

Absorption. The function of taking up substances from within or without the body.

Acetabulum. The bone socket which receives the head of the thigh bone.

Acne. Pimples upon the face, more common at the age of puberty.

Adipose Tissue. A thin membrane composed of cells which contain fat.

Adventitious. Acquired.

Albumen in urine in chemical composition resembles the white of an egg, and is detected by the application of heat, nitric acid, etc.

Albuminoid. Of the nature of albumen.

Albuminuria. A condition or disease in which the urine contains albumen. (See above.)

Alimentary Canal. The canal extending from the mouth to the anus, through which the food passes.

Allopathy. Allopathic school. Defined on page 293.

Alterative. A medicine which gradually changes the constitution, restoring healthy functions.

Alveolar process. The bony structure which contains the sockets of the teeth.

Amaurosis. Loss or decay of sight from disease of the optic nerve.

Amenorrhea. Suppression of the menses.

Amnion. A membrane enveloping the fœtus and the liquid.

Amputation. The operation of cutting off a limb.

Amyloid degeneration. Alteration in the texture of organs, which resembles wax or lard

Amyloids. Foods composed of carbon and hydrogen; as sugar, starch, etc.

Anæmia. Privation of blood. Lack of red corpuscles in the blood.

Anasarca. Dropsy attended with bloating all over the body.

Anatomy. The science of the structure of the body.

Anesthetic. An agent that prevents feeling in surgical operations, and in some diseases of a painful nature.

Angina (pectoris). Violent pain about the heart, attended with anxiety and difficult breathing.

Animalcula, Animalcule. An animal so small as to be invisible, or nearly so, to the naked eye.

Anodynes. Medicines which relieve pain.

Anteversion. The womb falling forward upon the bladder. Illus. p. 753.

Anthelmintics. Medicines which destroy or expel worms from the stomach and intestines.

Antidote. A remedy to counteract the effect of poison.

Antifebrile. A remedy which abates fever.

Antiperiodic. A remedy which prevents the regular appearance of similar symptoms in the course of a disease.

Antiseptic. Medicines which prevent putrefaction.

Antispasmodics. Medicines which relieve spasm.

Anus. The circular opening at the end of the bowel, through which the excrement leaves the body.

Aorta. The great artery of the body arising from the heart. Illus. page 58.

Aperient. A medicine which moves the bowels gently.

Aphthæ. Sore mouth, beginning in pimples and ending in white ulcers.

Aphthous. Complicated with aphthæ.

Apnœa. Short, hurried breathing.

Apoplexy. The effects of a sudden rush of blood to an organ; as the brain, lungs, etc. Brain pressure, from rupture of a blood-vessel.

Aqueous humor. The clear fluid contained in the front chambers of the eye.

Arachnoid. A thin, spider-web like membrane covering the brain.

Areolar Tissue. The network of delicate fibres spread over the body, binding the various organs and parts together,

Artery. A vessel carrying blood from the heart to the various parts of the body; usually red in color.

979

prehend the work, and profit by its perusal. Written as it is amid the many cares attendant upon a practice embracing the treatment of thousands of cases annually, and therefore containing the fruits of a rich and varied experience, some excuse exists for any literary imperfections which the critical reader may observe. THE AUTHOR

Buffalo, N. Y., July, **1875**

INTRODUCTORY WORDS

———⟨∞⟩———

Health and disease are physical conditions upon which pleasure and pain, success and failure depend. Every individual gain increases public gain. Upon the health of its people is based the prosperity of a nation; by it every value is increased, every joy enhanced. Life is incomplete without the enjoyment of healthy organs and faculties, for these give rise to the delightful sensations of existence. Health is essential to the accomplishment of every purpose; while sickness thwarts the best intentions and loftiest aims. . . .

The profession of medicine is no sinecure; its labors are constant, its toil unremitting, its cares unceasing. The physician is expected to meet the grim monster, "break the jaws of death, and pluck the spoil out of his teeth." His ear is ever attention to entreaty, and within his faithful breast are concealed the disclosures of the suffering. Success may elate him, as conquest flushes the victor. Honors are lavished upon the brave soldiers who, in the struggle with the foe, have covered themselves with glory, and returned victorious from the field of battle; but how much more brilliant is the achievement of those who overwhelm disease, that common enemy of mankind, whose victims are numbered by millions! Is it meritorious in the physician to modestly veil his discoveries, regardless of their importance? If he have light, why hide it from the world? Truth should be made as universal and health-giving as sunlight. We say, give light to all who are in darkness, and a remedy to the afflicted everywhere.

We, as a people, are becoming idle, living in luxury and ease, and in the gratification of artificial wants. Some indulge in the use of food rendered unwholesome by bad cookery, and think more of gratifying a morbid appetite than of supplying the body with proper nourishment. Others devote unnecessary attention to the display of dress and a genteel figure, yielding themselves completely to the sway

of fashion. Such intemperance in diet and dress manifests itself in the general appearance of the unfortunate transgressor, and exposes his folly to the world, with little less precision than certain vices signify their presence by a tobacco-tainted breath, beer-bloated body, rum-emblazoned nose, and kindred manifestations. They coddle themselves instead of practicing self-denial, and appear to think that the chief end of life is gratification, rather than useful endeavor.

I propose to express myself candidly and earnestly on all topics relating to health, and appeal to the common sense of the reader and render it a practical common-sense guide to the farmer, mechanic, mariner, and day-laborer, yet I trust that it may not prove less acceptable to the scholar, in its discussion of the problems of life. Not only does the method adopted in this volume of treating of the Functions of the Brain and Nervous System present many new suggestions, in its application to hygiene, the management of disease, generation and the development and improvement of man, but the conclusions correspond with the results of the latest investigations of the world's most distinguished *savants*. My object is to inculcate the facts of science rather than the theories of philosophy.

CHAPTER I

MARRIAGE-LOVE

Love, that tender, inexplicable feeling which is the germinal essence of the human spirit, is the rudimental element of the human soul. It is, therefore, a Divine gift, a blessing which the creator did not withdraw from his erring children, when they were driven from a paradise of innocence and loveliness into a world of desolation and strife. He left it as an invisible cord by which to draw the human heart ever upward, to a brighter home—the heavenly Eden. Love is the very essence of Divine law, the source of inspiration, even the fountain of life itself. It is spontaneous, generous, infinite. To its presence we are indebted for all that is good, true, and beautiful in Art and Nature. It endows humanity with countless virtues, and throws a mystic veil over our many faults. It is this feeling, this immutable law, which controls the destiny of the race. From its influence empires have fallen, scepters have been lost. Literature owes to Love its choicest gems. The poet's lay is sweeter when Cupid tunes the lyre. The artist's brush is truer when guided by Love. . . .

The materialism of the nineteenth century has sought to degrade Love; to define it as purely physical. The result has been a corresponding degradation of art, and even literature has lost much of its lofty idealism. Nudity has became a synonym of vulgarity; Love, of lust. "Evil be to him who evil thinks." True Love never seeks to degrade its object; on the contrary, it magnifies every virtue, endows it with divinest attributes, and guards its chastity, or honor, at the sacrifice of its own life. It increases benevolence by opening the lover's heart to the wants of suffering humanity. Ideality is the canvas, and imagination the brush with which Love delineates the beauties of the adored. Love heightens spirituality, awakens hope, strengthens faith, and enhances devotion. It quickens the perceptions, intensifies the sensibilities, and redoubles the memory. It augments muscular activity, and imparts grace to every movement. The desire to love and to be loved is innate, and forms as much a part of our being as bone or reason. In fact, Love may be considered as the very foundation of our spiritual existence, as bone and reason are the essential bases of our physical and intellectual being. Every man or woman feels the influence of this emotion, sooner or later. It is the Kadesh-barnea of human existence; obedience to its intuitions insures the richest blessings of life, while neglect or perversion enkindles God's wrath, even as did the disobedience of the wandering Israelites. . . .

CONJUGAL LOVE

. . . The consummation desired by all who experience this affection is the union of souls in a true marriage. Whatever of beauty or romance there may be in the lover's dream, is enhanced and spiritualized in the intimate communion of married life. The crown of wifehood and maternity is purer, more divine, than that of the maiden. Passion is lost; the emotions predominate.

The poet's lay is sweeter when Cupid tunes the lyre. The artist's brush is truer when guided by Love. Greece was the cradle of letters and art. Her daughters were queens of beauty, fitted to inspire the Love of her noblest sons.

The materialism of the nineteenth century has sought to degrade Love; to define it as purely physical. The result has been a corresponding degradation of art, and even literature has lost much of its lofty idealism. Nudity has become a synonym of vulgarity; Love, of lust. "Evil be to him who evil thinks." True Love never seeks to degrade its object; on the contrary, it magnifies every virtue, endows it with divinest attributes, and guards its chastity, or honor, at the sacrifice of its own life. It increases benevolence by opening the lover's heart to the wants of suffering humanity. Ideality is the canvas, and imagination the brush with which Love delineates the beauties of the adored. Love heightens spirituality, awakens hope, strengthens faith, and enhances devotion. It quickens the perceptions, intensifies the sensibilities, and redoubles the memory. It augments muscular activity, and imparts grace to every movement. The desire to love and to be loved is innate, and forms as much a part of our being as bone or reason. In fact, Love may be considered as the very foundation of our spiritual existence, as bone and reason are the essential bases of our physical and intellectual being. Every man or woman feels the influence of this emotion, sooner or later. It is the Kadesh-barnea of human existence; obedience to its intuitions insures the richest blessings of life, while neglect or perversion enkindles God's wrath, even as did the disobedience of the wandering Israelites.

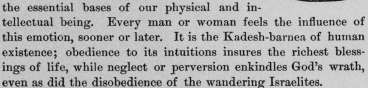

Fig. 96.

The one great fact which pervades the universe is *action*. The very existence of Love demands its activity, and, hence, the highest happiness is attained by a normal and legitimate development of this element of our being. The heart demands

The connubial relation is not an institution; it was born of the necessities and desires of our nature. "It is not good for man to be alone," was the Divine judgment, and so God created for him "an helpmate." Again, "Male and female created He them"; therefore, sex is as divine as the soul. It is often perverted, but so is reason, aye, so is devotion.

The consummation of marriage involves the mightiest issues of life. It may be the source

of infinite happiness or the seal of a living death. . . . Many unhappy marriages are traceable to one or both of two sources, Physical Weaknesses and Masquerading. Many are the candidates for marriage who are rendered unfit therefor from weaknesses of their sexual systems, induced by the violation of well-established physical laws.

We cannot too strongly urge upon parents and guardians the imperative duty of teaching those youths who look to them for instruction, in all matters which pertain to their future well-being such lessons as are embraced in the chapter of this book entitled "Hygiene of the Reproductive Organs." By attending to such lessons as will give the child a knowledge of the physiology and hygiene of his whole system, the errors into which so many of the young fall.

Masquerading is a modern accomplishment. Girls wear tight shoes, burdensome skirts, and corsets, all of which prove very injurious to their health. At the age of seventeen or eighteen, our young ladies are sorry specimens of womankind, and "palpitators," cosmetics, and all the modern paraphernalia of fashion are required to make them appear fresh and blooming. Man is equally to blame. A devotee to all the absurd devices of fashion, he practically asserts that "dress makes the man." But physical deformities are of far less importance than moral imperfections. Frankness is indispensable in love. Each should know the other's faults and virtues. Marriage will certainly disclose them; the idol falls and the deceived lover is transformed into a cold, unloving husband or wife. By far the greater number of unhappy marriages are attributable to this cause. In love, especially, honesty is policy and truth will triumph.

THE PERPETUATION OF THE SPECIES

The third essential object of marriage is the perpetuation of the species. The desire for offspring is innate in the heart of every true man or woman. It is thus a law of our nature, and, as such, must have its legitimate sphere. The essential features of reproduction proclaim monogamy to be the true method of procreation. Promiscuity would render the mother unable to designate the father of her children. Among lower animals, pairing is an instinctive law whenever the female is incapable of protecting and nourishing her offspring alone. During at least fifteen years, the child is dependent for food and clothing upon its parents, to say nothing of the requisite moral training and loving sympathy, which, in a great measure, mould its character. Fidelity to one promotes multiplication. It has been argued by the advocates of polygamy that such a system interferes with woman's natural right to maternity. Of the many marriages celebrated yearly, comparatively few are sterile. The statement that many single women are desirous of having children, would apply only to a very limited number, as it is seldom that they would be able to support children without the aid and assistance of a father. Promiscuity diminishes the number and vitiates the quality of the human products. "Women of pleasure never give to the world sons of genius, or daughters of moral purity."

CHAPTER II

HYGIENE OF THE REPRODUCTIVE ORGANS

The structure and functions of organized bodies are subject to continual alteration. The changes of nutrition and growth, which are constantly taking place in the tissues render them at the same time the seat of repair and waste, of renovation and decomposition, of life and death. The plant germinates and blossoms, then withers and decays; animal life, in like manner, comes into being, grows to maturity, fades and dies. It is, therefore, essential to the perpetuation of life, that new organisms be provided to take the place of those which are passing out of existence. There is no physiological process which presents more interesting phenomena than that of reproduction, which includes the formation, as well as the development of new beings.

Since self-preservation is Nature's first law, the desire for food is a most powerful instinct in all living animals. Not inferior to this law is that for the perpetuation of the race; and for this purpose, throughout the animal and vegetable kingdoms, we find the Biblical statement literally illustrated: "Male and female created He them."

Health is the gauge by which the prosperity of a people may be measured. Were we to trace the history of nations,—their rise and fall,— we would find that much of the barbarism and crime, degradation and vice, as well as their decline and final extinction, was due to licentiousness and sexual excesses. Since there is an intimate relation between mind and body, when the body is enfeebled the mind becomes enervated. Morbid conditions of the body prevent the highest mental development, and, on the other hand, when the mind is debilitated, general depravity, physical as well as mental, is the result. The highest development of the body results from the equal and harmonious cultivation of the mental powers. The perfect

INVALIDS' HOTEL

A MODEL SANITARIUM AND SURGICAL INSTITUTE.

NOT A HOSPITAL, BUT A PLEASANT REMEDIAL HOME,

ORGANIZED WITH

A FULL STAFF OF EIGHTEEN PHYSICIANS AND SURGEONS

AND EXCLUSIVELY DEVOTED TO THE

TREATMENT OF ALL CHRONIC DISEASES.

This imposing Establishment was designed and erected to accommodate the large number of invalids who visit Buffalo from every State and Territory, as well as from many foreign lands, that they may avail themselves of the professional services of the Staff of Skilled Specialists in Medicine and Surgery that compose the Faculty of this widely-celebrated institution.

development and health of the physical organs is therefore essential to the happiness of mankind. But, before health can be insured the nature and general functions of the physical system must be understood. This being done, the question naturally arises: How can health be best maintained and longevity secured?

INFLUENCE OF FOOD—Excessive stimulation excites the sexual passions. For this reason, children should not be immoderately indulged in highly seasoned foods. Those persons who have great muscular vigor are endowed with violent passions, and unless restrained by moral considerations are very likely to be overcome by their animal propensities.

Alcoholic stimulants have a debasing influence upon the whole system, and especially upon the sexual organs; they excite the animal and debase the moral nature; they exhaust the vitality, and, after the excitement, which they temporarily induce, has passed away, the body is left in a prostrated condition.

PHYSICAL LABOR MODIFIES THE PASSION—Labor consumes the surplus vitality which a person may possess, and no better protective can be found against the gratification of the passions, unless it be high moral training, than daily toil extended to such a degree as to produce fatigue. . . .

INFLUENCES OF CLIMATE—Individuals possess distinguishing peculiarities characteristic of the nation to which they belong. Climate exerts a powerful influence upon mankind. In tropical regions the inhabitants are enervated, effeminate, and sensual. The rich live in luxury and ease, vice is unrestrained and license unbridled. When the animal propensities are allowed to predominate, the mental faculties are kept in subjection. Hence races that inhabit those latitudes rarely produce scholars or philosophers. A warm climate hastens the development of the reproductive organs. Men and women become mature at a much earlier age in those regions, than in countries where the temperature is lower. In like manner there is a tendency to premature enfeeblement, for the earlier the system matures, the sooner it deteriorates.

MAN IS A SOCIAL BEING—History demonstrates that when man is deprived of the society of women, he becomes reckless, vicious, depraved, and even barbarous in his habits, thus illustrating the maxim: "It is not good for man to be alone." Social intercourse promotes mental and physical development. . . . Nothing so regulates and restrains passion as a healthy condition of the organs through which it finds expression. And every organ of the body is powerful in proportion to its soundness. . . . Boys are more liable to be morbidly excited when secluded from the society of girls, and vice versa.

The passions may be aroused by the language, appearance, or dress of the opposite sex. A word spoken without an impure intent is often construed in a very different sense by one whose passions color the thought, and is made to convey an impression entirely unlike that which was intended by the speaker. Also, the dress may be of such a character as to excite the sexual passion. The manner in which the apparel is worn is often so conspicuous as to become bawdy, thereby appealing to the libidinous desires.

OBSCENE LITERATURE—Literature is a powerful agent either for good or evil. If we would improve the morals, choice literature must be selected, whether it be that which realizes the ideal, or idealizes the real. Obscene literature, or books written for the express purpose of exciting or intensifying sexual desires in the young, goads to an illicit gratification of the passions, and ruins the moral and physical nature.

SELF-ABUSE—Untold miseries arise from the pollution of the body. Self-pollution, or onanism, is one of the most prolific sources of evil, since it leads both to the degradation of body and mind. It is practiced more or less by members of both sexes, and the habit once established, is overcome with the greatest difficulty. It is the source of numerous diseases which derange the functional activity of the organs involved, and eventually impair the constitution. This vicious habit is often practiced by those who are ignorant of its dangerous results. Statistics show that insanity is frequently caused by masturbation.

Immoderate indulgence in any practice is deleterious to the individual. Emphatically true is this with regard to sexual excesses. . . . The abuse of the conjugal relation produces the most serious results to both parties, and is a prolific source of some of the gravest forms of disease. . . .

The health of the reproductive organs can only be maintained by leading a temperate life. The food should be nourishing but not stimulating. Lascivious thoughts should be banished from the mind, and a taste cultivated for that literature which is elevating in its nature, and the associations should be refining and ennobling. . . .

Woman, from the nature of her organization, has less strength and endurance than man. Much, however, of the suffering and misery which she experiences arises from insufficient attention to the sexual organs. . . . Young women, should, therefore, properly protect themselves, and avoid extremes of heat and cold.

CHAPTER III

CHAPTER III

REMEDIES FOR

DISEASE

It will be our aim, throughout this book, to prescribe such remedies as are within the easy reach of all, and which may be safely employed. Many of those of the vegetable class are indigenous to this country, and may be procured in their strength and purity, at the proper season, by those residing in the localities where they grow, while all others advised may be obtained at any good drug-store. We shall endeavor to recommend such as can be procured and prepared with the least trouble and expense to the patient, when it is believed that they will be equally as efficacious as more expensive medicines.

PROPRIETARY MEDICINES

Having the invalid's best interests in view, it will often happen that we cannot prescribe better or cheaper remedies nor those which are more effective or easily obtained, than some of our standard preparations, which are sold by all druggists. We are aware that there is a popular, and not altogether unfounded prejudice against "patent medicines," owing to the small amount of merit which many of them possess. The term "Patent Medicine" does not apply to Dr. Pierce's remedies, as no patent has ever been asked or obtained for them, nor have they been urged upon the public as "cure-alls." They are simply favorite prescriptions, which, in a very extensive practice have proved their superior remedial virtues in the cure of the disease for which they are recommended.

From the time of Hippocrates down to the present day, physicians have classified diseases according to their causes, character or symptoms. It has been proved that diseases apparently different may often be cured by the same remedy. The reason for this singular fact is obvious. A single remedy may possess a variety of properties. Quinine, among other properties has a tonic which suggests its use in cases of debility; an anti-periodic, which renders it efficient in ague; and an anti-febrile property, which renders it efficacious in cases of fever. The result produced varies with the quantity given, the time of its administration, and the circumstances under which it is employed. Every practicing physician has his favorite remedies, which he oftenest recommends or uses, because he has the greatest confidence in their virtues. The patient does

THE
Invalids' Hotel and Surgical Institute

SOME OF THE CAUSES THAT LED TO ITS ERECTION, AND THE ADVANTAGES WHICH IT AFFORDS.

The destinies of institutions, like those of men, are often determined by pre-existing causes. The destinies of some men are like those of way-side plants, springing up without other apparent cause than the caprice of nature, developing without any apparent aim, yielding no

One of the Private Consultation-rooms, Gentlemen's Department.

perfected fruit, and, finally, dying, leaving scarcely a trace of their existence. Thus it is with institutions which have their origin only in man's caprice. To be enduring, they must be founded upon the needs and necessities of humanity. Many of the great men of the world owe their greatness more to surrounding circumstances than to the genius

not know their composition. Even prescriptions are usually written in a language unintelligible to anybody but the druggist. As much secrecy is employed as in the preparation of proprietary medicines. Does the fact that an article is prepared by a process known only to the manufacturer render that article less valuable? How many physicians know the elementary composition of the remedies which they employ, some of which never have been analyzed? Few practitioners know how morphine, quinine, podophyllin, lepfandrin, pepsin, or chloroform are made, or how nauseous

HOW TO AVOID SWINDLERS

Who Sometimes Infest the Cars and Depots in and Near this City.

We warn all those who contemplate visiting us, that we have the most *positive proofs* that a gang of confidence men have at different times made it their business to watch for sick and infirm people on the way to our institutions, and divert them into the hands of "sharpers," confidence men and swindlers. These men have watched for the coming of invalids on the cars, in and around the depots, in the offices of the hotels located near the depots, and if inquiry was made for our institutions, or if the object of the visit to the city was made known or suspected from the invalid appearance of the traveler, they at once commenced weaving their skillfully-wrought web to catch a victim.

WE, THEREFORE,

Advise all those Desiring to Visit Us,

FIRST.—To ask for no information from policemen, or those appearing to be policemen, in or about our depots. Confidence men often assume a style of dress similar to that worn by policemen.

SECOND.—Let the object of your visit to the city be known to no one whom you meet on the cars, or in the depots or near them.

THIRD.—If you have a check for baggage, when the baggage-man comes through the cars, as one does on every train before it reaches the city, asking if you will have your baggage delivered anywhere in the city, or, if you will have a carriage; if you have a trunk, give him the check for it, pay him 25 cents only and he will have it delivered at the INVALIDS' HOTEL AND SURGICAL INSTITUTE, 663 Main Street. (Do not forget the number). You had

990 ☞

drugs are transformed into palatable elixirs; yet they do not hesitate to employ them. Is it not inconsistent to use a prescription the composition of which is unknown to us, and discard another preparation simply because it is accompanied by a printed statement of its properties with directions for its use?

Various journals in this country, have at different times published absurd formulae purporting to be receipts for the preparation of "Dr. Sage's Catarrh Remedy" and Dr. Pierce's standard medicines, which, in most instances, have not contained a single ingredient which enters into the composition of these celebrated remedies.

In the manufacture of any pharmaceutical preparation, two conditions are essential to its perfection, viz: purity and strength of the materials, and appropriate machinery. The first is insured by purchasing the materials in large quantities, whereby the exercise of greater care in selecting the ingredients can be afforded; and the second can only be accomplished where the business is extensive enough to warrant a large outlay of capital in procuring proper chemical apparatus. These facts apply with especial force to the manufacture of our medicines, their quality having been vastly improved since the demand has become so great as to require their manufacture in very large quantities. Some persons, while admitting that our medicines are good pharmaceutical compounds, object to them on the ground that they are too often used with insufficient judgment. We propose to obviate that difficulty by enlightening the people as to the structure and functions of their bodies, the causes, character, and symptoms of disease, and by indicating the proper and judicious employment of our medicines, together with such auxiliary treatment as may be necessary. Such is one of the designs of this volume.

PROPERTIES OF MEDICINE

It is generally conceded that the action of a remedy upon the human system depends upon properties peculiar to it. The effects produced suggest the naming of these qualities, which have been scientifically classified. We shall name the diseases from their characteristic symptoms, and then, without commenting upon all the properties of a remedy, recommend its employment. Our reference to the qualities of any remedy when we make a particular allusion to them, we shall endeavor to make as easy and familiar as possible.

THE PREPARATION OF MEDICINES.

The remedies which we shall mention for domestic use are mostly vegetable. Infusions and decoctions of these will often be advised on account of the fact that they are more available than the tinctures, fluid extracts, and concentrated principles, which we prefer, and almost invariably employ in our practice. Most of these medical extracts are prepared in our chemical laboratory under the supervision of a careful and skilled pharmaceutist. No one, we presume, would expect with only a dish of hot water and a stew-kettle, to equal in pharmaceutical skill the learned chemist with all his ingeniously devised and costly apparatus for extracting the active, remedial principles from medicinal plants. Yet the infusions and decoctions are not without their value; and from the inferior quality of many of the fluid extracts and other pharmaceutical preparations in the market, it may be questioned whether the former are not frequently as valuable as the latter. So unreliable are a majority of the fluid extracts, tinctures, and concentrated, active principles found in the drug-stores, that we long since found it necessary to have prepared in our laboratory, most of those which we employ. To the reliability of the preparations which we secure in this way we largely attribute our great success in the treatment of disease. Tinctures and fluid extracts are often prepared from old and worthless roots, barks, and herbs which have wholly lost their medicinal properties. Yet they are sold at just as high prices as those which are good. We manufacture our tinctures, fluid extracts, and concentrated, active principles from roots, barks, and herbs which are fresh, and selected with the greatest care. Many of the crude roots, barks, and herbs found in the market are inactive because they have been gathered at the wrong season. These, together with those that have been kept on hand so long as to have lost all medici-

nal value, are often sold in large quantities, and at reduced prices, to be manufactured into fluid extracts and tinctures. Of course, the preparations made from such materials are worthless. Whenever the dose of fluid extracts, tinctures, and concentrated active principles, is mentioned in this chapter, the quantity advised is based upon our experience in the use of these preparations, as they are made in our laboratory, and the smallest quantity which will produce the desired effect is always given. When using most of the preparations found in the drug-stores, the doses have to be somewhat increased, and even then they will not always produce the desired effect, for reasons already given.

ALTERATIVES

Alteratives are a class of medicines which in some inexplicable manner, gradually change certain morbid actions of the system, and establish a healthy condition instead. They stimulate the vital processes to renewed activity, and arouse the excretory organs to remove matter which ought to be eliminated. They facilitate the action of the secretory glands, tone them up, and give a new impulse to their operations, so that they can more expeditiously rid the system of worn-out and effete materials. In this way they alter, correct, and purify the fluids, tone up the organs, and re-establish their healthy functions. Alteratives may possess tonic, laxative, stimulant, or diuretic properties all combined in one agent. Or we may combine several alteratives, each having only one of these properties in one remedy.

THE COMPOUNDING OF ALTERATIVES

The efficacy of this class of remedies can be greatly increased by properly combining several of them into one compound. This requires a knowledge of Pharmaceutical Chemistry; i.e., the preparation of compounds founded on the chemical relation and action of their several remedial, active principles. Many practitioners make combinations of remedies which neutralize each other's influence, instead of extending their efficacy and curative power.

DR. PIERCE'S Golden Medical Discovery, or Alterative extract. This compound is a highly nutritive and tonic preparation, combining the remedial properties of the best vegetable alteratives at present known to the medical profession. In perfecting this alterative compound, and likewise other standard preparations of medicine, we have made an outlay of many thousands of dollars for chemical apparatus, and special machinery by the aid of which these remedies have been brought to their present perfection. Great pains are taken to obtain the materials at the right season of the year, properly cured so that none of their remedial qualities may be impaired. We, therefore, can with great confidence recommend Dr. Pierce's Golden Medical Discovery as one of the best preparations of the alterative class. Like all others of this type, its action is insensible, producing gradual changes, arousing the excretory glands to remove morbid materials, and at the same time toning the secretory organs. The manufacture of this compound is under the special supervision of a competent chemist and pharmaceutist, and it is now put up in bottles wrapped with full directions for its use.

DR. PIERCE'S Pleasant Purgative Pellets. These pellets combine the pure, concentrated, active principles of several vegetable alteratives, and the result is, that within the small compass of a few grains he has most happily blended and chemically condensed these properties, so that their action upon the animal economy is sanative and universal. They awaken the latent powers, quicken the tardy functions, check morbid deposits, dissolve hard concretions, remove obstructions, promote depuration, harmonize and restore the functions, equalize the circulation, and encourage the action of the nervous system. They stimulate the glands, increase the peristaltic movement of the intestines, tone the nutritive processes, while aiding in evacuating the bowels. All this they accomplish without corroding the tissues or vitiating the fluids. Their assistance is genial, helping the system to expel worn out materials, which would become noxious if retained. Having expended their remedial powers upon the various functions of the body, they are themselves expelled along with other waste matter, leaving behind them no traces of irritation. This cannot be said of mercurials, or of other harsh, mineral alteratives. These Pellets may be safely employed when the system is feeble, frail, and delicate, by giving them in less quantities.

ANODYNES

Anodynes are those medicines which relieve pain by blunting the sensibility of the nerves,

or of the brain, so that it does not appreciate the morbid sensation. An anodyne may be a stimulant in one dose, and a narcotic in a larger one. The properties of different anodyne agents vary, consequently they produce unlike effects.

DR. PIERCE'S Compound Extract of Smart-weed. This anodyne compound is made by uniting several of the most valuable agents of this class, and its medicinal qualities are rendered still more efficacious by the addition of certain stimulating articles. It is free from narcotic properties which are liable to produce deleterious results, and has been found to be not only harmless in its action, but very genial and effectual withal, and most reliable as a stimulant and diaphoretic remedy.

ANTIPERIODICS

It is well understood that malarial diseases are characterized by a periodicity which indicates their nature. Antiperiodics prevent the recurrence of the periodic manifestations, and hence their name.

The Golden Medical Discovery has gained an enviable reputation in malarial districts for the cure of ague. From observing its action in the cure of this and other miasmatic diseases and knowing its composition, we are thoroughly satisfied that it contains chemical properties which neutralize and destroy the miasmatic or ague poison which is in the system, and, at the same time, produces a rapid excretion of the neutralized poisons. One strong proof of this is found in the fact that persons who are cured with it are not so liable to relapse as those in whom the chills are broken with Quinine or other agents. No bad effects are experienced after an attack of ague which has been cured with the Golden Medical

Discovery. This cannot be said of Quinine, Peruvian Bark, Arsenic, and Mercurials, which comprise nearly the whole list of remedies usually resorted to by physicians for arresting ague. The Golden Medical Discovery not only has the merit of being a certain antidote for miasmatic diseases, but is pleasant to the taste, a matter of no small importance, especially when administered to children. To break the chills, this medicine should be taken in doses of four teaspoonfuls three times a day, and if this treatment pursued for three days, does not entirely arrest the chills, these doses may be repeated in alternation with five-grain doses of quinine for the three succeeding days. But in no case should more than this amount of the Golden Medical Discovery be given.

CATHARTICS

DR. PIERCE'S Pleasant Pellets being entirely vegetable in their composition, operate without disturbance to the system, diet, or occupation. Put up in glass vials. Always fresh and reliable. As a laxative, alterative, or gently acting but searching cathartic, these little Pellets give the most perfect satisfaction. Sick Headache, Bilious Headache, Dizziness, Constipation, Indigestion, Bilious attacks, and all derangements of the stomach and bowels, are promptly relieved and permanently cured by the use of Dr. Pierce's Pleasant Pellets. In explanation of the remedial power of these Pellets over so great a variety of diseases, it may truthfully be said that their action upon the system is universal, not a gland or tissue escaping their sanative influence.

Everybody, now and then, needs a gentle laxative to assist nature a little; or, a more searching and cleansing, yet gentle cathartic, to remove offending matter from the stomach and bowels and tone up and invigorate the liver and quicken its tardy action. Thereby the Pleasant Pellets cure biliousness, sick and bilious headache, costiveness, or constipation of the bowels, sour stomach, windy belchings, "heart-burn," pain and distress after eating, and kindred derangements of the liver, stomach and bowels.

Persons subject to any of these troubles should never be without a vial of the Pleasant Pellets at hand. In proof of their superior ex-

cellence it can be truthfully said that they are always adopted as a household remedy after the first trial.

The Pleasant Pellets are far more effective in arousing the liver to action than "blue pills," the old-fashioned compound cathartic pills, calomel, or other mercurial preparation, and have the further merit of being purely vegetable in their composition and perfectly harmless in any condition of the system. Furthermore, no particular care is required while using them. . . .

If people generally, would pay more attention to properly regulating the action of their bowels, they would have less frequent occasion to call for their doctor's services to subdue attacks of dangerous diseases. Hence it is of great importance to know what safe, harmless agent best serves the purpose of producing the desired action.

DIAPHORETICS

Diaphoretics are medicines which increase perspiration. Those which occasion profuse sweating are termed Sudorifics. The two terms indicate different degrees of the same operation. They constitute an important element in domestic practice, on account of the salutary effects which generally follow their action. Their operation is favored by warmth externally, and warm drinks, when they are not given in hot infusion.

DR. PIERCE'S Compound Extract of Smart-weed. This is unsurpassed as a diaphoretic agent, and is much more certain in its operation than any simple diaphoretic.

EMMENAGOGUES

Emmenagogue is a term applied to a class of medicines which have the power of favoring the discharge of the menses. We shall mention only a few of those which are best adapted to domestic use.

DR. PIERCE'S Compound Extract of Smart-weed is an excellent emmenagogue. Dr. Eberle, a very celebrated medical writer, and author of a work on medicine which is very popular with the profession, says that he has used the Extract of Smart-weed in twenty cases of amenorrhea (suppressed menstruation), and affirms "With no other remedy or mode or treatment have I been so successful as with this." Full directions accompany every bottle. It is sold by all druggists.

DR. PIERCE'S Favorite Prescription is an efficient remedy in cases requiring a medicine to regulate the menstrual function. Full directions accompany every bottle.

LINIMENT

Liniments are medicines designed for external application. The benefits arising from their use depend upon their derivative power, as well as upon the anodyne properties which many of them possess, rendering them efficacious for soothing pain. We cannot mention a more valuable agent of this class than

DR. PIERCE'S Compound Extract of Smart-weed. As an external application this preparation subdues inflammation and relieves pain. For all wounds, bruises, sprains, bee-stings, insect and snake-bites, frost-bites, chilblains, caked breast, swollen glands, rheumatism, and, in short, for any and all ailments, whether afflicting man or beast, requiring a direct external application, either to allay inflammation or soothe pain, the Extract of Smart-weed cannot be excelled.

NERVINE

These are medicines which act on the nervous system, soothing excitement and quieting the condition known as "nervousness."

DR. PIERCE'S Favorite Prescription. This is a tonic nervine of unsurpassed efficacy, combined in such a manner, that, while it quiets nervous irritation, it strengthens the enfeebled nervous system, restoring it to healthful vigor. In all diseases involving the female reproductive organs, with which there is usually associated an irritable condition of the nervous system, it is unsurpassed as a remedy. It is also a uterine and general tonic of great excellence. It is sold by all druggists.

STIMULANTS

Stimulants are medicines which have the power of increasing the vital activity of the body. Some have a very transient action, while others are more permanent in effect.

DR. PIERCE'S Compound Extract of Smart-weed. This quickly diffusible stimulant and genial anodyne we have spoken of under the head of Anodynes. But its medicinal properties equally entitle it to a place and mention under the class of stimulants. As a stimulant it spurs the nervous system and arouses the circulatory forces. Congestion of the lungs, liver, bowels, or uterus, embarrasses the functions of these organs. Frequently this congestive difficulty may be entirely obviated, and the circulation of the blood restored to the surface of the body, by the administration of a few doses of this pleasant remedy.

TONICS

Tonics are remedies which moderately exalt the energies of all parts of the body, without causing any deviation of healthy function. While stimulants are transient in their influence, tonics are comparatively permanent.

DR. PIERCE'S Favorite Prescription. The Favorite Prescription, in addition to those properties already described, likewise combines tonic properties. In consequence of the never ceasing activities of the bodily organs, the system requires support, something to permanently exalt its actions. In all cases of debility, the Favorite Prescription tranquilizes the nerves, tones up the organs and increases their vigor, and strengthens the system.

DR. PIERCE'S Golden Medical Discovery. In addition to the alterative properties combined in this compound, it possesses important tonic qualities. While the Favorite Prescription exerts a tonic influence upon the digestive and nutritive functions, the Golden Medical Discovery acts upon the excretory glands. Besides, it tends to retard unusual waste and expenditure. This latter remedy tones, sustains, and at the same time regulates the functions. While increasing the discharge of noxious elements accumulated in the system, it promptly arrests the wastes arising from debility, and the unusual breaking down of the cells, incident to quick decline. It stimulates the liver to secrete, changes the sallow complexion, and transforms the listless invalid into a vigorous and healthy being. At the same time, it checks the rapid disorganization of the tissues and their putrescent change, while it sustains the vital processes. It is, therefore, an indispensable remedy in many diseases.

The Indian Vegetable Family Instructor

Indian Hemp.

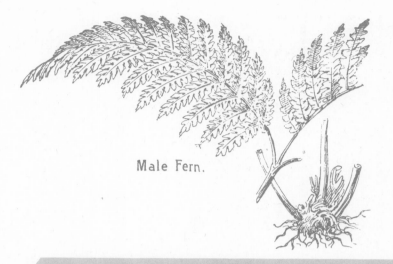

Male Fern.

KICKAPOO

Indian Worm Killer.

—PREPARED FROM—

NATURAL ROOTS and HERBS.

Two to four doses will be sufficient. A Pleasant, Safe, Reliable and Prompt Remedy for the removal of Stomach and Seat or Pin Worms from Child or Adult.

IT IS EASY TO TAKE,
NEVER FAILS,
ABSOLUTELY HARMLESS,
AND REQUIRES NO PHYSIC.

Price, 25 Cents a Package, 5 for $1.00.

FOR SALE BY ALL DRUGGISTS

Throughout the United States.

43

THE

INDIAN VEGETABLE

FAMILY INSTRUCTER:

CONTAINING

THE NAMES AND DESCRIPTIONS OF ALL THE MOST USEFUL HERBS AND PLANTS THAT GROW IN THIS COUNTRY, WITH THEIR MEDICINAL QUALITIES ANNEXED;

ALSO,

A TREATISE

ON MANY OF THE LINGERING DISEASES TO WHICH MANKIND ARE SUBJECT, WITH NEW AND PLAIN ARGUMENTS RESPECTING THE MANAGEMENT OF THE SAME;

WITH

A LARGE LIST OF RECIPES,

WHICH HAVE BEEN CAREFULLY SELECTED FROM INDIAN PRESCRIPTIONS AND FROM THOSE VERY PERSONS WHO WERE CURED BY THE SAME AFTER EVERY OTHER REMEDY HAD FAILED.

DESIGNED FOR THE USE OF FAMILIES IN THE UNITED STATES.

BY PIERPONT F. BOWKER.

UTICA:
PUBLISHED BY JARED DOOLITTLE
1851.

Onion.

KICKAPOO

INDIAN ✳ SAGWA.

Is a compound of the virtues of Roots, Herbs,
Barks, Gums and Leaves. Its elements are

BLOOD-MAKING, BLOOD-CLEANSING AND LIFE-SUSTAINING.

It is the Purest, Safest, Most Effectual Medicine known to the public. **By**
. its searching and cleansing qualities it drives out the foul corruptions .
. . which contaminate the blood and cause derangement and decay. . .
. . . . It stimulates and enlivens the vital functions, promotes en- . . .
. . . . . ergy and strength, restores and preserves health and in- . . . .
. . . . . fuses new life and vigor throughout the whole system. . . . .
. . . . No sufferer from any disease which arises from impurity . . . .
. . . of the blood need despair who will give Indian Sagwa a . . .
. . fair trial. The sciences of Medicine and Chemistry have never . .
. produced so valuable a remedy, nor one so potent to cure all diseases .
. . . . . arising from an impure blood. **SAGWA** will cure . . . . .

CONSTIPATION, LIVER COMPLAINT, DYSPEPSIA, INDIGESTION, LOSS OF APPETITE, SCROFULA, RHEUMA-TISM, CHILLS AND FEVER,

or any Disease arising from an Impure Blood or Derangement of the
STOMACH, LIVER OR KIDNEYS.

Price, $1.00 per bottle ; 6 bottles for $5.00.

FOR SALE BY ALL DRUGGISTS.
43

Juniper

SPRING

Now comes the soft season of buds and bowers.
The opening of bells and the blooming of
flowers,
The hill-tops and meadows are verdant and
gay,
O this is the month, the fair blooming May.
See yonder she comes with a wreath on her
brow,
How grateful and gay is a glance at her now;
Fair sunshine's her mantle, it dazzles the eye,
Her vestments are bright as the heavenly sky.
O'er the wide peopled earth she is every where
seen,
With a foliage of lively and beautiful green,
She invites the fair damsel there heedlessly
stray.
And follow the flourish along the smooth way.
Learn the true use of herbs, of trees, and of
flowers,
Then wander afar, for wide are her bowers,
And easy the task and more useful than
wealth,
'T is earth's sweetest treasure, the sure way to
health.

Vegetation is now springing forth; it is the
season of sunshine and showers; sweet spring,
like a herald from heaven, invites our footsteps
abroad over the green fields that surround our
native dwellings. If you have a leisure hour,
employ it in minutely searching God's works.
Cull medicine and prepare it ready against
sickness and distress. Say not I have not, for
sickness will surely come. Our fields abound
with vegetable medicine and the fertile
meadows, the witness of your labor, produce
many, yes, very many, a valuable root. It is
now the season of complaint. Jaundice and
universal weakness of the whole system is
common. The remedy is simple and easy. Expense is out of the question entirely. Roots
and herbs are at the command of every one,
and nature's prescriptions are all free gratis.
She demands not your money for her services,
but like a kind patron and friend invites you
to partake of her blessings, and her only
reward is to come and taste more. There is no
excuse for you to lay and suffer if you are sick.
No; this physician is kind and charitable. The
rich and poor may share the blessing alike.

Equality and equal rights is the motto. Very little trouble when you are well will procure a store of medicine against the day you may become diseased. But I have insensibly deviated from the path I was tracing. Return again to spring. If you are in the habit of being unwell about this time, all you have to do is to cleanse and promote a free circulation of the blood. This may be easily done. Root beers and vegetable bitters are simple and easy medicines. These are the cheapest and best restoratives to human nature ever known. An enlightened and civilized republic, it is hoped, will shortly see the day when the bands of thraldom to apothecary medicine will be loosed, and like the shackles of royalty that would fain encumber our liberty, sleep with the dust of ages or remain to dupe mortals of another country with its oppression. America! the land of the free! may thy name and nature accord in golden harmony together!

AN INVOCATION

That nice machine, the human frame!
O God! inspire my mind,
That I may understand the same,
No more to nature blind.

Inspire my tongue, inspire my heart,
And useful knowledge give,
That knowledge, too, may I impart,
And teach mankind to live.

To thee, great God, to this I look,
For naught there is but thine;
A lesson teach, 'tis nature's book,
To read it then incline.

All mortals here ope wide your eyes
And view all nature's ways,
Thou are the great Physician, Lord,
To thee be all the praise.

RECIPES

If all knew the right rules of prescribing, how much would it prevent of premature death and pain. For instance, it is now dead of night—it matters not who, perhaps a parent, is taken ill; one thing after another is tried; their small store of skill is exhausted; it has done no good; all avail nothing. Ah! says a watchful friend, with tearful eye, "we have done all we can; call in one who knows still more." Away they go, post haste; the night is dark, and even

raining; it is ten, twelve, or perhaps even twenty miles to his dwelling, and ere they reach home, the unfortunate man is no more. The physician looks grave, "then he is gone— a pity I had not been a moment sooner; I could no doubt have saved his life." He orders his horse, pockets a five dollar bill, and is gone. He has left you in the dark; you have paid him—for what? he has prepared no medicine, prescribed no rule to you for a similar occurrence; not even remotely hinted at the nature of the disorder that has thus spread terror and dismay over your household.

We use our native language in all our common
   deal,
What use is Greek or Latin to tell us how we
   feel?
It is because to keep ignorant's part,
And to deceive us with deceitful art?

Mustard.

FOR A COUGH, OR PHTHISIC

Take the dried leaves of rosemary, shred small, and smoke them in a tobacco pipe. It will help those that have a cough or phthisic, or consumption, by warming and drying the thin distillations which cause these diseases.

FOR THE KING'S EVIL, OR KERNEL OF THE EARS

Take the root of bastard rhubarb, dry it, and boil it in wine. Bathe the part affected, and drink a glass of it three times a day, before eating. It is also good for the stone or gravel, to drink the steepings of the root in Holland gin.

AN EXCELLENT REMEDY TO STOP VOMITING

Take green wheat or green grass, pound it and pour on boiling water, and sweeten with loaf sugar. Press out the juice, and let the patient drink a table-spoonful every ten minutes. Or, take gum camphor, pounded fine, mix it with boiling water, sweetened. The same quantity will answer for a dose as the other.

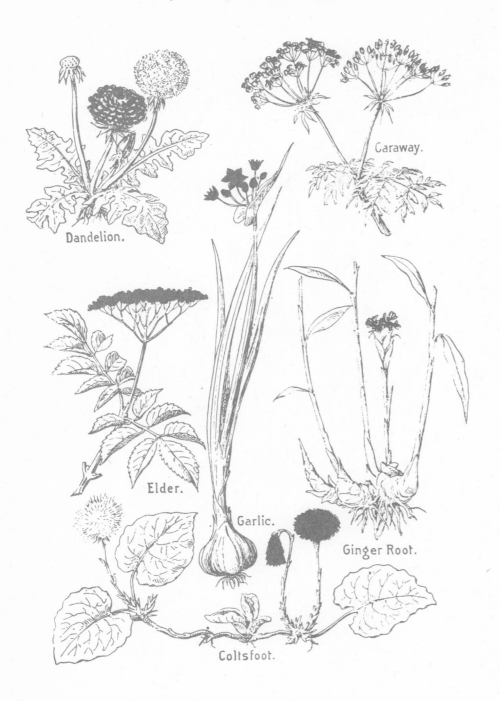

Dandelion.

Caraway.

Elder.

Garlic.

Ginger Root.

Coltsfoot.

AN EXCELLENT WASH FOR SORE MOUTHS, OR CANKER

Take plaintain, honeysuckle, sage, and rosemary, equal parts, and boil them in sour wine; add thereto a little honey and alum. Wash the mouth with this as often as necessary. A few times will be sufficient. It is very harmless, but not more so than it is healing.

FOR DEAFNESS, SINGING IN THE EARS, &C.

Take the juice of sow-thistle, and heat it with a little oil of bitter almonds, in the shell of a pomegranate, and drop some of it into the ears. It is a good remedy for deafness, singings, and other diseases of the head and ears.

FOR INFLAMMATION OF THE HEART

Make a decoction of red roses with wine, apply it to the region of the heart, with a sponge; or let the leaves remain in, and bring them on, over where your heart beats, shifting them often.

This is very good for St. Anthony's fire, and many other diseases of the stomach, also for pains in the head, and hot and inflamed eyes. Be sure to remember that red roses strengthen the heart, liver, stomach, and retentive faculties.

FOR A BURN

Take an onion and cut it in halves, warm it a very little, (but not roast it, for that decreases its strength, and consequently its virtues,) bind it on the affected part. It will stop the soreness and inflammation, by drawing out the humors, which always accompany a burn, if not prevented.

FOR A CONSUMPTIVE COUGH, OR PAIN IN THE BREAST

Take a table-spoonful of tar, three spoonfuls of honey, the yolks of three eggs, beat them well together, then add half a pint of wine, and beat them again. Then cork it up tight for use. Take a teaspoonful three times a day, before eating. Be sure to drink nothing but barley tea for your constant tea.

FOR THE ITCH

Make a syrup of the juice of sorrel and fumitory. This is a sovereign remedy for that troublesome disorder. Use it inwardly, and the juice of sorrel and vinegar, as a wash, outwardly.

A CURE FOR BLEEDING AT THE STOMACH

Take one pound of yellow dock root, dry it thoroughly, and pound it fine. Boil this in a quart of milk, and strain it off. Use one gill three times a day, also one pill a day, made of turpentine, from the end of a white pine log, and honey, equal parts. This will heal the vessels that leak.

PILLS FOR THE HYSTERICS

Take the leaves of motherwort and thoroughwort, and poplar bark, from the root of a tree. Pound these fine, and sift them through a fine sieve. Mix with molasses and make it into pills, and take four of them when the disorder is coming on. This will settle the head, and make every thing as calm as a clock!

FOR THE RHEUMATISM

Take a table-spoonful of pitch from a white pine log, the same quantity of sulphur, and a spoonful of honey. Add these to two quarts of the best fourth-proof brandy, and shake till it is dissolved. Cork it up tight for use. Take a table-spoonful three times a day, before eating, and bathe the part affected in salt, and some of the same brandy, as hot as you can bear it.

FOR WEAKNESS AND GENERAL DEBILITY OF THE WHOLE SYSTEM

Take of lovage root half a pound, four ounces of burdock roots, and half a pound of comfrey roots to four quarts of water, and let it boil moderately for the space of two hours, strain it off and then continue to boil it down to one quart, add half a pint of the best Holland gin, and one pound of honey, or loaf sugar will do if honey cannot be procured; put it into a bottle and cork it tight for eight and forty hours, when it will be fit for use. Dose, a table-spoonful three times a day before eating. This syrup has been known to perform a great many cures after every other remedy had failed and the most celebrated physicians' skill entirely baffled.

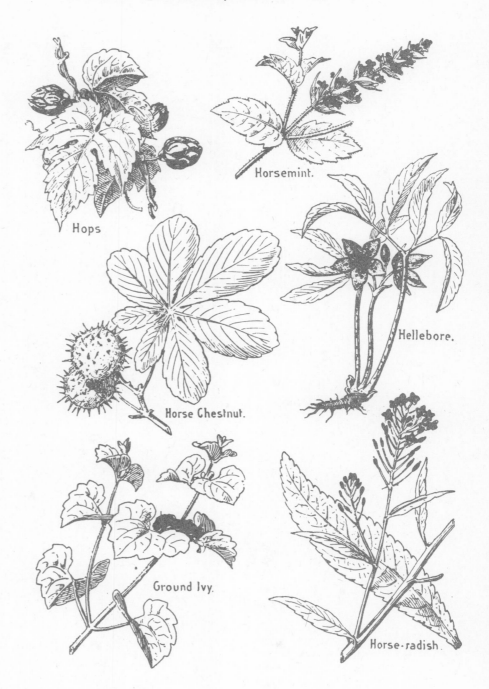

Hops

Horsemint.

Horse Chestnut.

Hellebore.

Ground Ivy.

Horse-radish

FOR CHILDREN TROUBLED WITH WORMS

There are many things good for children in this case. The leaves of sage, powdered fine, and mixed with a little honey, a tea-spoonful for a dose; or flour of sulphur, mixed with honey, is good for worms.

FOR THE TOOTHACHE

If the tooth be hollow, put in as much blue vitriol as it will contain. This repeated for a few days will kill the marrow.

FOR A PERSON THAT IS STRAINED, OR WEAK ACROSS THE KIDNEYS

Take one pound of the inner bark of witch hazel to two quarters of milk, and the same quantity of water, all boiled together, and drink of it three or four times a day, about one gill at a time. This treatment for a few days, will generally give relief.

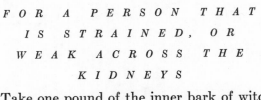

Mullein.

Lovage

A CURE FOR THE JAUNDICE

Take a half a pint of the last milk that can be obtained from a cow, and a small handful of yellow blowed celandine; put it into a cloth and pound it; then squeeze it till the juice is out, and then mix and drink, the whole, while warm, every morning before eating, for the space of nine mornings in succession, which will generally be sufficient; but if obstinate, or of long standing, it will be necessary to omit it for nine mornings, and then take it for the same space as before, which will be sufficient to cure the disorder in its worst form and longest standing.

FOR A COUGH

Take of hoarhound a small handful, and about as much garden colt's foot, two table-spoonfuls of sage, and one of saffron, well simmered together. Strain it off, add half a pint of molasses, and simmer it again for the space of three hours, with a moderate fire, and while it is hot, add one gill of the best Holland gin. Dose, three times a day. Commence with a table-spoonful, and increase to half a wine glass full. This is a safe remedy, and may be relied on for a cough of any kind except whooping cough.

FOR SWELLINGS THAT COME OF THEIR OWN ACCORD

Take an ointment made of melilot, saffron, aldertags, and sugar of lead, simmered in hog's lard; strain it, anoint the affected part and take something to guard the stomach before ointing. If done in season, it will scatter the swelling.

A CURE FOR CORNS

Spread a plaster of white pine turpentine, put it on the corn, let it stay till it comes off of its own accord. Repeat this three times.

FOR A STIFF JOINT, OR SHRUNK SINEW

Take an ointment made of melilot, saffron, large as a chestnut, half an ounce of green melilot, half an ounce of oil amber, half an ounce of yellow besilicom. Simmer them to an ointment. Apply this to the affected part, and put it on the joint above. This often repeated, will effect a cure.

FOR A STRAINED STOMACH

Take one third of a pound of pitch from the end of a white pine log, the same quantity of sulphur and half a pound of honey; simmer well together, take two pills of this every day before eating. There is but one chance in this medicine for a person to be disappointed. That is, it generally effects a cure before the medicine is half used up.

A GOOD MEDICINE FOR INWARD HURTS OR ULCERS

Take genseng roots, angelica, elecampane, masterwort, comfrey and spikenard roots, a pound of each, one pound of camomile, two pounds of fir boughs; put them into one gallon of rum and two gallons of water; still these, and draw off six quarts. Take a small glass night and morning.

A VALUABLE REMEDY FOR THE BILIOUS CHOLIC

Take one gill of West India molasses, one gill of West Indian rum, one gill of hog's lard, and the urine of a beast one gill. Simmer these well together. This will seldom fail of performing a cure.

FOR WEAK AND INFLAMED EYES

Take the pith from the stalk of a sassafras bush, mix it with a very little water, about blood warm. Wash the eyes three or four times a day. This is far superior to the most celebrated eye water. Keep clear of greasy victuals.

A CURE FOR THE GRAVEL IN THE BLADDER, OR KIDNEYS

Take the herb called heart's ease, make a strong tea of it, and drink plenty; or make the root of Jacob's ladder into a tea, and drink of that. It is a most sure remedy, and has proved to be the best thing known.

CURE FOR THE ASTHMA

Take two ounces of elecampane root, two ounces of sweet flag, two ounces of spikenard root, two ounces of common chalk; beat them in a mortar, till they become very fine, then add one pound of honey, and beat them altogether. Take a tea-spoonful three times a day.

Iceland Moss

A CURE FOR WOMEN'S SORE NIPPLES

When the infant stops nursing, apply clear molasses. This seldom fails of a cure. It is a very easy medicine.

A BEER TO GUARD AGAINST BILIOUS FEVER

Take elder roots, burdock roots, spruce boughs, white ashbark, sarsaparilla roots, hops and spikenard. Make a small beer of this, and drink of it often. Take powdered bloodroot, and mandrake roots, mixed together, once a quarter, for physic, and you will seldom, if ever, have an attack of the bilious fever.

FOR THE RICKETS IN CHILDREN

If any part of the body be outwardly affected with this disorder, bathe it thoroughly with a good brandy, and take turkey root, steeped in wine, for a drink, three times a day.

TO DESTROY WORMS IN SICKNESS OR HEALTH

Take a table-spoonful of molasses, and mix it with a tea-spoonful of the rust of tin. This is a safe remedy.

GOOD SALVE FOR WOMEN'S SORE BREASTS

Take one pound of spikenard, half a pound of comfrey, and one pound of tobacco; boil these in three quarts of chamber lye till almost dry, then press out the juice, and add to it pitch and beeswax enough when simmered, to give it the consistency of salve. Apply this to the part affected.

A BEER FOR THE LIVER COMPLAINT

Take a fever bush, wintergreen, checkerberries, hops, and black birch twigs. Make these into a beer, and after it is fermented, bottle it up. Add a tea-spoonful of ginger and loaf sugar, to a tumbler full of the beer, before drinking. It is a healthy and good drink.

FOR FITS CAUSED BY WORMS

Take cream sweetened with molasses, and pour it down the throat of the child; it will immediately give relief, and turn the worms. It is one of the best things known, and very harmless.

FOR WIND IN THE CHILDREN

Take genseng roots, pound or grate a little into warm water, and sweeten it with loaf sugar. This given warm will afford relief.

TO DRIVE OUT HUMORS

Take saffron and snakeroot, equal parts of each; make this into a strong tea, and drink of it occasionally. This is good to drive out humors, and keep any kind of disorder from striking to the stomach.

FOR A PERSON THAT HAS BEEN TROUBLED WITH A WEAK STOMACH FOR A LONG TIME

In the first place omit taking all kinds of medicine whatever. Take rye, wash it clean, and boil it in the same manner as you would rice. Make this your constant diet. This may be eaten with molasses, or in milk. Be sure and not take any other kind of food whatever, till you are thoroughly satisfied you can bear it. Drink a tea of white pine bark and slippery elm. This has been known to cure persons who have been troubled with a weak stomach for years, and become so much reduced as not to be able to bear half a cracker at a meal.

A CURE FOR FROST BITTEN FEET

Take the inner bark of elder and simmer it in hen's oil, and rub the affected part with it twice a day over a warm fire; at the same time wrap the frost bitten part in a piece of woolen cloth well greased with the same. In a few days this will effect a cure.

FOR CHILDREN THAT CANNOT HOLD THEIR WATER

Take the bark off a green red beech tree; dry this and pound it up fine; steep it in wine; give a table-spoonful at a time once a day.

FOR ANY HEMORRHAGE OF THE BLOOD

Take a handful of bloodweed, if green pound it and press out the juice; let the patient take a table-spoonful at a time, once an hour, till it stops. If the herb is dry, boil it very strong, and give three or four spoonfuls of the tea at a time.

TO CURE THE BITE OF A RATTLESNAKE

Take green hoarhound tops, pound them up fine and squeeze out the juice; let the patient take a table-spoonful three times a day; apply the pounded herbs to the bite, and change them twice a day. The patient may also drink a spoonful of sweet olive oil. This generally effects a cure.

TO CURE A SWELLED FACE OR SCURVY IN THE TEETH

Take scurvy grass and prince of pine, boil them in water, strain it, and add a little honey and rum, hold it in the mouth as hot as possible, boil a large quantity of the herbs and sweat the head over it.

CURE FOR SPRAINS

Use a table-spoonful of honey, the same quantity of fine bay salt, and the white of a hen's egg. Beat the whole up together for two hours at least. Let it stand one hour and anoint the sprained part with the oil which is produced from the mixture, keeping it well bound with a flannel bandage. This will generally enable a person to walk free from pain in one day.

Hemlock.

Hedge-Mustard.

No. 112

U. U.

Herb Compound

This herb compound contains: Marshmallow, Uva Ursi, Saw Palmetto, Cubebs, Juniper Berries, Cheese Plant, Fennel, Sweet Fern, Licorice, Pipsissewa.

The contents of this package is guaranteed, by replacement, to contain standard ingredients of high quality.

Directions:

Place 1 teaspoonful in a cup of boiling water, stir, allow to stand for 15 to 30 minutes and strain. Take when cold 1 to 2 cupsful a day. This tea should be freshly made each day.

Packed and Sold by
ILLINOIS HERB COMPANY
Chicago, Ill.

Net weight 5½ ounces

No. 749

SONADA

HERB COMPOUND

This herb compound contains: Senna, Licorice, Sassafras, Calamus, Yellow Dock, Mate, Alfalfa, Yerba Santa, Boldo, Damiana.

Directions:

Place 1 teaspoonful in a cup of boiling water and allow to stand 15 to 30 minutes. Take when warm or cool, 1 to 2 cupsful a day. Make this tea fresh daily.

To avoid dependence on laxatives or cathartics do not use continuously, nor in the presence of vomiting, nausea or abdominal pains which may indicate symptoms of organic disease, such as appendicitis.

Packed and Sold by
ILLINOIS HERB COMPANY
Chicago, Ill.

Net weight 2½ ozs.

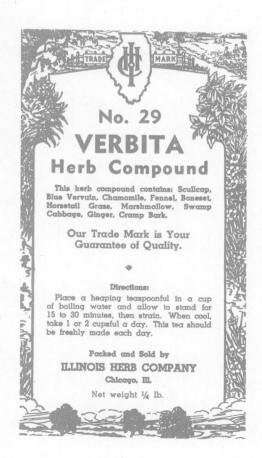

No. 29

VERBITA

Herb Compound

This herb compound contains: Scullcap, Blue Vervain, Chamomile, Fennel, Boneset, Horsetail Grass, Marshmallow, Swamp Cabbage, Ginger, Cramp Bark.

Our Trade Mark is Your Guarantee of Quality.

Directions:

Place a heaping teaspoonful in a cup of boiling water and allow to stand for 15 to 30 minutes, then strain. When cool, take 1 or 2 cupsful a day. This tea should be freshly made each day.

Packed and Sold by
ILLINOIS HERB COMPANY
Chicago, Ill.

Net weight ¼ lb.

BEST METHOD OF CURING A WEN

Bake a live bull frog in one pound of fresh butter. Keep the frog's back down until he is thoroughly baked through; strain off the butter into a tight vessel and keep it for use. Anoint the wen a dozen times every day. Any person who happens to be troubled with a wen, would do well to give this a fair trial, for it is sure, and can be easily obtained. It can frequently be squeezed out from three to six months.

FOR A SORE THROAT

Steam the throat with hot water, in which some hops are infused. After the hops have been thoroughly scalded, apply them externally to the diseased part of the throat.

OINTMENT FOR WEAK JOINTS

Boil together a sweet apple tree, and white oak bark, with a piece of cod-fish's skin, till you obtain the extract. Make a plaster of this and wear it on the affected part. It seldom fails of a cure.

FOR A WEAK STOMACH

Let your diet be milk, with a table-spoonful of the best brandy you can get into it, and any kind of light bread, and drink a tea made of strawberry leaves, with a red pepper broke in it. This is a safe remedy.

FOR WIND IN THE STOMACH

Take a tea-spoonful of saffron, chew and swallow the spittle. This is easy and sure to give relief in most cases.

FOR INDIGESTION

Swallow six gravel-stones the size of a small pea, from a cool brook, every morning. Repeat nine mornings in succession. Burn beef bones, pound them fine and sift them. Take a tea-spoonful of the powder every time before you eat. This will cause your food to pass off without distressing you. There is no danger in the remedy.

FOR WEAK NERVES

Take the roots of Indian umbel, or as some call it, nervine, or ladies' slipper. Pound them fine and sift them through a fine sieve. Cork it up tight from the air. Take half a tea-spoonful for a dose in hot water, sweetened. This is used by the Indians for all disorders of the nerves.

EXCELLENT FAMILY PILLS

Take the inner bark from the roots of a butternut, scraped down; balm of Gilead and white ash bark. Boil these in fair water until all the strength is out. Take out the bark, and continue to boil it down until you can work it into pills. This is a healthy physic, and good in all cases where cathartics are needed.

A BEER FOR CANCERS

Take the tops and roots of the whortleberry bush, sarsaparilla roots, and hop roots, one pound of each; three ounces of blood root, three ounces of unicorn roots, and half a peck of barley malt; make of these ingredients seven gallons of beer. Take half a gill for a dose, three times a day. This beer is very palatable.

TO MAKE WALKER'S LINIMENT

To one gallon of Alcohol add one pound of oil of cedar, half a pound of squaw weed oil, half a pound of oil origanum, half a pound of wormwood, half a pound of spearmint, half a pint of tincture of lobelia. Color with red sanders.

EYE WASH

Pulverized slippery elm bark in cold water.

FOR A DRY COUGH, WHEEZING, OR SHORTNESS OF BREATH

Take liquorice and boil it in spring water, with some maidenhair and figs, and use it for constant drink. It is good for all diseases of breast and lungs.

WALKER'S CURE FOR CORNS

Take mullein leaves and pound them and moisten with soft soap.

FOR WOMEN'S SORE NIPPLES

Take balsam fir, make a plaster of it, and apply it as often as possible. It will effect a cure in a few days.

FOR A STIFF JOINT AND SHRUNK SINEWS

Take a skin of a codfish, wet it in strong red pepper water. Bind this on the joint, taking care to have it come at least six inches above and below the joint. Change this as often as dry, use considerable friction, and anoint the cords with a salve made of the following materials. Take white oak bark and sweet apple tree bark, equal parts, boil these in three quarts of water till all the strength is out; strain off and simmer again till quite thick, add the same quantity of goose grease that you have of syrup. Mix these while warm, and anoint the joints and cords.

STEAM HEMLOCK SWEAT

When we have taken a very hard cold, and are of a very feverish disposition, with catarrh in the head, falling into the throat, it is very good to take a steam hemlock sweat. For this purpose get and break up hemlock boughs, and boil them. Heat two or three pieces of brick or stone, or have them heating. Some of the hemlock liquor should be put into a tin pan, but not so very hot but what you can stand in it. Let the one to be sweated strip entirely in the bedroom, and put a large quilt or the like around him. Then walk deliberately and take the stand in the tin pan. Then put the quilt right over your head, and let it be full all around you. The kettle or pail of hemlock preparation should be set as close as may be to the tin pan. The shroud about the person should include both kettle and pan. The hot bricks then can be thrown into the kettle at the patient's pleasure to make the sweat start and even run.

THE ART OF MAKING POULTICES.

The moist heat, which acting alone will quell all but the most violent inflammations, is often most conveniently attained by means of poultices, which it is desirable that every girl who is studying household duties should learn to make. We give below authoritative directions for making those most commonly used:

Flaxseed Poultices—Pour sufficient boiling water over the ground flaxseed to make it as thick as thick cream, and let the mixture simmer a few minutes. Apply as hot as can be borne.

Mustard Poultices—Mix equal quantities of mustard, corn-meal and flour in warm water until just thick enough not to run. Spread it over the poultice cloth, and if a very quick action of the poultice is desired, sprinkle a little clear mustard on before folding the cloth over it. Apply this side next to the skin.

Bread-and-Milk Poultice—Simmer old bread in milk until soft enough to mash smoothly. Crackers may be used instead of bread, if necessary.

Indian-Meal Poultice—Stir the corn-meal into water, and cook like mush for five minutes or more.

Slippery-Elm Poultice—Pour boiling water over slippery-elm bark (powdered) and add a little powdered charcoal, if necessary.

All classes of poultices should be spread on one-half of an oblong piece of thin muslin; the other half should then be folded over the spread mass, and the loose edges carefully joined with needle and thread.

*A MORE DISORDERED
STATE OF THROAT
AND LUNGS*

Here I would make some remarks on the application of cold water to the human system. We by observation think that quick changes of weather from cold to heat, and from heat to cold, act with a depressing unhealthy effect upon us. The writer, in his travels, has seen quite a number in young and middle age, sinking away with the disease called consumption. He has asked them if they had tried the cold water remedy. They have answered, "O yes, but it did not good. It made us chill." The writer has, in some degree, been so diseased. Made an application of the cold water by being packed in a wet sheet, which was done by wetting a sheet in cold water all through. Then it was spread out on a tick of straw, which lay on a bedstead. The writer with expedition laid his entire naked body down on the sheet, his arms extended down the body entirely their whole length. The sheet was then put over him each way, and the edges packed under as tight as well might be, except his head. A feather tick was immediately put over him, with some heavy quilts on the top. Then a hot stone was put to my feet. My nurse and benefactor in doing this good work for me, was a deacon, and apparently a good Christian man, whom I much to this day respect. . . . In lying in the bath about three hours, toward the last of it, I had some perspiration and got to feeling quite comfortable. My covering was then removed. I washed myself in front while another washed my back parts in warm water. This got off the gluten or slime-like matter, which obstructs the pores.

ARTS REVEALED AND UNIVERSAL GUIDE

THE DOCTOR AT HOME

New Cure for Consumption, Scrofula, general Infantile Atrophy, Rickets, Diarrhoea, and Tuberculous Diseases—Eight grains of phosphate of lime, administered in cod-liver oil three times a day.

Liquorice.

Cure for a Nail run into the Foot—Fresh beet, thoroughly pounded. Apply to the part frequently.

Fever and Ague—Pound a piece of alum and nutmeg in half a tumbler of water. Take it when you find the fever coming on.

Cure for Tooth-ache—Put a piece of cotton, dipped in collodion, into the tooth. When hardened, it will adhere strongly and stop the pain.

A Very Strengthening Drink—Put a tea-cupful of pearl barley into a sauce-pan and three pints of cold water, the rind of a lemon, and a small piece of cinnamon; boil gently till the barley becomes tender, strain it and sweeten with sugar or molasses.

Cure for Rheumatism—One gill of alcohol, one of beef's gall, one of spirits of turpentine, one of sweet oil, and four ounces of camphor gum. Put them all in a bottle and shake it up; use it two or three times a day, a teaspoonful at a time. Apply it to the parts affected before the fire. It is good also for frost-bites.

Very Valuable Remedy for Rheumatism—Peel off the outside bark of the elder, scrape of the green bark that is under it, and stew in lard till it is crisp.

Cure for Hydrophobia—Take the root of the common upland ash, generally known as black ash, peel off the bark, and boil it to a strong decoction. Take one gill three times a day for eight or ten days.

Tonic—The following is the tonic used by reformed drunkards to restore the vigor of the stomach. Take of gentian root two drams, bitter orange peel three drams, rhubarb root two drams, valerian root one dram, cardamom seeds half an ounce, and cinnamon bark one dram. Having bruised all the above together in a mortar, (the druggist will do it if requested,) pour upon it one and a half pints of boiling water, and cover up close; let it stand till cold; strain, bottle, and cork securely; keep in a dark place. Two table-spoonfuls may be taken every hour before meals, and half that quantity whenever the patient feels that distressing sickness and prostration, so generally present for some time after alcoholic stimulants have been abandoned.

Bowel Complaints—Tea and coffee, and toast without butter, arrow-root, crackers of any kind, and chicken broth, or anything else of that nature, will not be injurious; and enough of it should be taken to keep the strength and spirits as much unimpaired as possible, as no treatment is more dangerous than to have nothing to eat; but on no account should a patient be permitted to have access to fruit of any kind (with the exception, perhaps, of figs, which may be eaten freely), or to use meat, until recovered.

Inflammation of the Bowels—Apply a mustard plaster until sufficient irritation is produced, and, on taking it off, flannel dipped in hot water should be applied every half hour until relief is obtained. Great care should be used as to diet, the simplest and most nutritious alone being safe; and on no account should any fruit be allowed to pass into the bowels while suffering from the complaint.

Common Canker—Take a pound of canker root, wash it well and pound it fine. Soak it in warm water three hours, stirring it up well occasionally, so as to extract its strength. Wash the canker with it, and drink of it three times a day for a week.

Gravel—Make a strong tea of the root of the plant called Jacob's ladder, and drink five or six times a day, in doses of half a pint at a time. It is an infallible cure.

Preventive of Bilious Fever—If you are bilious in the spring, it will be well to physic with a syrup made of four ounces of rhubarb, four ounces of blood root, four ounces of mandrake root, ground or pounded fine, and stirred in half a pint of molasses, of which two table-spoonfuls is a dose. Then make a beer of equal parts of elder roots, burdock·roots, sarsaparilla and spikenard roots, and white-ash bark and hops, and four times their weight of spruce boughs; add sufficient water, and place over a fire until sufficient mixture and extraction of the strength of the ingredients has taken place, then add yeast and put into a keg; after twelve hours, bottle, cork and tie down the corks.

Consumption—Take a peck of barley malt, add to it nine gallons of water boiling hot. Let it stand six hours, then add to the water

in which the malt was soaked a peck of white-pine bark, half a pound of spikenard root, and half a pound of Syria grass. Boil half away, then put the liquid part into a keg, adding a quart of brewer's yeast.

Hypochondria, or Hysteric Passion—These disorders are most common to women, and imitate almost all diseases. They complain of almost every thing, although all have not the same complaints. Sometimes they have ague or hot sweats, and faintness comes on them; but the symptoms are varied according to the temper and constitution of the patient, and her mode of living. All that can give rest or relief, is to administer things to strengthen the blood—Filings of iron steeped in wine, sundue, goldthread, rue, burdock-seeds, and mustard-seed, pulverized and put into brandy, is a superior medicine in cold, phlegmatic temperaments. These hysteric fits differ according to the nature of the patient; therefore the medicine that will help one will hurt another. Sanguine persons cannot bear spirit or cordial, but must have such as tend to quench, in some degree, the animal spirits, as assafoetida, castor, and all foetid medicines used in pills, with aloes and myrrh. Let these be given as an attenuative every night. If the person be pale, of a cold, phlegmatic constitution, give ens. veneris, and a preparation of steel, dissolved; also, ens. veneris, given in a powder, two or three grains at a time, every morning, and a tea of rue, sage, pennyroyal, and sweet flagroot, in brandy is good. Hysteric women generally obtain their disease by taking cold in their feet, which stops their menses or courses, and, in a few months, brings on spasms, occasioned by a suffocation of the womb. These fits are exceedingly violent, and will not be cured until blood-root in powder is mixed with brandy and taken. . . .

Rabies or Hydrophobia—This is a sort of disorder occasioned by the bite of a mad dog, or the saliva of some animal which is in rage with this disease. This poison is very strong, so that the cure is difficult after the madness has come on; but as soon as the bite is made, it may be drawn out by many things, as onion beat out with salt and applied to the wound, jalop pounded on, and often sifted, till the saliva be drawn out. Give internally snakeroot

Tea.

Sassafras.

Thorough Wort.

and camphor, some burn the place with a hot iron. Others apply a cupping-glass. All that have a great dread of water die of this disorder.

Piles—Make an ointment of equal parts of sage, parsley, burdock, and chamomile leaves, simmer half an hour in fresh butter or sweet oil and lard; then rub the parts affected with, and drink half a gill of tar water twice a day; if the piles are inward, take the same quantity of tar water, and half a small glass of the essence of fir each night, on going to bed. Continue this course two months, and it will do you more good than all the quack medicines in existence.

Dysentery—In diseases of this kind, the Indians use the roots and leaves of the blackberry bush—a decoction of which in hot water, well boiled down, is taken in doses of a gill before each meal, and before retiring to bed. It is an almost infallible cure.

Pain in the Breast or Side—The Indian remedy for this is, two pounds of fir boughs, a quarter of a pound of spikenard, half a pound of red clover, and a gallon of sweet cider, boiled to three pints. Drink half a gill of the mixture each night on going to bed, and morning, on getting up.

Inward Ulcers—Take a quarter of a pound of sassafras root bark, a quarter of a pound of colt's foot root, two ounces of gum myrrh, two ounces of winter bark, and two ounces of succatrine aloes; boil them well in four quarts of spirits, and drink a small glass every morning, fasting.

Sore Eyes—A teaspoonful of sugar of lead, same quantity of white vitriol, and two ounces of gunpowder, mixed well together in a quart of soft water, applied to the eyes as a wash three times a day for a week, will cure the most inveterate case.

The following recipes accompany this system of practice, one of which is worth more than twenty times the cost of this book.

These preparations should be made and kept on hand by every family. The expense is but little, and in certain cases, the patient may die before they can be obtained; and besides, age improves their quality, provided they are kept from the air, by being tightly corked in bottles.

Soothing Lotion—Two quarts of alcohol, six ounces fine castile soap, one ounce of camphor, one ounce of laudanum, one ounce of rosemary.

Invalid Cordial—An excellent article to strengthen and restore the tone of the stomach. It prevents faintness or a sinking feeling at the stomach, and for persons subject to low and depressed spirits, it affords great relief. It is made thus:

Dissolve gum arabic, 2 oz. in 1 pint of rain water, and 1½ wine-glass of best brandy, take a table-spoonful three or four times a day.

Balm of Life—This is a most excellent medicine for consumptive complaints. It is very good for pain in the stomach or side, or for a feverish stomach; it strengthens weak lungs, and helps the whooping-cough. It is a relief from suffering, in nearly all diseases.

It is made thus: Gum benzoin 4 oz., gum storax callintee 3 oz., balsam tolu 1 oz., gum aloes, sucatine, 1½ oz., gum myrrh 1½ oz., root of angelica 2 oz., tops of Johnswort 2 oz. Pound all these together, and put them into about three pounds of rectified spirits of wine in a glass bottle. Let them stand in the spirits four weeks in a moderate heat; shake them once a day, strain it off, and it is fit for use. If the gums are not all dissolved, add a little more spirits to the same; shake it and let it stand as before. The patient should take 12 to 15 drops in a glass of wine, in the morning, before eating.

For Cleansing and Purifying the Blood—Take 1 lb. sarsaparilla, ½ lb. guaiacum shavings, 1 oz. sassafras, ½ lb. elder-flowers, ½ lb. alder buds, ½ lb. burdock root; put all these together, and add 2 quarts of boiling water to one-third of it. Take a wine-glassful three times a day and a dose of pills twice a week.

Head-ache drops—For the cure of nervous, sun, and sick head-ache, take 2 quarts alcohol, 3 oz. castile soap, 1 oz. camphor, and 2 oz. ammonia. Bathe forehead and temples.

For Strengthening and Invigorating the Nerves—1 oz. juniper berries, 2 oz. orris root, 1 oz. bitter bufle, 3 oz. chamomile flowers;

break them up fine, steep 1 table-spoonful in a half a pint of boiling water, and drink it through the day.

A Shrunk Sinew, or Stiff Joint—Mix half an ounce, each of green meliot, yellow besilicon, oil of amber, and a piece of blue vitriol as large as a thimble, well together, simmer over a slow fire, to the consistency of salve, in two ounces of lard; apply the salve (rubbing it in well each time to the shrunken part, and joint next above it,) at least three times a day.

CANCER OF THE BREAST

It is indeed a sad reflection, that women, from the performance of duties most endearing to her offspring, should become the frequent victim of the most intractable diseases that afflict her. Cancer of the breast, although it occasionally originates in males and unmarried females, is far more frequent among those who are nursing, or have nursed, one or more children. It is most likely to show itself between the thirtieth and forty-fifth years; the cases increasing in frequency as the female approaches the cessation of the menstruating period.

Symptoms—The first appearance of cancer is generally that of a small tumor, the size of a cranberry, situated deep in the substance of the breast. This, if taken hold of, and handled freely between the thumb and two fingers will be found perfectly movable with the substance or mass of the breast, and more or less hard. If not removed, and it really be a cancer, it gradually becomes immovable, from attachment to the parts beneath it, larger, harder, and more or less painful. All these characteristics increase, with greater or less rapidity, until the skin becomes congested and attached to the tumor, and alters its hue, growing redder and more tense; the tumor then attaches itself to the body, and becomes immovable—increases in size, either on one side, elevating that part of the breast into an irregular surface, or it surrounds the nipple, swallowing it up as it were in itself. The pain becomes of a cutting or lancinating kind, and it gradually opens and discharges a thin and unhealthy sort of bloody matter. When the disease has proceeded to this extent, its further progress, with affection of the health is rapid.

Remedy—This is one of those diseases which it is almost impossible to cure. Its progress, however, may sometimes be retarded, and some of its most disagreeable symptoms mitigated, by proper applications. One misfortune attending the disease is, that the unhappy patient often conceals it too long. Were proper means used in due time, a cancer might often be prevented; but after the disorder has arrived at a certain height, it often sets all medicine at defiance.

The fact respecting a cancer, however, is this; it is canker making its appearance in one part of the body, showing that the whole body is more or less affected with the same. Many appearances in the body are called cancer, which are only warts or things which never injure the system; and often men have the name of curing a cancer, when they have only removed something else. A real cancer may be taken out, but this can never cure the disease in the person, for it is in every part, more or less. To cure a real cancer, whether the common kind, or what is called a rose cancer, the whole system must be first cleared of canker. When this is done, there is nothing left to support what is called the cancer.

My method of curing, is, first to clear the system with the emetic, &c., giving powders, bitters, &c., to help the digestion; and continue this course until the whole body is cleared of what makes and supports the cancer. While attending to this, apply the cancer plaster, which goes into the sore, and lessens it. The cancer eats the plaster, instead of being drawn out by the plaster. When the plaster is all gone from the soft leather bladder on which it is spread, more must be put on, until a cure is performed—this is very simple, safe and generally effectual remedy. The best cancer plaster with which I have any knowledge is the extract of clover. However there is an Infallible Cure for Cancer: take arsenic and pulverized root of cokeberry, in equal parts, and sprinkle upon a bread and milk poultice, which keep moist, and renew every 36 hours. In a few days every fibre of the cancer will be destroyed. This remedy being very poisonous, cannot interfere with respiration.

Dr. Chase's Recipes;
– or –
Information for Everybody

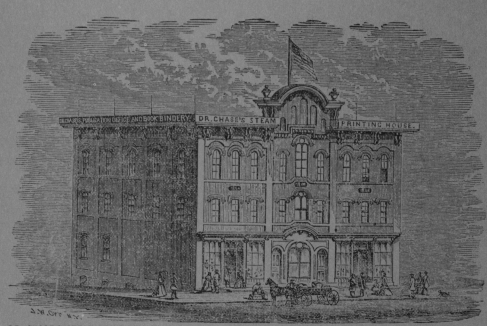

DR. CHASE'S STEAM PRINTING-HOUSE, R. A. BEAL, PROPRIETOR, 39, 41 & 43 N. MAIN ST., ANN ARBOR, MICH.

In bringing a permanent work, or one that is designed so to be, before the public, it is expected of the Author that he give his reasons for such publication. If the reasons are founded in truth, the people consequently seeing its necessity, will appreciate its advantages, and encourage the Author by quick and extensive purchases, they alone being the judges. Then:

FIRST—Much of the information contained in "Dr. Chase's Recipes; or Information for Everybody," has never before been published, and is adapted to everyday use.

SECOND—The Author, after having carried on the Drug and Grocery business for a number of years, read Medicine, after being thirty-eight years of age, and graduated as a Physician to qualify himself for the work he was undertaking; for having been familiar with some of the Recipes, adapted to these branches of trade, more than twenty years, he began in "Fifty-six," seven years ago, to publish them in a Pamphlet of only a few pages, since which time he has been traveling between New York and Iowa, selling the work and Prescribing, so that up to this time, "Sixty-three," over twenty-three thousand copies have been sold. . . .

THIRD—Those remarks, explanations, and suggestions accompanying the Recipes, are a special feature of this work, making it worth double its cost as a ready book, even if there was not a prescription in it. . . .

SIXTH—In ague sections of country, none should be without the information on this subject; and in fact, there is not a medical subject introduced but what will be found more or less valuable to every one; even Physicians will be more than compensated in its perusal; whilst Consumptive, Dyspeptic, Rheumatic, and Fever patients ought, by all means, to avail themselves of the advantages here pointed out. The treatment of Female Debility, and the observations on the Changes in female life are such that every one of them over thirteen or fourteen years of age should not be without this work. The directions in Pleurisy and other Inflammatory diseases cannot fail to benefit

DR. CHASE'S RECIPES;

OR,

INFORMATION FOR EVERYBODY:

AN INVALUABLE COLLECTION OF

ABOUT EIGHT HUNDRED

PRACTICAL RECIPES,

FOR

Merchants, Grocers, Saloon-Keepers, Physicians, Druggists, Tanners, Shoe Makers, Harness Makers, Painters, Jewelers, Blacksmiths, Tinners, Gunsmiths, Farriers, Barbers, Bakers, Dyers, Renovaters, Farmers, and Families Generally,

TO WHICH HAVE BEEN ADDED

A Rational Treatment of Pleurisy, Inflammation of the Lungs, and other Inflammatory Diseases, and also for General Female Debility and Irregularities:

All arranged in their Appropriate Departments.

BY A. W. CHASE, M. D.,

STEREOTYPED

CAREFULLY REVISED, ILLUSTRATED, AND MUCH ENLARGED, WITH REMARKS AND FULL EXPLANATIONS.

We Learn to Live, by Living to Learn.

IN CLOTH, $1.25; PAPER COVERS, $1.00; MOROCCO GILT, $2.00. THE GERMAN IN CLOTH ONLY, $1.25.

ANN ARBOR, MICHIGAN PUBLISHED BY THE AUTHOR. 1867.

every family into whose hands the book shall fall.

The Good Samaritan Liniment, we do not believe, has its equal in the world, for common uses, whilst there are a number of other liniments equaly well adapted to particular cases. And we would not undertake to raise a family of children without our Whooping Cough Syrup and Croup Remedies, knowing their value as we do, if it cost a hundred dollars to obtain them. . . .

Another gentleman recently said to me: "Your Eye Water is worth more than $20."

I could fill pages of similar statements that have come to my knowledge since I commenced the publication of this work, but must be content by asking all to look over References, which have been voluntarily accumulating during the seven years in which the work has been growing up to its present size and perfection; and the position in society, of most of the persons making these statements is such, many of which are entire strangers to

REASONS WHY

Everybody Should Have Dr. Chase's Recipe Book as Improved by the Publisher.

EVERY HOUSEKEEPER NEEDS IT,

To know how to wash, to cook, to preserve, to brew, to keep the house clean and sweet, to know how to color in modern style and newest colors, to understand household management and economy, and for its practical "Hints on Housekeeping."

EVERY MOTHER NEEDS IT,

To understand and provide for the care, dress, management, and bringing up of children; to understand and cure the diseases peculiar to childhood; and for the "Advice to Mothers," which should make the RECIPE BOOK a welcome friend to every mother and family in the land.

EVERY WOMAN NEEDS IT,

For its plain and practical treatment and cure of all female complaints and irregularities; to know how to care for the sick; and for its "Management of the Sick Room," and advice to them especially.

EVERY MAN NEEDS IT,

To know how to act promptly in all kinds of "Accidents and Emergencies," and for its 2,000 invaluable Recipes in its various Departments, upon almost every subject.

EVERY YOUNG LADY NEEDS IT,

For its "Hints upon Etiquette;" to know to dress becomingly; to know how to beautify the person and complexion; to know how to soften and whiten the skin and hands; to know how to promote the growth and beauty of the hair; to know how to remove superfluous hair, or make it curl; to know how to remove freckles, pimples, and blotches; to know how to remove sun burn and tan; to know how to make perfumes, pomade, tooth-wash, hair oils, etc., etc.

EVERY YOUNG MAN NEEDS IT,

For its "Hints upon Personal Manners;" for its "Rules for the Preservation of Health;" for its advice and counsels upon habits, business, etc.

EVERY SICK PERSON NEEDS IT,

To know how to regain their health, and for its priceless recipes and cures for almost all kinds of sickness and disease.

EVERY WELL PERSON NEEDS IT,

To know how to preserve their health, and for its rules for the prevention of sickness and promotion of health.

EVERY FARMER NEEDS IT,

For its complete Farrier Department, which has no superior; to know how to manage Bees, and for hundreds of recipes especially in his line, which he will have almost daily occasion to use or refer to.

EVERY MECHANIC NEEDS IT,

As blacksmiths, tinners, gunsmiths, jewelers, cabinet makers, tanners painters, barbers, shoe and harness makers, for its recipes and advice in these various branches of industry.

THE YOUNG FOLKS AND CHILDREN NEED IT,

For its "Counsels to the Young," and its amusements and indoor games.

EVERY FAMILY NEEDS IT,

As a household work, to consult upon almost every conceivable subject; with its 2,000 practical recipes for almost everything and everybody; to consult upon all the leading diseases of man, woman, or child, as it points out in plain language the symptoms cause, and cure; to consult upon all matters of housekeeping, cooking, coloring, etc.; to consult in all cases of accidents, of poisoning, burns scalds, bruises, cuts, bites, wounds, etc.; to consult upon a thousand other things of every-day occurrence; in short, as a Family Guide and Physician.

To, conclude, every person should have it, whether young or old, married or single, whether farmer, mechanic, or professional, as a book to refer to in a thousand matters of daily occurrence, as it will not only save you many dollars, but perhaps life itself, and will add to your comfort, pleasure and happiness.

Carefully examine the "Index" of the Recipe Book, which you will find in this Circular, which will show you more fully the character and worth of the Book, and the various subjects treated of, and see if *you* do not *need* it, or if two dollars could be expended more satisfactorily, and if you can afford to be without it.

the Author and to each other, that any person can see that no possible complicity could exist between us, even if we desired it. . . .

FINALLY—In this edition you get a dollar's work of book, even if common reading matter, besides the most reliable practical information, by which you will often save, not only dollars and cents, but relieve suffering and prolong life . . . especially when we assure you that the book is sold only by Traveling Agents, that all may have a chance to purchase; for if left at the Book Stores, or by Advertisement only, not One in Fifty would ever see it. . . .

It is hoped that all purchasers may have sufficient confidence in the work not to allow it to lay idle; for, that the designed and greatest possible amount of good shall be accomplished by it, it is only necessary that it should be generally introduced, and daily used, is the positive knowledge of the

AUTHOR

MEDICAL DEPARTMENT

I would give an introductory word of *Caution* in this Department.

Whenever you buy an article of medicine which is not regularly *labeled* by the Druggist, have him, in all cases, *write* the name upon it. In this way you will not only save *money*, but perhaps *life*. Arsenic, phosphorus, laudanum, acids, &c., should always be put where children cannot get at them. And always purchase the best quality of drugs to insure success.

ALCOHOL—IN

MEDICINES,

PREFERABLE TO

BRANDY, RUM, OR

GIN OF THE

PRESENT DAY

There is no one thing doing so much to bolster up the tottering yet strong tower of Intemperance, as the old Fogy Physicians, who are constantly prescribing these articles to their patients, and one-half of the reason for it is to cover the faults of their own constant use of these beverages. This unnecessary call for these articles thus used as a medicine, keeps up a large demand; and when we take into consideration the almost impossibility of obtaining a genuine article, the sin of prescribing them becomes so much the greater, when it is also known by all really scientific men that with alcohol (which is pure) and the native fruit wines, cider, and cider wines, (which every one can make for themselves, and can thus know their purity,) that all the indications desired to be fulfilled in curing disease can be accomplished without their use.

Then, when it is deemed advisable to use spirits to preserve any bitters or syrups from souring, instead of 1 qt. of brandy, rum or gin, use the best alcohol ½ pt., with about 2 or 3 ozs. of crushed sugar for this amount, increasing or lessening according to the amount desired in these proportions. If a diuretic effect is desired, which is calculated to arise where gin is prescribed, put 1 dr. of oil of juniper into the alcohol before reducing with the water; or if the preparation admits of it you may put in from 1 to 2 ozs. of juniper berries instead of the oil. . . .

If the strength of wine only is desired, use 1 qt. of the ginger wine, or if that flavor is not fancied, use any other of the wines as preferred by the patient.

But no one should use any of the descriptions of alcohol as a constant beverage, even in medicine, unless advised to do so by a physician *who is not himself a toper*.

If families will follow the directions above given, and use proper care in making some of the various fruit wines as given in this book for medical use, preparing cider, &c., which is often used in prescriptions, they would seldom, if ever, be obliged to call for the *pretended* pure brandies, rums, gins, &c., of commerce, and intemperance would die a natural death for want of support.

And you will please allow me here to correct a common error, with regard to the presence of alcohol in wines. It is generally supposed that wine made from fruit, without putting some kind of spirits into it, does not contain any alcohol; but a greater mistake does not exist in the world. Any fruit, the juice of which will not pass into vinous fermentation by which alcohol is produced, will not make wine at all; distillation will produce brandy or alcohol from any of these fermented liquors. . . .

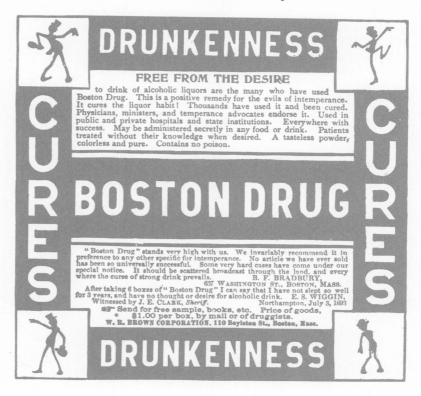

※※※※※※※※※※※※※※※※※※※※※※※※※※※※※※※※※※※※※※※

Ginger Beer.—The following recipe for making a very superior ginger beer is taken from the celebrated treatise of Dr. Pereira on Diet. The honey gives the beverage a peculiar softness, and from not being fermented with yeast, it is less violent in its action when opened, but requires to be kept a somewhat longer time before use. White sugar, five pounds; lemon juice, one quarter of a pint; honey, one quarter of a pound; ginger, bruised, five ounces; water, four gallons and a half. Boil the ginger in three quarts of the water for half an hour, then add the sugar, lemon juice and honey, with the remainder of the water, and strain through a cloth ; when cold, add a quarter of the white of an egg, and a small teaspoonful of essence of lemon; let the whole stand four days and then bottle; it will keep for many months. This quantity will make 100 bottles; the cost being, sugar, five pounds, 2s.; lemon juice, 2d.; honey, 3d.; best white ginger, 2d.; egg and essence of lemon, 2d.: total, 2s. 9d. Ginger-beer bottles may be obtained at the potteries at 10s. to 12s. per gross, and corks at 8d. to 1s. per gross.

※※※※※※※※※※※※※※※※※※※※※※※※※※※※※※※※※※※※※※※

So it will be seen that every quart of fruit wine not made for medicine, or sacramental purposes, helps to build up the cause (intemperance) which we all so desire not to encourage. And for those who take any kind of spirits for the sake of the spirit, let me give you the following:

Spiritual Facts—That whis-key is the *key* by which many gain entrance into our prisons and almshouses.

Fig. 23.

THE MAN WHO DRINKS MODERN LIQUORS.

Fig. 24.   Fig. 25.

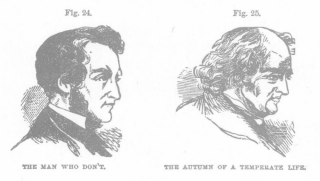

THE MAN WHO DON'T.   THE AUTUMN OF A TEMPERATE LIFE.

That *brandy brands* the noses of all those who cannot govern their appetites.

That *punch* is the cause of many *unfriendly punches.*

That *ale* causes many *ailings*, while *beer brings* to the *bier.*

That *wine* causes many to take a *winding* way home.

That *cham*-pagne is the source of many *real* pains.

That *gin slings* have "*slewed*" more than *slings of oak.*

AGUE MEDICINES

Soot Coffee—Has cured many cases of ague, after "everything else" had failed; it is made as follows:

Soot scraped from a chimney, (that from stove pipes does not do) 1 table-spoon, steeped in water, 1 pt., and settled with 1 egg beaten up in a little water, as for other coffee, with sugar, and cream, 3 times daily with the meals, in place of other coffee.

It has come in very much to aid restoration in Typhoid Fever, bad cases of Jaundice, Dyspepsia, &c., &c.

Many persons will stick up their noses at these "Old Grandmother prescriptions," but I tell many "upstart Physicians" that our grandmothers are carrying more information out of the world by their deaths, than will ever be possessed by this class of "sniffers," and *I* really thank God, so do *thousands* of others, that He has enabled *me*, in this work, to reclaim such an amount of it for the benefit of the world.

DYSPEPSIA

In the good old days of corn bread and crust coffee, there was but little trouble with Dyspepsia; but since the days of fashionable intemperance, both in eating and drinking, such as spirituous liquors, wines, beers, ale, tea, and coffee, hot bread or biscuit, high seasoned food, over-loading the stomach at meals, and constant eating and drinking between meals, bolting the food, as called, that is swallowing it without properly chewing, excessive venery, want of outdoor exercise, with great anxiety of mind as to how the means can be made to continue the same indulgences, &c., all have a tendency to debilitate the stomach, and bring on, or cause Dyspepsia. . . .

This overindulgence would not be continued, nor would it have been allowed, had they known its awful consequences. I know that this was true in my own case, in all its points; this was, of course, before I studied, or knew but little, of the power of the human system, or the practice of medicine, and it was for the purpose of finding something to cure myself, that I commenced its study; for it was by years of over-indulgence at table, and between meals, in the grocery business which I was carrying on, that I brought on such a condition of the stomach that eating gave me the most intolerable suffering—a feeling almost impossible to describe; first a feeling of goneness or want of support at the stomach, heat, lassitude, and finally pain; until a thousand deaths would have been a great relief. . . .

All physicians whose books I have read, and all whose prescriptions I have obtained, say: "Eat little and often; drink little and often." I say eat a little, and at the right time, that is, after digestion, and it is of just as much importance to eat and drink the right thing, as at the right time.

Persons have been so low in Dyspepsia, that even one tea-spoon of food on the stomach would not rest; in such cases, let nothing be taken by mouth for several days; but inject gruel, rice water, rich broths, etc.; but these cases occur very seldom.

First—Then, with ordinary cases, if there is much heat of the stomach, at bed time, wet a towel in cold water, wringing it out that it may not drip, and lay it over the stomach, having a piece of flannel over it to prevent wetting the clothes. This will soon allay the heat, but keep it on during the night, and at any subsequent time, as may be needed.

Second—In the morning, if you have been in the habit of eating about two large potatoes, two pieces of steak, two slices of bread, or from four to six pancakes, or two to four hot biscuits, and drinking one to three cups of tea

PUDDING—Biscuit Pudding, Without Re-Baking.—Take water, 1 qt.; sugar, ¼ lb.; butter, the size of a hen's egg; flour, 4 table, spoons; nutmeg, grated, ½ of one.

Mix the flour with just sufficient cold water to rub up all the lumps while the balance of the water is heating, mix all and split the biscuit once or twice, and put into this gravy while it is hot, and keep hot until used at table. It uses up cold biscuit, and I prefer it to richer puddings. It is indeed worth a trial. This makes a nice dip gravy also for other puddings.

2. Old English Christmas Plumb Puddings.—The Harrisburg *Telegraph* furnishes its readers with a recipe for the real "Old English Christmas Plumb Pudding." After having given this pudding a fair test, I am willing to endorse every word of it; and wish for the holiday to come oftener than once a year:

"To make what is called a pound pudding; take of raisins well stoned but not chopped, currants thoroughly washed, 1 lb. each; chop suet, 1 lb., very finely, and mix with them; add ¼ lb. of flour or bread very finely crumbled; 3 ozs. of sugar; 1½ ozs. of grated lemon peel, a blade of mace, ½ of a small nutmeg, 1 tea-spoon of ginger; ½ doz. of eggs, well beaten; work it well together, put it in a cloth, tie it firmly, allowing room to swell; put it into boiling water, and boil not less than two hours. It should not be suffered to stop boiling.

The cloth, when about to be used, should be dipped into boiling water, squeezed dry, and floured; and when the pudding is done, have a pan of cold water ready, and dip it in for a moment, as soon as it comes out of the pot, which prevents the pudding from sticking to the cloth. For a dip gravy for this or other puddings, see the "Biscuit Pudding without Re-Baking," or "Spreading Sauce for Pudding."

3. Indian Pudding, To Bake.—Nice sweet milk, 1 qt.; butter, 1 oz.; 4 eggs, well beaten; Indian meal, 1 tea-cup; raisins, ½ lb.; sugar, ¼ lb.

Scald the milk, and stir in the meal whilst boiling; then let it stand until only blood-warm, and stir all well together, and bake about one and a half hours. Eaten with sweetened cream, or either of the pudding sauces mentioned in the "Christmas Pudding."

or coffee,—hold, hold, you cry; no, let me go on. I have many times seen all these eaten, with butter, honey, or molasses, too large in amount to be mentioned, with a taste of every other thing on the table, such as cucumber, tomatoes, &c., &c., and all by dyspeptics. But you will stop this morning on half of one potato, two inches square of steak, and half of one slice of cold, wheat bread—or I prefer, if it will agree with you, that you use the "Yankee Brown Bread," only the same quantity: *very slow, chew perfectly fine, and swallow it without water, tea, or coffee;* neither must you drink any, not a drop, until one hour before meal-time again, then as little as possible, so as you think not quite to choke to death. . . .

Lastly—You now have the whole secret of curing the worst case of dyspepsia in the world. You will, however, bear in mind that years have been spent in indulgence; do not therefore expect to cure it in day, nay, it will take months, possible a whole year of self-denial, watchfulness and care: and even then, one over loading of the stomach at a Christmas pudding will set you back again for months. . . .

CAUTION—I may be allowed to give a word of caution to Mothers, as well as to all others. One plate of food is enough for health—two, and even three, are often eaten. Most persons have heard of the lady who did not want a "cart load," but when she got to eating, it all disappeared, and the retort, "Back up your cart and I will load it again," was just what I would have expected to hear if the load had been given to a Dyspeptic, which it no doubt was; then learn the proper amount of food necessary for health, and when that is eaten, by yourself, or child, stop. If pudding is on the table and you choose to have a little of it, it is all right,—have some pudding; if pie, have a piece of pie; or cake, have a piece of cake; but do not have all, and that after you have eaten twice as much meat victual as health requires. If apples, melons, raisins or nuts are on the table, and you wish some of them, eat them before meal, and never after it; if surprise is manifested around you, say *you eat to live, not live to eat.* The reason for this is, that persons will eat all they need, and often more, of common food, then eat nuts, raisins, melons, &c., until the stomach is not only filled beyond comfort, but actually distended to its utmost capacity of endurance; being led on by the taste, when if the reverse course is taken, the stomach becomes satisfied when a proper amount of the more common food has been eaten after the others.

You may consider me a hard Doctor, be it so then; the drunkard, calls him hard names who says give up your "cups," but as sure as he would die a drunkard, so sure will you die a Dyspeptic unless you give up your over-eating and over-drinking of water, tea, coffee, wine, beer, ale, &c. Now you know the consequences, suit yourselves; but I have paid too dearly for my experience, not to lift a warning voice, or spare the guilty. . . .

Old "Father Pinkney," a gentleman over 90 years of age, assures me that he had cured many bad cases of Dyspepsia, where they would give up their over indulgences:

Blue flag root, washed clean, and free from specks and rotten streaks, then pounding it and putting it into a little warm water, and straining out the milky juice, and adding sufficient peppersauce to make it a little hot. DOSE—one table-spoon 3 times daily.

It benefits by its action on the liver, and it would be good in Liver Complaints, the pepper also stimulating the stomach.

LARYNGITIS

Inflammation of the Throat. This complaint, in a chronic form, has become very prevalent, and is a disease which is aggravated by every change of weather, more especially in the fall and winter months. It is considered, and that just, a very hard case to cure, but with caution, time, and a rational course of treatment, it can be cured.

The difficulty with most persons is, they think that it is an uncommon disease, and consequently they must obtain some uncommon preparation to cure it, instead of which, some of the more simple remedies, as follows, will cure nearly every case, if persevered in a sufficient length of time.

Gargle For Sore Throat—Very strong sage tea ½ pint; strained honey, common salt, and strong vinegar, of each 2 table-spoons; cayenne, the pulverized, one rounding tea-spoon; steeping the cayenne with the sage, strain, mix, and bottle for use, gargling from 4 to a dozen times daily according to the severity of the case.

CANCER

Dr. H. G. Judkins's Method—This gentleman, of Malaga, Monroe Co., O., takes: Chloride of zinc the size of a hazel nut, and puts enough water with it to make a thin paste, then mixes with it equal parts of flour, and finely pulverized charcoal, sufficient to form a tolerable stiff paste.

He spreads this on a soft piece of sheep skin, sufficiently large to cover the tumor, and applies every two days until it is detached, then dresses it with "Judkins' Ointment," which see.

L. S. Hodgkins' Method—This gentleman is a merchant, of Reading, Mich. The method is not original with him, but he cured his wife with it, of cancer of the breast, after having been pronounced incurable. Some would use it because it contains calomel—others would not use it for the same reason; I give it an insertion from the fact that I am well satisfied that it has cured the disease, and from its singularity of composition.

Take a white oak root and bore out the heart and burn the chips to get the ashes, ¼ oz.; lujar caustic, ¼ oz.; calomel, ¼ oz.; salts of nitre (salt petre) ¼ oz.; the body of a thousand-legged worm, dried and pulverized, all to be made fine and mixed with ¼ lb. of lard.

Spread this rather thin upon soft leather, and apply to the Cancer, changing twice a day; will kill the tumor in three or four days, which you will know by its general appearance; then apply a poultice of soaked figs until its comes out, fibres and all; heal with a plaster made by boiling red beech leaves in water, straining and boiling thick, then mix with beeswax and mutton tallow to form a salve of proper consistency. To cleanse the system while the above is being used, and for some time after:

Take mandrake root, pulverized, 1 oz.; epsom salts 1 oz.; put into pure gin 1 pt., and take of this 3 times daily, from 1 tea to a tablespoon, as you can bear. He knew of several other cures from the same plan.

Great English Remedy—by which a brother of Lowell Mason was cured, is as follows:

Take chloride of zinc, blood-root pulverized, and flour, equal quantities of each, worked into a paste and applied until the mass comes out, then poultice and treat as a simple sore.

The Rural New Yorker, in reporting this case, says in applying it, "First spread a common sticking-plaster much larger than the cancer, cutting a circular piece from the center of it a little larger than the cancer, applying it which exposes a narrow rim of healthy skin; then apply the cancer plaster and keep it on twenty-four hours. On removing it, the cancer will be found to be burned into, and appears the color of an old shoe-sole, and the rim outside will appear white and boiled, as it is burned by steam.

"Dress with slipper-elm poultice until suppuration takes place, then heal with any common salve."

C O S T I V E N E S S

To Cure—Costive habits are often brought on by neglecting to go to stool at the usual time, for most persons have a regular daily passage, and the most usual time is at rising in the morning, or immediately after breakfast; but hurry or negligence, for the want of an understanding of the evil arising from putting it off, these calls of nature are suppressed; but it be understood, *nature*, like a good workman or student, has a time for each duty; then not only let her work at her own time, but if tardy not only aid but solicit her call, or in other words:

> *When nature calls, at either door, do not*
> *   attempt to bluff her;*
> *But haste away, night or day, or health is*
> *   sure to suffer.*

The above attention to diet, using milk, roasted apples, and if not dyspeptic, uncooked apples, pears, peaches, &c., at meal time, "Yankee Brown Bread," or bread made of unboled wheat, if preferred, and avoiding a meat diet, will in most cases soon remedy the difficulty, HOWEVER:

Corn Meal 1 table-spoon stirred up in sufficient cold water to drink well, and drunk in the morning, immediately after rising, has with perseverance, cured many bad cases.

S I C K   H E A D A C H E

To Cure—Sick headache, proper, arises from acidity, or over-loading the stomach; when it is not from over eating, all that is

necessary, is to soak the feet in hot water about twenty minutes, drinking at the same time some of the herb-teas, such as pennyroyal catnip, or mint, &c., then get into bed, cover up warm and keep up a sweating process for about an hour, by which time relief will have been obtained; but when food has been taken which remains in the stomach, it is much the best way to take an emetic.

After the operation, and when the stomach becomes a little settled, some nourishment will be desired, when any of the mild broths, or gruel, should be taken, in small quantities, without fear of increasing the difficulty.

Females in a weak and debilitated condition, often have a headache which is purely sympathetic; this they will distinguish by their general weakness, irregularities, and the light-headedness, often amounting to real pain; in such cases take the following:

Headache Drops—Castor, gentian, and valerian roots, bruised, ¼ oz.; laudanum 1 oz.; sulphuric ether 1½ oz.; alcohol ½ pt.; water ½ pt.; put all into a bottle and let stand about 10 days. DOSE—A tea-spoon as often as required, or 2 or 3 times daily.

BURNS

Salve for Burns, Frost-Bites, Cracked Nipples, &c.—Equal parts of turpentine, sweet oil, and beeswax; mix the oil and wax together, and when a little cool, add the turpentine, and stir until cold, which keeps them evenly mixed.

Apply by spreading upon thin cloth—linen is the best. I used this salve upon one of my own children only a year and a half old, which had pulled a cup of hot coffee upon itself, beginning on the eye lid and extending down the face, neck and breast, also over the shoulder, and in two places across the arm, the skin coming off with the clothes; in fifteen minutes from the application of the salve, the child was asleep, and it never cried again from the burn, and not a particle of scar left. . . .

Dr. Downer, of Dixboro, within six miles of our city used it (another preparation) in a case where a boy fell backwards into a tub of hot water, scalding the whole buttock, thighs, and privates making a bad scald in a bad place, but he succeeded in bringing him successful through, and from its containing

opium, it might be preferable to the first in deep and extensive burns, but in that case the opium might be added to the first salve.

CHILBLAINS

To Cure—Published by Order of the Government of Wirtemburg.—Mutton tallow and lard of each ¾ lb.; melt in an iron vessel and add hydrated oxide of iron 2 oz.; stirring continually with an iron spoon, until the mass is of uniform black color; then let it cool and add Venice turpentine 2 oz.: and Armenian bole 1 oz; oil of burgamot 1 dr.; rub up the bole with a little olive oil before putting it in.

Apply several times daily by putting it upon lint or linen—heals the worst cases in days.

Chilblains arise from a severe cold to the part, causing inflammation, often ulcerating, making deep, and very troublesome, long continued sores.

LINIMENTS

Good Samaritan, Improved—Take 98 per cent alcohol 2 qts., and add to it the following articles: Oils of sassafras, hemlock, spirits of turpentine, tincture of cayenne, catechu, guac, and laudanum, of each 1 oz. tincture of myrrh 4 ozs.; oil origanum 2 ozs.; oil of wintergreen ½ oz.; gum camphor 2 ozs.; and chloroform 1½ ozs.

I have used the above liniment over five years, and cannot speak too highly of its value; I have cured myself of two severe attacks of rheumatism with it, the first in the knee and the last in the shoulder, three years after; my wife has cured two corns on the toes with it, by wetting them twice daily for a few days; and it is hard to think of anything which it has not cured, such as sprains, bruises, cuts, jams, rheumatism, weak back, reducing swellings, curing leg-ache in children from over-playing, for horseflesh, &c., &c. . . .

Toad Ointment—For sprains, strains, lame-back, rheumatism, caked breasts, caked udders, &c., &c.

Good sized live toads, 4 in number; put into boiling water and cook very soft; then take them out and boil the water down to ½ pt., and add fresh churned, unsalted butter 1 lb. and simmer together; at the last add tincture of arnica 2 ozs.

This was obtained from an old Physician, who thought more of it than of any prescription in his possession. Some persons might think it hard on toads, but you could not kill them quicker in any other way.

HYDROPHOBIA AND SNAKE BITES

To Prevent, and Cure—A. Hubbard, of Boone Co., Ill. in a letter to the St. Louis *Republican,* says: "Eighteen years ago my brother and myself were bitten by a mad-dog. A sheep was also bitten at the same time. Among the many cures offered for the little boys, (we were then ten or twelve years old,) a friend suggested the following which he said would cure the bite of a rattlesnake:

"Take the root of the common upland ash, commonly called the black ash, peel off the bark, boil it to a strong decoction, and of this drink freely. Whilst my father was preparing the above, the sheep spoken of began to be afflicted with hydrophobia. When it had become so fatigued from its distracted state as to be no longer able to stand, my father drenched it with a pint of the ash root ooze, hoping to ascertain whether he could depend upon it as a cure for his sons. Four hours after the drench had been given, to the astonishment of all, the animal got up and went quietly with the flock to graze. My brother and myself continued to take the medicine for 8 to 10 days, 1 gill 3 times daily. No effects of the dread poison were ever discovered on either of us. It has been used very successfully in snake bites, to my knowledge."

EYE PREPARATION

For Excessive Inflammation of the Eyes—Poultice by boiling a handful of hops in water, putting in from ½ to 1 dr. of opium, while boiling; when still warm, lay the hops over the eyes and keep them wet with the water in which they were boiled.

A lady who had been blistered and starved, according to the old plan, in this disease, was soon cured by this poulticing and washing the eyes often with the hop-water containing the opium, with generous diet, &c., contrary to the expectations of friends, and the predictions of enemies, to the plan.

FIGURE 2.
MAD DOG OR POISONOUS REPTILE BITES.

What to Do.—This class of common and dangerous emergencies may be successfully met on the moment by the simple means shown in the adjoining plate. By preventing the poison from entering the system, time is gained for the use of the remedies given on pages 365, 664, 1034.

The Band.—The band, fillet or ligature used may be a strap, cord, rope or handkerchief—anything, in fact, which can be drawn and tied tightly; or which, if tied loosely, will permit of a stick being placed within it, and a tight twisting of the same, after the manner of a *tourniquet* (see page 660), in order to stop the blood circulation more effectively.

How to Do.—1. If the bite be on the arm, bind the cord, or ligature, tightly around the limb at the point indicated by the head of the *"arm"* arrow.

2. If the bite be on the hand, bind the cord tightly around the wrist at the point indicated by the head of the *"hand"* arrow.

3. If the bite be on the upper part of the leg, bind the cord tightly around the limb at the point indicated by the head of the *"upper limb"* arrow.

4. If the bite be below the knee, bind the cord tightly around the limb at the point indicated by the head of the *"lower limb"* arrow.

5. **Further Precautions.**—It is perhaps unnecessary to add that in the emergency of a mad dog bite the band for preventing the virus from entering the system should be applied as quickly and tightly as possible. If the material is at hand, several of such bands, tied one above the other, will prove more effective than a single one. An additional emergency measure, and a very proper one, is to quickly cut the wound out with a sharp knife, and then to cauterize it with a hot iron, or such other means as may prove to be at hand. Make all haste to get the victim within reach of the remedies given in the pages above mentioned.

The Snake Bite.—The snake bites that are dangerously poisonous are those of the copperhead, water-moccasin, rattlesnake and viper. As in the case of the mad dog bite, several bands, tied one above the other, are better than one. The wound should be cut out, and then sucked. No harm can come from this if the mouth be free from sores, or the poison is not swallowed. In the absence of other means of cauterizing a snake bite wound, hunters pour powder upon it and explode it with a spark. The band or bands used should not be removed for some time, and in case of more than one, the uppermost one should be removed first.

658

Indian Eye Water—Soft water 1 pt.; gum arabic 1 oz.; white vitriol 1 oz.; fine salt ½ tea-spoon; put all into a bottle and shake until dissolved. Put into the eye just as you retire to bed.

I paid Mrs. Pinny, south of Ypsilanti, Mich., fifty cents for this prescription. . . .

VERMIFUGES

Worm Cake, English Remedy—Wheat flour and jalap of each ½ lb.; calomel, grain-tin, and ginger, of each 1 oz. Mix thoroughly and wet up as dough, to a proper consistence to roll out; then roll out as lozenge cakes, to three-sixteenths of an inch in thickness; then cut out ¾ inch square and dry them. . . .

"Children may eat them, or they can be shaved off very fine and mixed in a little treacle, honey, or preserves. If after taking the first dose, they do no work as you desire increase the dose a little. The patient to take the medicine twice a week—Sundays and Wednesdays. To be taken in the morning, fasting, and to be worked off with a little warm tea, water gruel, or warm broth. N.B.—Milk must not be used in working them off, and be careful of catching cold."

I obtained the above of an English family who praised it very highly as a cathartic for common purposes, as well as for worms. . . .

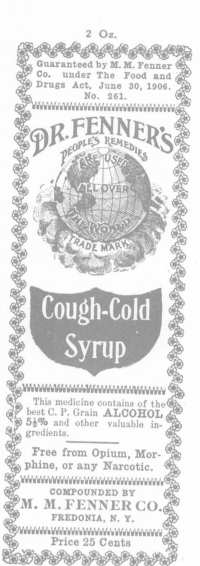
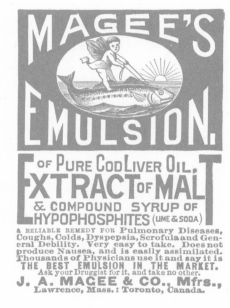

WHOOPING COUGH

Syrup—Onions and garlics, sliced, of each 1 gill; sweet oil 1 gill; stew them in the oil, in a covered dish, to obtain the juices; then strain and add honey 1 gill; paregoric and spirits of camphor, of each ½ oz.; bottle and cork tight for use. DOSE—For a child of 2 or 3 years, 1 tea-spoon 3 or 4 times daily, or whenever the cough is troublesome, increasing or lessening, according to age.

This is a granny's prescription, but I care not from what source I derive information, if it gives the satisfaction that this has done upon experiment. This lady has raised a large family of her own children, and grandchildren in abundance. We have tried it with three of our children also, and prescribed it in many other cases with satisfaction for over seven years. It is excellent also in common cold extended with much cough. This is from experience, too, whom I have found a very competent teacher. . . .

DIARRHEAS

Cordial—The best rhubarb root, pulverized, 1 oz.; peppermint leaf 1 oz.; capsicum ⅛ oz.; cover with boiling water and steep thoroughly, strain, and add bi-carbonate of potash and essence of cinnamon, of each ½ oz.; with brandy or good whisky equal in amount to the whole, and loaf sugar 4 oz. DOSE—For an adult 1 to 2 table-spoons; for a child 1 to 2 tea-spoons, from 3 to 6 times per day, until relief is obtained.

This preparation has been my dependence, in my travels and in my family for several years, and it has never failed us.

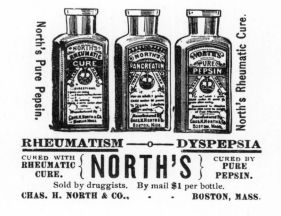

Medicology

NECESSITY OF THIS BOOK

If each inhabitant of America could have an experienced doctor constantly at his elbow to advise him in all the medical and sanitary emergencies of life, these pages would never be needed. As, however, such a desirable precaution is an impracticable one, this work is offered as a substitute for the medical guide, who should be sent for as quickly as possible whenever any emergency arises or any departure from perfect health makes itself manifest. On the other hand when, as must frequently happen, in small towns, villages, in rural districts, at sea, or whilst traveling in foreign lands, a doctor cannot be procured immediately, prompt treatment by an intelligent person as directed in this work will surely result in saving an immense number of lives and a vast amount of human suffering.

PATENT MEDICINES

A cure for biliousness and relief from asthma were but two of the almost limitless promises made by patent medicines. Any doubters were beguiled by testimonials, of which those on the Pe-Ru-Na ad at left are typical. Along with the rich and famous (such as actress Julia Marlowe) testimonials were credited to ordinary people who might live in or near your own home town.

Take Hood's Sarsaparilla

100 Doses One Dollar

SUFFERERS FROM ASTHMA
CAN GET INSTANT RELIEF BY USING THE
Excelsior Asthma Remedy.
Send 3c. Stamp for SAMPLE PACKAGE, or 50c. for
LARGE PACKAGE. Address,
EXCELSIOR ASTHMA REMEDY, Montpelier, Vermont.

DR. GROSVENOR'S
LIVER AID,
ENSURES
APPETITE & DIGESTION
SMALL DOSES, PROMPT EFFECT.

Use TARRANT'S
SELTZER
APERIENT,
To Regulate
The Stomach,
The Liver,
The Bowels.

TARRANT'S
SELTZER
APERIENT.

To cure
Indigestion,
Biliousness,
Constipation.

A most important and useful lesson in regards to the wisdom of sanitary precautions and surgical or medical treatment may be drawn from the common accident of having a cinder enter the eye (as it is called) on a railway journey. Trivial as this misfortune seems at first, the painful irritation which the tiny particle of coal, if not removed, soon sets up under the lid is far more troublesome than the hygienic precaution of wearing wire-gauze spectacles for a lifetime of railroad traveling would be. . . .

OUTWARD ENEMIES OF HEALTH

Heat and Disease—Heat becomes a predisposing cause of disease as soon as the temperature rises above 70 degrees or 80 degrees. When it begins to affect healthy life the pulse, the heart action and respiration are quickened. The skin and lungs are unable to equalize temperature, and the condition of the entire body becomes one of susceptibility to disease.

The Sun's Heat—Exposure of the body for long periods to the heat of the sun is apt to result in more or less serious disturbances, such as congestions, brain hemorrhages, meningitis, etc. Hence the need of protection against direct rays of sun.

Sunstroke—Sunstroke, or thermic fever, is the result of exposure to heat rays. Its early symptoms are faintness, thirst, great heat and dryness of the skin, with prostration. As quickly as possible the body should be subjected to the ice or cold water treatment to neck and head.

Traveling in Hot Climates—Do not travel during the heat of the day. Protect the person by some covering which will reflect the sun's rays. Rest during the mid-day hours. Content yourself with a scanty, unstimulating diet. Use gently stimulating baths. Wear thin, light, loosely-fitting clothes.

Cold as a Disease Producer—Cold becomes a disturber of bodily function as soon as it falls to a temperature which ceases to be agreeable. The tissues shrink, the capillaries grow sluggish, perspiration is suppressed, sensibility is impaired.

Sudden Cold—Sudden falls of temperature are marked by a long train of diseases, or by aggravated or fatal turns to existing diseases. This is particularly true of consumption, catarrh, influenza or grippe and bronchitis.

Cold and Elderly People—From thirty years on the human body, begins to draw on its surplus power. This power is constantly diminishing as we age. Hence cold affects the aged most seriously by calling largely on a diminishing power. It is difficult to sustain a "blood heat."

Cold and Perspiration—Cold produces disease by checking perspiration, thus preventing the escape of injurious materials from the blood, and throwing more work on kidneys and lungs, which often become overtaxed.

Cold and the Blood—Cold tends to drive the blood from the blood-vessels to the surface, thus filling one or more of the circulating organs too full of blood. If any of these vessels be weak the man is handicapped in his battle against disease.

Regulation of Clothing—Garments worn next to the skin should be of wool or silk, as best absorbents of perspiration, and as nonconductors of heat. Weights may be light or heavy according to the seasons or different constitutions. White or gray clothes are preferable to black, when one is subjected to direct solar heat.

Poisoned Clothing—Clothes made of dyed materials are sometimes injurious to health, as containing poisons. This is particularly so of bright colored stockings or underclothing.

Local Injuries—Cold gives rise to painful local affections, such as frost-bite and chilblains, the former involving the nose, ears and fingers, the latter the feet. Heat applications in any of these cases must be avoided. The cold treatment is best.

Light—Light has a powerful effect on the system, through both the blood and nerves. It is, therefore, an active agency in the generation of diseases and their cures. It is essential to all growth, and particularly affects the outer tissues as well as the internal organization.

Colored Light—Many advantages are claimed for colored light. Blue and green lights are preferable to orange, yellow or red for the eyes. Certain of the colored lights act beneficially on animal and vegetable growths, and have a great influence in hastening the cures of certain diseases.

Electricity—Electrical conditions of the atmosphere have a direct effect on the human system. On the approach of a thunder storm, one may frequently notice a difficulty of breathing. Rheumatics are painfully affected, neuralgia is intensified. Many existing maladies are aggravated by electrical conditions.

Electricity in Medicine—As a medical agent electricity has grown rapidly in favor. As a remedy for many nervous diseases and for pain the galvanic battery has come into quite general use. It is a clean, convenient and safe remedy. It is also economic, for the cost of an electrical machine is within the means of most every one, and it can be self-operated.

Diseases Affected by Climate—Among the diseases favorably affected by a change of climate are consumption, bronchial affections, diseases of the throat, asthma, chronic gout and rheumatism, dyspepsia, kidney affections, especially Bright's disease, and neuralgia. The advantages of a climate where sea air abounds, or where the air is rarefied and dry, are fully recognized by medical men.

Soils—These affect health in the most direct manner, and through their mineral, animal and vegetable matter, also their air and water. Diseases connected with moist soils are of almost every type, rheumatism catarrh and typhoid being most general. Moist soils are favorite breeding places for germs affecting health, and drainage systems should be made as perfect as possible.

Morbid Poisons—With regard to the co-operative effect of fermentation, putrescence or decomposition there is some reason to believe that it may quicken the activity or facilitate the development of specific morbid poisons in the way of a predisposing cause to their reproduction. There is no small amount of circumstantial evidence tending to show that conditions of this kind may be thus favorable to the propagation of specific diseases, even to the extent of rendering them epidemics in consequence of the predisposing agency of putrefying emanations.

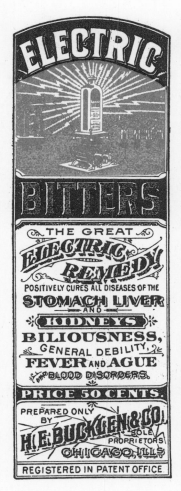
ELECTRICITY IN MEDICINE.

Introduction.—For half a century there has been a steady growth in the use of electricity as a medical agent. At this date many institutions are organized for the purpose of applying electrical treatment to various diseases and medical-healing is taught in nearly all the medical colleges.

Application.—At first electricity was thought to be useful for only that class of diseases due to the nerves and it was generally applied by means of the galvanic battery, which was made in various forms for home use. But the treatment has grown to embrace a variety of diseases.

Dyspepsia.—Electricity is found to be an excellent treatment for dyspepsia on account of the relief it affords to both the physical and mental conditions that accompany the disease. It gives tone to the appetite, cures sleeplessness, removes distress after eating, strengthening the powers of digestion and drives away despondency and gloom.

Fits, Epilepsy, Falling Sickness.—These diseases being nervous in character yield satisfactorily to the electric treatment. Any nervous disease is more readily reached by electricity than by other remedies and some remarkable cures have been placed to its credit.

Anemia.—This means want of blood and the patient becomes pale and weak. The disease is a general condition, and as a cure electricity is found efficacious. It stimulates the same as oxygen, produces more red corpuscles in the blood, imparts increased vital energy to the blood currents and does away with languidness and depression.

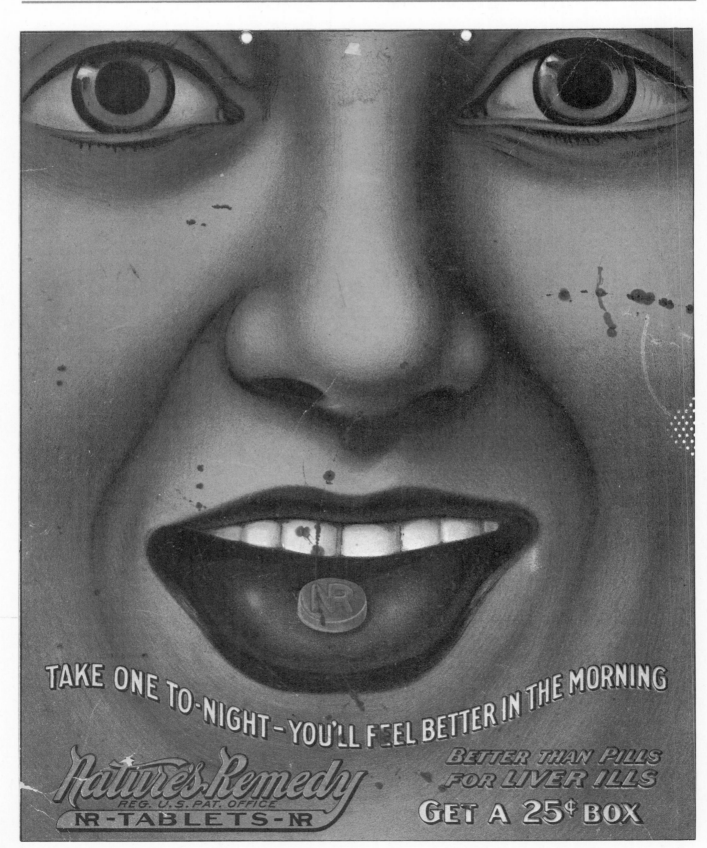

Patent medicine advertisements shocked, stunned, and bludgeoned the consumer to gain his attention. Garish illustrations vied with extravagant claims—and sometimes with whimsical ideas like that of Dr. Myles. Once a product gained the public fancy—as Lydia Pinkham's Compound did so successfully—its makers could eschew sensationalism and produce ads that were subdued and dignified.

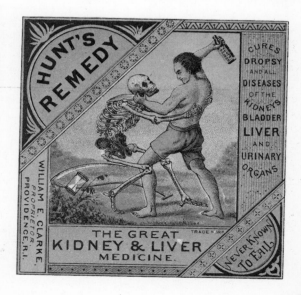

Advertisements

Since the advertising media were more limited in scope
in the 1800's than they are now,
most of the newspapers and magazines
were filled with advertisements extolling the
virtues of the various patent medicines.
They ran in size from full page ads for something like
Hale's Honey of Horehound to a few lines
of type for the curing of the opium habit.
Everyone and everything was advertised.
These advertisements in the following section are typical of the many
to be found at that time with the extravagant claims and testimonials used.
There also were many advertisements to be found at the
back of home medicine books and cookbooks.

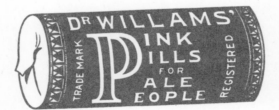

SCOTT'S EMULSION

A Quick Return to Rosy Health

The Experience, Doings and Sayings of a Bright Little Southern Girl

"Under the Doctor's Care for Three Years"—"A Fearful Cough That Baffled Their Skill"—"Became Thin and Weak and Nervous"—"Doctors All Said She Had Consumption"—"Last Winter They About Gave Her Up"—Doctors Agreeing, They Tried Scott's Emulsion—Again "Plump and Rosy."

ELIZABETH CITY, N. C., June 28, 1892.

Messrs. Scott & Bowne, New York.

GENTLEMEN:—It has been a pleasure to me to advise, in many instances, my friends to use your **Emulsion**, and thus far to know of their rapid improvement. I cite one case in particular. A dear little girl of nine years, a music pupil of mine, had been under the doctor's care for three years or more before I knew her. Her trouble was a fearful cough which defied their treatment and baffled their skill. The poor child became so thin and weak and nervous that she could do nothing. The doctors all said she had Consumption.

This last winter they about gave her up. I was there one day and her parents were telling me that they had done everything, and I asked whether they had ever given her **Scott's Emulsion** of Cod Liver Oil. She shuddered at the name. They said "No," and I asked them to try it faithfully. They did. Within a month, in fact, less than a month, she was out and has not been sick since. She continues taking the **Emulsion**, and her cough is nearly well, and she begins to look so plump and rosy, as though she had never been ill.

The other day as she was taking her lesson, she looked up at me and said, "I thought it was going to be bad, but I like it now." Not knowing what she had on her mind, and supposing she was speaking of the music, I asked her what she meant, and she greatly amused me by replying, "Why, I meant my **C. O. D.**" She is very bright, and can fully appreciate a joke. Wishing you all manner of success,

Yours very truly,

SCOTT'S EMULSION of Cod Liver Oil with Hypophosphites of Lime and Soda *restores healthy flesh,* dissipated through ANY cause at ANY period of life. Where it is required and used once in Consumption it does service a score of times in the treatment and prompt cure of Coughs, Colds and Throat Affections, so often *sources* of Consumption. In this preparation the cod liver oil is freed from its drawbacks of taste and indigestibility, and becomes *a practical medicine, a practical food.* Partly digested by chemical process, it is easy of assimilation, and available when all other forms of flesh-producing foods fail. It *strengthens* digestion, and renews failing appetite. It arrests wasting diseases by rapidly and abundantly supplying *sound tissue, pure blood* and *nerve force.*

Scott's Emulsion IS SOLD BY DRUGGISTS THE WORLD OVER. THE GENUINE IS ALWAYS ENCLOSED IN A SALMON COLORED WRAPPER, WITH LABEL OF MAN WITH FISH ON BACK.

PREPARED BY SCOTT & BOWNE, CHEMISTS

New York   London   Paris   Barcelona   Milan   Belleville, Canada

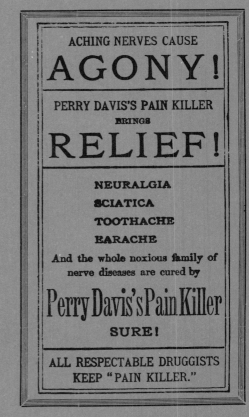
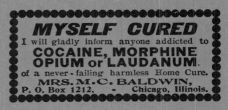

35 Pounds of Fat.

DR. EDISON'S OBESITY PILLS AND REDUCING TABLETS CURED MRS. MANNING.

No Other Remedies But Dr. Edison's Reduce Obesity—
Take No Others.

SAMPLES FREE—USE COUPON.

MRS. MANNING

Mary Hyde Manning, one of the best known of Troy's, New York, society women, grew too fleshy, and used Dr. Edison's Obesity Remedies. Read the letter telling of her reduction and restoration to health:—"In six weeks I was reduced 35 pounds, from 171 to 136, by Dr. Edison's Obesity Pills and Reducing Tablets. I recommend these remedies to all fat and sick men and women."

The following well-known men and women have been reduced by DR. EDISON'S OBESITY REMEDIES:

Mrs. H. Mershon, 156 South Jackson St., Lima, O., 148 lbs.
Mrs. Josephine McPherson, 7916 Wright St., Chicago, 42 lbs.
Rev. Edward R. Pierce, 410 Alma St., Chicago, 42 lbs.
C. C. Nichols, 145 Clark St., Aurora, Ill., 36 lbs.
Mrs. W. Davlin, Whitemore, O., 149 lbs.
W. H. Webster, 618 2d Ave., Troy, N. Y., 26 lbs.
J. M. McKinney, 4504 State St., Chicago, 30 lbs.
Mrs. J. M. McKinney, 4504 State St., Chicago, 33 lbs.
Mrs. A. Walker, 1104 Milton Place, Chicago, 20 lbs.

WARNER'S OBESITY TABLETS

The original Warner harmless effective cure for gradually reducing obesity and over fatness.

Made after the composition of the famous Vichy and Kissingen spring waters and prepared in such a form that one or two tablets added to a glassful of water will make the exact spring water. By using Vichy tablets one day and Kissingen the next, any excessive fat will be gradually reduced without in the least endangering the patient's health. The treatment should be continued until the desired weight is obtained. Full directions given.

No. 8F46 Complete treatment of 40 tablets. Price, per box 43c

How to Treat Itching Piles.
How to Treat Blind Piles.
How to Treat Bleeding Piles.
How to Treat Ulcerated Rectum.
How to Treat Hemorrhoids.

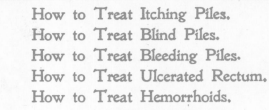

DR. KILMER & CO'S HARD RUBBER

PILE PIPE

Use Dr. Kilmer's U & O Anointment.

It does not irritate and make the disease worse.

The First application will give the patient immediate relief, comfort and rest.

Piles, if allowed to continue, very often develop into Fistula, a most serious trouble which often proves fatal.

How to Apply U & O Anointment.

☞ In all ordinary cases the application of U & O Anointment may be made with the end of finger, sponge or linen cloth.

☞ If the disease has become deep-seated, with much soreness, pain, tenderness, and up out of reach of finger, the **Pile Pipe** should be used.

☞ If the patient suffers during evacuation of the bowels, application with the **Pile Pipe** should be made before and after the bowels move.

☞ In all cases, application of Dr. Kilmer's U & O Anointment may be made as often as the case would seem to require—1, 2, 3 or 4 times a day.

It is a vegetable product and contains no opiates or minerals.

How to Get the Pile Pipe.

The Dr. Kilmer & Co. Pile Pipe can be obtained at druggists, or we will send it by mail upon receipt of 50 cents in postage stamps. We have received many letters from people who have used the Pile Pipe with the most pleasing satisfaction. In bad cases the Pile Pipe will place our U & O Anointment just where it is most needed to heal. The price is within reach of all.

Directions for Using the Pile Pipe.

The patient can use it in a simple and cleanly manner without pain, inconvenience or soiling the linen. It is so compact that it can be carried in the pocket, filled with Dr. Kilmer's U & O Anointment ready for use.

Remove the screw plunger from the ointment barrel, then place a sufficient quantity of ointment in the barrel for several applications; replace the plunger, turning it sufficiently to force the ointment into the small perforated end of pipe; when thus prepared, insert the tube of pipe within the rectum, turn the plunger two or three revolutions (having a milled head that it may be done easily), thereby forcing the ointment through the perforation of the pipe; turn pipe around once or twice, making a more effectual distribution of the ointment to the parts afflicted; then withdraw pipe, when it will be found that the contraction of the muscles has effectually removed and distributed all the ointment from the surface of the tube, retaining it where it has been deposited, the application being exceedingly simple and *free from all irritation and pain.*

Two or three applications daily will be found quite sufficient for desired effect

In some cases, when the disease is of long standing and chronic, the use of Dr. Kilmer's Swamp-Root and Liver Pills are advised to rid the blood of impurities, mucus (matter), irritating acids, etc., which will result in removing from the system the causing conditions that bring on the piles.

HOW TO GET THE REMEDIES.

Dispensed by Druggists and Dealers in Medicines.

☞ If they do not have them in stock when you call, they will get them for you if requested; if not, send direct to Dr. Kilmer & Co.

Swamp-Root, fifty-cent and dollar size, are large bottles, and the Postoffice Department will not allow us to send them by mail.

If you send fifty cents or one dollar for **one bottle** of either size, **you** will have to pay express.

☞ Send us $5.00 and we will send you five large dollar bottles or five dollars' worth assorted, and we will prepay all express charges.

Dr. Kilmer's U & O Anointment, 25c. | Pile Pipe, - - - 50c.
Dr. Kilmer's U & O Anointment, 50c. | Parilla Liver Pills, 25c.

One or more of the above will be sent by mail upon receipt of price.

☞ *Get them from your Druggist if you can.*

Trading Cards

*Every manufacturer of proprietary medicines had trading cards
which either came with the medicine or else were sent for with a label from the package.
Trading cards were important to the young boy to use in his
games, while his sister took the cards and put them into albums.
Some of the cards were in the form of puzzles such as some that
Carter's Iron pills issued. Other cards were comic or just plain pretty.
When one sees the number of cards that were issued,
one wonders whether the trading cards were issued to advertise the product—
or did one buy the product to get the cards?*

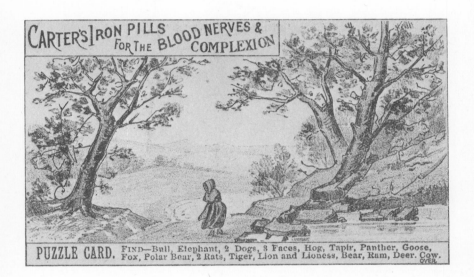

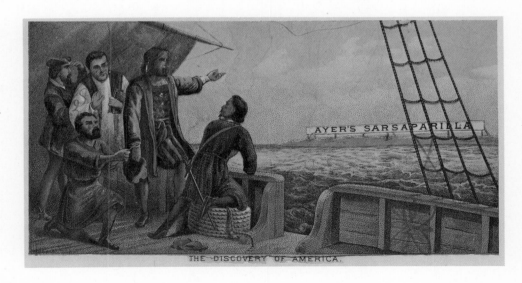

COMPLIMENTS OF
DR. J. MELVIN CO.,
WOBURN, MASS.,
PROPRIETORS OF
Melvin's Vegetable Pills,
Nerve Liniment, and
Cough Syrup.

AYER'S SARSAPARILLA
Purifies the Blood,
Stimulates the Vital Functions, restores
and preserves Health, and infuses New
Life and Vigor throughout the whole System.

Prepared by Dr. J.C. Ayer & Co., Lowell, Mass., U.S.A.

My name is
Residence

"AND THIS
IS MY SISTER"

AFTER READING JAM
CONVINCED THAT MURDOCK'S
LIQUID FOOD WILL MAKE
BLOOD FASTER THAN ALL
PREPARATIONS KNOWN
AND THAT WILL CLEANSE
THE SYSTEM of
DISEASE

Copyright 1890 by A.L.Murdock

Fall River Litho & Co. Fall River, Mass.

over

CURES
NEURALGIA,
"SAPANULE"
DIPTHERIA,
RHEUMATISM
&C.
TRADE MARKS.
REGISTERED
1878

DANDY:—"Inform me, sir, why your quadruped should have the audacious effrontery to exhale his obnoxious, reprehensible, odious and offensive breath directly under my nostrils."

URCHIN:—"Can't you understand your relation better than that? He's only blowing for Kendall's Spavin Cure, 'cause it cured ____ ____ hat awful bad spavin."

AYER'S CHERRY PECTORAL
Cures Colds, Coughs, and all Diseases of the Throat and Lungs.

Presented by
Morse Yellow Dock Root Syrup Co
Providence, R.I.

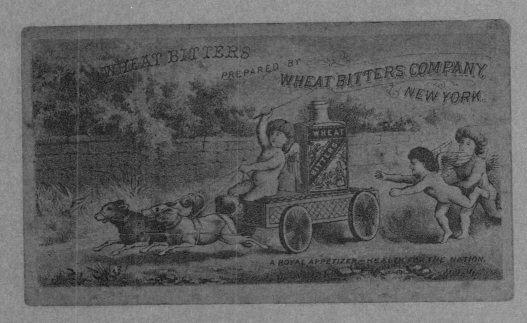

WHEAT BITTERS PREPARED BY WHEAT BITTERS COMPANY, NEW YORK.
A ROYAL APPETIZER — HEALTH FOR THE NATION.

Medicinal Plants

Yellow Flag.

Since most remedies were basically vegetable in origin, there were many books that described the various herbs and how to use them. Some of the books were herbals, others were home medicine books which contained sections on medicinal plants. This practice dates back to the Bible where various plants were mentioned as medicine.

Along with the vegetable garden, every household had an herb corner for those herbs used constantly in the cure of various ailments. The wife and mother also used plants of the forest and field that she did not cultivate. Indian influence was strong and the settlers relied upon herbs and root doctors.

Since herbs were used in remedies so widely, root and herb collecting and cultivating became a routine activity for many pioneers and a part-time vocation for some. The Shakers thrived on the sale of dried herbs, packed and shipped to the various parts of the country.

The largest portions of medicinal substances are extracted from the vegetable world. They consist of leaves, flowers, seeds, barks, and roots. These lose much or all of their medicinal powers unless gathered at the right seasons of the year, and then properly cured. The different parts of a plant are to be gathered when their peculiar juices are most abundant in them. Since the roots of annual plants are best supplied with their juices before they are in flower, they should be gathered at this time. The roots of biennial plants should be gathered in the autumn, after the first year's growth.

The roots of perennial plants are most effective when collected in the spring before vegetation has begun. Before they are dried, the solid parts of these roots are to be washed and cut in slices. The small fibres, unless they are the parts used, are to be thrown away.

Bulbous roots are best when gathered at the time their leaves decay. Their outer covering being rejected, they must be sliced, strung upon thread, and hung in a warm, airy room to dry. After being dried, roots should be packed in barrels or boxes, and kept as free as possible from moisture.

Barks, whether of the roots, trunk, or branches, should be gathered either in autumn

Aloes.

Arnica.

Barley.

Arrow Root.

Burdock.

Balm Mint.

or early in the spring, when they peel off most easily. The dead outside and all rotten parts being separated, they must be dried in the same manner as roots. The most active barks are generally from young trees.

Leaves are to be gathered when they are full grown, and just before the fading of the flower. Those of biennial plants are not to be collected until the second year. For drying,

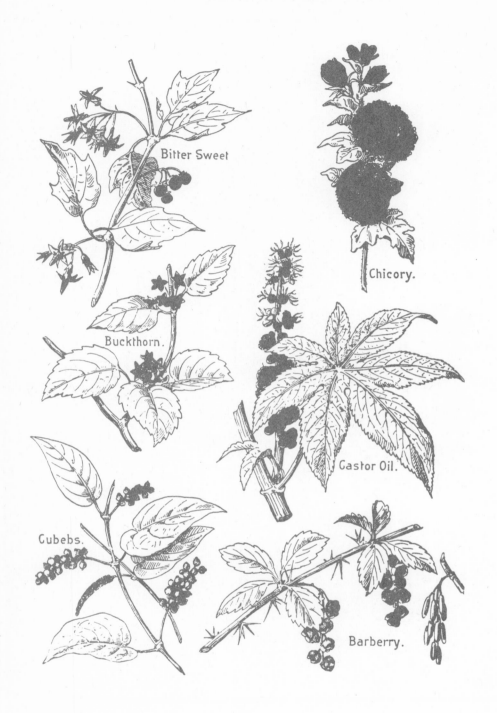

Bitter Sweet

Chicory.

Buckthorn.

Castor Oil.

Cubebs.

Barberry.

they should be thinly spread on the floor of a room through which a current of air passes. For preservations, they should be packed in vessels, and kept free from moisture and insects.

Flowers must generally be collected about the time of their opening, either a little before or just after. They should be dried as rapidly

as possible, but not in the sun, and may be packed away in the same manner as leaves.

Fruits, berries, etc., may be spread thinly upon the floor, or hung up in bunches to dry.

MEDICINAL PLANTS

VIOLETS—THE BLOWS

These are pretty garden flowers, sometimes called "Ladies' Delights," and well known to the florist. They are of a mucilaginous nature and effective in treating canker and strengthening the stomach; they are also good in syrups.

DWARF ELDER—THE BERRIES

This species of elder grows chiefly in pastures and is commonly found among raspberry bushes. The stalk runs up high, with several small berries on the top, resembling whortle berries. They are good for all rheumatic complaints, dropsy, and swollen limbs. Steep the berries in spirit, and take them in small doses before eating.

DOG ACNA

This bush grows commonly in wet places, and is covered with a smooth, speckled bark, of light and dark green. It branches out very much like dog wood. The bark of this, when made into a tea and used as a wash, is good for canker.

RUNNING HEMLOCK

A small bush, this species grows wild in the woods. Light green in color, it has small red berries which are good for a weak stomach. The bush when boiled in water is said to produce a solution effective in curing swollen limbs.

HOLLY

These familiar bushes grow in most places near the sea shore, by the sides of roads and as cultivated hedges. The leaf resembles that of an oak, except that it is prickly. The shrub's small black berries, as well as the bark are made into a solution that is both an astringent and a tonic.

JILL GROW OVER THE GROUND

A common herb, this plant is found in door-yards and by the side of the road. It is a small running vine, resembling low mallow, except that the leaf is smaller. Taken green and pounded up, the herb is beneficial when applied to a fresh wound, or where humors prevail. It is also "the best thing known" to correct female irregularities.

JUNIPER BUSH

The berries of this common bush do not ripen the first year, but continue green two summers and one winter, at which time they are of a black color. Therefore green berries are always to be found upon the bush. The berries are ripe about the falling of the leaf. This admirable solar shrub is "rarely to be paralleled for its virtues." The berries are hot in the third degree, and dry; but in the first, being a most admirable counter-poison, and as great a resister of the pestilence as any thing that grows. They are excellent for the biting of venomous beasts; they provoke urine exceedingly, and therefore are very available in dysurics and stranguaries. . . . They strengthen the stomach exceedingly and expel the wind; indeed there is scarce a better remedy for wind in any part of the body, or the cholic, than the chemical oil drawn from the berries. Such people as know not how to extract this oil, may content themselves by eating ten or a dozen of the ripe berries every morning, fasting. They are good for a cough, shortness of breath, and consumption. They fortify the eye sight by strengthening the optic nerves. The ashes of the wood are especially beneficial to such as have the scurvy, to rub their gums with. The berries stop all fluxes, help the hemorrhoids, or piles, destroy worms in children, procure a lost appetite, and are good for palsies and falling sickness.

GERMANDER

Common Germander shoots forth a number of stalks, with small and somewhat round leaves, dented about the edges. The flowers stand at the tops, of a deep purple color. The roots are composed of divers sprigs, which

Home Remedies and How to Use Them.

HOME REMEDIES, AND HOW TO USE THEM.

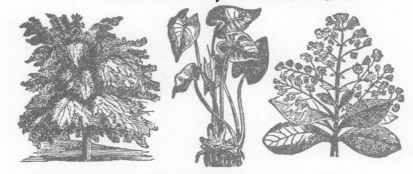

How to Gather and Prepare Medicinal Plants and Barks.

1. BARKS should be gathered as soon as they will peal easily in the spring.
2. LEAVES AND HERBS should be collected just before they begin to fade in autumn.
3. FLOWERS, when they first begin to blossom.
4. SEEDS, just before they are ripe.
5. ROOTS may be dug at any time, thoroughly washed, cleaned and dried.

THE AMERICAN POPLAR.

This is a good tonic, and is a good remedy for *chronic rheumatism, dyspepsia* and general *debility.* Use only the inner part, dried and powdered.

DOSE, a heaping teaspoonful three or four times a day.

shoot forth, round about, quickly overspreading the ground. It grows usually in gardens, and flowers in June and July. This herb is considered to strengthen the brain and apprehension exceedingly. This taken with honey is a remedy for coughs, hardness of the spleen, and difficulty of urine, and helps those that are fallen into dropsy, especially at the beginning of the disease. It is most effectual against the poison of all serpents, being drunk in wine; and the bruised herb outwardly applied, used with honey, cleanses old and foul ulcers. It is good in all diseases of the brain, as continual headache, falling sickness, melancholy, drowsiness and fullness of the spirits, convulsions and palsies. One drachm of the seeds taken in powder will purge by urine, and is good for the yellow jaundice.

LOOSE STRIPE OR WILLOW HERB

The most common kind is called Yellow Loose Stripe. It grows to be four or five feet high or more, with large round stalks, a little crested, and diversely branched from the middle of them to the top into great and long branches. At all the joints there grow long and narrow leaves, but broader below, and usually two at a joint, yet sometimes more, something like willow leaves, smooth on the edges, and of a fair green color. From the upper joints of the branches, and at the tops of them, also stand yellow flowers, of five leaves each, with yellow thread in the middle, which turn into small round heads containing small cornered seeds. The root creeps under ground like couch grass roots, but larger, and shoots up every spring, brownish heads, which afterwards grow up into stalks; it has neither scent nor taste, but is astringent. It grows in moist meadows, and by the side of water. This is good for all manner of bleeding at the mouth and nose, and all fluxes, either to drink, or taken by clyster. It is also good for green wounds to stop the bleeding, and quickly close together the lips of the wound. The juice of the herb is used in gargles, for sore mouths.

YELLOW ROOT (Hydrastis Canadensis).

Part used—the root.

Possesses the virtues of the ordinary bitters and popularly employed as a tonic. Used in dyspepsia and stomach affections, and as a topical application to ulcers and sores in the form of a decoction made with a drachm of the dried root to a pint of water and a syringeful injected three times a day. It is most useful in gonorrhœa.

(1356)

ACONITE

Liniment: Tincture of aconite root, two ounces; opium liniment, 2 ounces; useful in neuralgia, rheumatism and other painful affections.

Liniment of ointment rubbed over a painful brow will cut short the pain of a sick headache. If rubbed over the face, be careful to keep away from the eyes; will help neuralgia of the face.

Mixture of equal parts of aconite and iodine painted on jaw after tooth has been extracted will stop pain.

For typhoid fever: two drops every hour of the tincture with ten drops of sweet spirits of nitre.

For epilepsy, paralysis, gout: Fluid extract, dose: two to five drops: solid extract, dose: one quarter of a grain to a grain.

For fevers and inflammations: Of the tincture of the root, from one-half to 2 drops, in a spoonful of water.

ACORN COFFEE

(1856) A coffee made from one ounce of roasted acorns and a pint of boiling water and used in the dose of three or four teacupfuls in the day, is highly extolled in scrofula, disease of the mesenteric glands, commencing rickets, asthma, and cough.

ADDER'S TONGUE

It is a fine cooling herb, and an excellent ointment is made from it. The leaves are to be chopped to pieces, and four pounds of them are to be put into three pounds of suet and one pint of oil melted together. The whole is to be boiled till the herb is a little crisp, and then the ointment is to be strained off; it will be of a beautiful green. Some give the juice of the plant, or the powder of the dried leaves, inwardly in wounds; but this is trifling.

AGRIMONY

Also called: Cockleburr and Sticklewort.

(1) Grows two to three feet high in hedges, etc. It blossoms in July, on long spikes which are yellow and the seeds of it in the fall of the year are remarkable for sticking to the clothes. Some people call it cuckold. In the form of a

tea it is a good drink in fever. The juice of this plant, sweetened with honey, is an excellent medicine for jaundice, scurvy, and diarrhoea. A wine glass full of the juice, three times a day is a proper dose. The herb is applied externally in fresh wounds.

(2) It is used for bedwetting and weakness of the bladder. It is also much used for loose coughs and sore mouths. The entire herb and dry root is made into an infusion, 1 ounce to the pint of boiling water, given in tablespoon doses every three hours; or in 2 tablespoon doses every four hours, and again in a very small amount of water just before retiring.

(3) The leaves are used fresh or dried; they have been recommended in the jaundice; but they are found by experience to be good in the diabetes and in incontinence of urine. No plant has been held in greater reputation for spitting of blood, bloody urine and disorders of the liver. The best method of using it is in fusion, a handful of the dried leaves are to be put into a vessel, and a quart of boiling water poured upon them and sweetened with a little sugar. By means of this drink some very obstinate liver complaints have been removed. It should be taken in the morning fasting, and repeated two or three times during the day. It has been considered one of the best herbs for cleansing the skin, and purifying the blood. It forms a good gargle for sore throats. Equal quantities of this herb, St. Johns Wort, Camomile flowers and Wormwood made into a strong decoction is a capital fomentation, for violent pains, cramps, etc.

ALDER

This is an astringent, useful in bleeding at the lungs, or as a wash for ulcers.

Alder bark tea is good for chills.

The bark is the part used. It is excellent in scrofula, syphilis, cutaneous and all blood diseases. Dose: Of decoction, one or two tablespoonfuls from 3 to 5 times daily; of tincture, 1 to 2 tablespoonfuls; of fluid extract, ½ to 1 teaspoonful.

Use bark to break out hives.

Both leaves and bark are used. Use the leaves when possible. Very useful for swellings of all kinds. Take green leaves, crush and lay them on painful swellings. Will relieve the

pain and take down the swelling. Make a poultice, crush the leaves. The green leaves, or dry leaves made into a poultice will allay the inflammation of a swollen and painful breast. Take a heaping tablespoonful to a pint of boiling water. Let steep half an hour. If used for poultices, take just enough water so leaves are moist. The fresh leaves are excellent for aching feet when placed in the shoes under the bare feet. Good to bathe the whole foot in strong tea.

ALFALFA

It is a tonic and a nutrient. It may be used where vitality is low as a tea with, or between, meals.

ALLSPICE

Promotes appetite and digestion and disguises the taste of unpalatable drugs, is one of the ingredients of spice plaster.

Allspice should not be used or given to anyone suffering with any form of stomach complaint.

It is of much benefit in ordinary diarrhoea. It is made more effective by adding a small amount of clove.

Allspice is a mild astringent. In cholera infantum it is of much benefit; relieves colic due to cold.

Allspice may be given as a tincture but is best as an infusion made by steeping a teaspoon of it in boiling water for 30 minutes, strain. Dose: a teaspoon in water every hour or oftener according to condition.

ALMOND

The almond tree grows in the south of Europe and Asia and yields the sweet and bitter almond. The sweet almond oil is used as a diuretic in coughs, hoarseness, scalding of urine, kidney troubles and to whiten and soften the skin. A dose is a teaspoonful. The oil of bitter almond is poisonous, and is occasionally used as a sedative. Its taste is like that of a peach kernel. Dose: one-quarter of a drop. Do not confound sweet with bitter.

Five almonds taken before drinking alcoholic beverages was considered the best bracer against intoxication and a preventive for hangovers.

Medical Folklore

Another source of home remedies was the folklore that was brought to the United States by settlers from other parts of the world.

Some beliefs of folklore had real value in remedies while others were incredible. In fact, not a few of the medicines used today are outgrowths of "Granny's Remedies." Digitalis is a perfect example of one of these remedies. It was developed in the Shropshire section of England where women brewed tea from foxgloves which they used for "dropsy." Another example is the old idea of using moldy bread as a poultice on wounds. Think for a moment and you will realize that it was the forerunner of today's antibiotics, such as penicillin. Grandma used lobelia for asthma. Today the alkaloid, lobeline, is used in modern medicine for asthma. There are many more examples of a similar nature to show that all folklore is not as weird as it may appear to be at first.

The folklore in this section can be found in various parts of the United States. Yet, since other folklore will be similar, though worded differently, the examples given here are necessarily limited. It would take pages and pages, properly indexed, to comb all the health superstitions.

Asthma

Take one ounce of Low Beta Leaves and one ounce of the pods and one ounce of Skunk Cabage put them in to ½ pint of elkahall let them stand 24 hours then strain them & them add 1 ounce of rattle snake oil. Let the patient take ½ teaspunfull

MEDICAL FOLKLORE
or
"GRANNY'S CURES"

WHOOPING COUGH

Put nine worms into a bottle and hide it.

Cat soup is good for whooping cough.

Wear the rattles of a rattlesnake.

Water of baptism is good for whooping cough.

A wood louse suspended from the neck in a bag is good for whooping cough.

Tea made of blue clover blossoms is good for whooping cough.

Drink stolen milk.

Steal a piece of blue ribbon and wear it.

Tie a spider into a thimble and suspend it from the neck of the ailing person.

Cut up and feed to the child the cast off skin of a snake.

Drink from a stolen blue tumbler.

Feed the child an egg gotten from persons who have not changed their names by marriage.

For whooping cough, a lock of hair cut from the head of a person who never saw his father, is to be tied up in a piece of cloth and worn around the neck.

Take a fish out of water and let the sufferer smell at it or let the fish breathe on the sufferer.

Put a trout's mouth into the patient's.

Cure a child of whooping cough by taking it through a tunnel.

A child can be cured of whooping cough by having a horse breathe into its face.

Squeeze the juice of two or three lemons into flaxseed tea and sweeten with honey.

Cook sunflower seed until you have a thick liquid.

A black velvet band worn around the child's neck will prevent whooping cough.

CONVULSIONS

To cure a child of convulsions lay under its pillow a horseshoe containing the regulation number of horseshoe nails and which was cast by a horse.

When a child has convulsions cover it with its father's wedding coat.

Yarn that has never been wet and was spun by a child less than seven years of age will cure convulsions, if worn round the neck until it falls off.

A child will not have convulsions if the first chemise it ever wore has never been washed.

A child will not have convulsions if it eats the first hailstorm seen after its birth.

Suspend the eyetooth of a pig from a child's neck to cure convulsions.

The water used in baptizing a child should be poured over a peony bush to prevent convulsions in the child.

To stop convulsions in a baby that is teething, let the mother bite off the head of a mouse.

CROUP

Measure a child with an elderberry wand and put it where the rays of neither sun or moon strike it. The child will not have croup after it has grown taller than the wand.

To cure croup, the sufferer should stand on the warm spleen of a freshly slaughtered steer and remain standing on it until the spleen is cold.

A homespun woolen thread tied about the neck will cure croup.

A child suffering from croup can be cured if you place it against an oak tree and drive a nail into the tree above the child's head in such a manner that some of the child's hair is included.

Put some hair of a croupy child into a hole bored in the wall. Plug up the hole and the croup will be cured.

Poultice a baby's neck with bacon rind.

Croup can be cured by wrapping the child's neck with a rag that has been soaked in coal oil.

Beat egg yolks and stiffen with sugar and give for croup.

Let a child wear a piece of calfskin or leather around its neck and it will never have croup.

Slice an onion into a saucer, dust with sugar, and cover with another saucer for several hours. This makes a good syrup for croup.

Cover the chest with a poultice of cooked onions to cure croup.

Wrap an onion in brown paper, bake it in the oven, then remove the juice and give it to a baby with croup.

Take red pepper for croup.

Grease a black silk ribbon and let the child wear it about the neck as a preventive against croup.

Place a black silk ribbon around the child's neck and let it hang over the stomach, to prevent croup.

"Sheep nanny" tea is good for croup.

Rub skunk oil on the throat to cure croup.

Croup can be cured by bandaging the neck with a tobacco poultice that has been dipped into grease.

To cure croup, give the child a teaspoonful of urine three times a day.

R H E U M A T I S M

Wear the eyetooth of a pig.

Carry three potatoes in your pants pocket.

Carry in your pocket the triangular bone from a ham.

Put a copper cent into your shoe.

Carry a piece of burnt-out carbon from an arc light as a prevention or cure for rheumatism.

A ring made of a horseshoe nail is good for rheumatism.

Wear a brass ring to cure rheumatism.

To prevent rheumatism, put glass knobs under bed posts.

A dried eelskin tied about a joint cures and prevents rheumatism.

Do not throw out the water in which you washed your feet in the evening until the next day, for fear of rheumatism.

By all means throw out the water in which you washed your feet to prevent rheumatism.

Carry a coffin nail to prevent rheumatism.

A salted mackerel tied on the feet cures rheumatism.

A raw salt herring with the bone taken out applied to the neck, tying a handkerchief over it and keeping it on all night, cures rheumatism.

Rheumatism can be cured by sleeping on a sock that contains powdered alum.

A bee sting will cure rheumatism.

Keep a brass ring on the middle finger of the left hand to ward off rheumatism.

Rheumatism may be prevented by carrying a buckeye in your pocket.

Render a buzzard into grease and use this for rheumatism.

When going to bed tie a bag of camphor under each knee to prevent rheumatism.

Each night sleep with your feet against a cat and your rheumatism will go into the cat.

Boil three bunches of celery in two gallons of water until you have one gallon of liquid. Drink three glassfuls a day.

Take a chicken and cut it in two and leave all the entrails in. Put your foot right in the chicken and it will take all the rheumatism out of your body.

Sleep with a dog to cure rheumatism. The dog will absorb the disease and become crippled.

The rheumatic parts of your body can be cured by wrapping an eelskin around them.

Wear elder leaves in your shoes to ward off rheumatism.

A piece of red flannel worn about the wrist will cure rheumatism.

Rheumatism can be cured by alternately drinking three cupfuls of garlic tea daily for three days and then eating a garlic a day for five days.

To throw the cuttings from your hair on the floor will make your bones crack and give you rheumatism.

As a remedy for rheumatism, take a hot bath in water to which hayseed has been added.

Keep an Indian turnip in your pocket as a preventive against rheumatism.

Eat a lemon every morning one hour before breakfast until you have consumed 62 lemons, and you will have rheumatism.

Carry a potato in your pocket. If the potato rots, your rheumatism will leave; but if the potato becomes hard, the remedy will be ineffective.

Cut a potato in two and wear a half on each knee for a rheumatism remedy.

Spit on a rock for three mornings, then hide the rock under your front porch and forget about it; and this will cure your rheumatism.

Cure rheumatism by keeping salt in your shoes.

Skunk oil rubbed over any rheumatic part of the body will cure it.

Wear rattlesnake rattles in your hatband to prevent rheumatism.

For a rheumatism cure, keep a teaspoonful of sulphur in each shoe so that the sulphur will go up through your system.

Rheumatism can be cured by rubbing the ailing parts with the yellow meat of a turtle.

When you wash your hands and face in the morning, dry your hands first and you will never have rheumatism.

Mash up angleworms and let them decompose in the sun, and use this oil for rubbing rheumatic parts.

TO STOP A NOSEBLEED

1. Chew a newspaper.
2. Raise the arms above the head.
3. Stretch out the arm on the same side as the bleeding nostril and place it against the wall, and lean in that direction.
4. Make a cross of blood on the forehead, and put a dime on the forehead; then lie down.
5. Place a dime on the roof of the mouth and hold it there with the tongue for a few minutes.
6. Put a pair of scissors down your back to stop the blood.
7. Place a sharp knife on the back of the neck.
8. Sniff lemon juice into the bleeding nostril.
9. Put a small piece of paper between the upper teeth and lower lip.
10. Wrap the little finger tight with thread.
11. Stick the blade of an axe into the ground.
12. Wear a necklace of red beads.
13. It is lucky to have a nosebleed on Friday.
14. Hold a gold ring against the roof of the mouth.
15. Chew gum.
16. Dip a piece of cotton into good ink and place it in the nose.
17. Tie a bunch of keys on a green string and wear them around your neck.
18. Let the blood drop on a knife, and then stick the knife into the ground.
19. Leave rusty nails in cider vinegar until the rust comes off and then drink this liquid as a nosebleed remedy.
20. Chew a piece of brown wrapping-paper and place the wad under your upper lip.
21. Soak a piece of brown paper in vinegar and put it under your upper lip.
22. Go where you cannot be seen and let your nose bleed on a white rock, then turn the rock over and depart; your nosebleed will stop.
23. Suspend a dime from a red yarn string and tie it on your neck, and then open the Bible and say, "In the Name of the Father, Son and Holy Ghost—stop my nosebleed."
24. Cut two short twigs from a living branch, take off the bark, place the pieces (about two inches long) in the form of a cross; then let the blood from the nose drop on the twigs so as to make the entire length of each piece red. When they are colored, the bleeding will cease.

TO REMOVE WARTS

1. Rub warts with pebbles and throw them into a grave.
2. Rub warts with the blood of a chicken which has nothing but black feathers.

3. Rub warts with a piece of potato, which must then be buried under the eaves.

4. Rub warts with soft green walnuts.

5. Rub warts with the hand of a corpse.

6. Rub warts with the head of a rooster that has just been killed.

7. Rub warts with the rind of bacon, and then place the rind on a tree so that the birds may eat it.

8. Rub warts with saliva.

9. Scratch a wart with a nail taken from a coffin until the wart bleeds; it will then disappear.

10. Rub a bone over the wart, lay the bone down where you picked it up, walk off and don't look back.

11. Prick the wart, rub a piece of bread on it and get it bloody, then feed the bread to a black chicken.

12. Tie a hair around a wart and it will saw the wart off.

13. Tie as many knots in a string as you have warts, and when the string rots the warts will leave.

14. Cut holes in a piece of leather and place it over the warts. Fill the holes with sulfur, then set the sulfur afire.

15. Make the warts bleed, then take milk from milkweed and put it on the warts.

16. Throw a marble over your left shoulder and don't look back.

17. Strike a match, take off the burnt end, blindfold somebody and have him go in the back yard and bury the match. If no one sees you or digs up the match, the wart will go away in four days.

18. To remove a seed wart rub it hard, take a silver dollar and put it in a glass of buttermilk and drink for seven days.

19. Sell warts to remove them; have a mock sale of warts and put the money away and don't spend it.

20. Give someone a penny for each wart he has and they will come off.

21. Plant a pea for every wart you have and the warts will go away.

HICCOUGH

1. If a person has hiccough, he has told a lie.

2. Having hiccough means that someone is talking about you.

3. To stop a person's hiccoughs make him angry.

4. Lie on your back and stretch your arms straight up in the air.

5. Take teaspoonful doses of tea made from the dill plant.

6. Place your two little fingers in your ears and hold your breath.

7. Put the ends of your thumbs behind your ears and press them in tightly.

8. Hold both ears tightly closed and let someone give you a drink of water.

9. Hold your index fingers out in front of you and try to see how near you can bring them together without their touching.

10. Frighten a person to scare away his hiccoughs.

11. Check hiccoughs by standing on your head.

12. Rid yourself of hiccoughs by letting someone else place a knife blade under your tongue.

13. Take a glass of water and hold a knife down in the glass while you are drinking it.

14. Swallow a little sugar in a teaspoonful of lemon juice.

15. Wear a nutmeg around your neck and you will not have hiccoughs.

Pills of Health

4. oz Gumaloes   4 Cream Tarter
2 „   Liquorish Extract
2 „   Gumarabic
1 „   Colocynth or Bitter Apple
1 „   Gamboge
Mix the whole together dose 3 the common size

7,500 Rubber Pain-Relieving and Health-Giving Household Articles Offered to You.

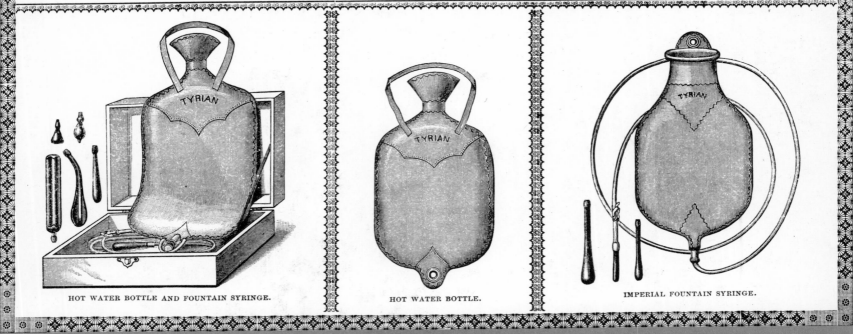

HOT WATER BOTTLE AND FOUNTAIN SYRINGE.

HOT WATER BOTTLE.

IMPERIAL FOUNTAIN SYRINGE.

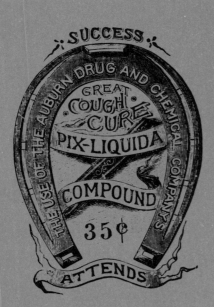

SUCCESS

THE USE OF THE AUBURN DRUG AND CHEMICAL COMPANY'S

GREAT COUGH CURE PIX-LIQUIDA COMPOUND

35¢

ATTENDS

⟐ 1879 ⟐

Nelson County, Ky.,
PURE RYE
WHISKEY.

Selected and put up for Medicinal Use, by

TRECO & WRIGHT,
Druggists.
23 Main St., ORION, ILL.

To Dye or Not to Dye

THAT
IS THE QUESTION

whether it is better

to wear that faded, shabby dress and endure the scornful looks of all your well-dressed neighbors, or to purchase a package of *DIAMOND DYES* and restore its freshness in another color —*making a new dress for ten cents.*

Diamond Dyes are made for home use. Absolutely reliable. Any color

Sold everywhere. 10 cts. a package. ☞ Direction book and 40 samples of colored cloth free.
WELLS, RICHARDSON & CO., Burlington, Vt.

THE
WASHINGTON
MONUMENT

Height 555 ft. Cost $1,187,710.
Corner Stone laid July 4, 1848.
Cap Stone Set Dec. 6, 1884.

Size at base 55 ft Square
Size at height of 500 ft. 34 ft. 6 in
Roof 55 ft. High
Total Height 555 ft from its floor
Weight 82,000 Long Tons
Weight of Crown Piece 3,300 lbs.
Area covered by foundation 16,002 sq. ft. There are 900 Steps to top of Shaft. Contains an Elevator of 7 tons capacity.

CELERY COMPOUND,
The Great Nerve Tonic and Alterative.
CURES NEURALGIA, DYSPEPSIA, CONSTIPATION, BILIOUSNESS, KIDNEY AND LIVER COMPLAINTS, AND ALL THEIR ATTENDANT EVILS, AND IS
The Best Blood Purifier in the Market.

Copyright 1885 by J.H.Bufford's Sons.